The Body & Mind Method

(Xíng Shén Zhuāng)

形神庄

Revised and Expanded Edition

Hou Hee Chan

Based on the teachings & writings of Dr. Pang Ming

Disclaimer

To reduce the risk of injury, consult your doctor before beginning this or any exercise program. The instructions and advice presented are in no way intended as a substitute for medical counseling. The author, the editors, Chilel Qìgōng, Inc., producers, participants and distributors of this book are not liable for any inadvertent errors or for misinterpretation or misuse of information presented here. The author, the editors, Chilel Qigong, Inc., producers, participants and distributors of this book disclaim any liability or loss in connection with exercise and advice herein.

Published by: Chilel Qìgōng, Inc.
PO Box 2097
Rockin, CA 95677

Website: www.chilelwellness.com
www.chilel.com

Email: info@chilelwellness.com

ISBN: 978-1-893104-13-6

SPECIAL THANKS TO DR. PÁNG MÍNG

Zhìnéng Qìgōng Founder：Páng Míng

智能氣功編創人:龐明

Páng (family name) Míng, also known as Páng Hè Míng (龐鶴明), was born in September 1940 in Hébĕi (河北), China. He is the founder of *the Huáxià Zhìnéng Qìgōng Clinic & Training Center (華夏智能氣功培訓中心),* He was an associate editor of the "Eastern Qìgōng" Magazine ("東方氣功" 雜誌常務副主編), and chairman of the Advisory Committee of Beijing Qìgōng Research Association (北京氣功研究會顧問委員會主任).

After graduating from the Beijing Physician School (北京醫士學校) in 1958, he worked as a Clinical Internist from 1958 to 1962. During that period of time, he studied Traditional Chinese Medicine at the Beijing Physician Association (北京醫師會) and has worked as a Traditional Chinese Medicine doctor since 1963.

From an early age, Dr. Páng has had a keen interest in Traditional Chinese Medicine (especially Acupuncture), Qìgōng and the Martial Arts. He has studied with nineteen teachers, beginning with teachers of Buddhist Qìgōng, and then Martial Art Qìgōng. In the 1970s, he began to study and did research on Dàoist Qìgōng and Folk Qìgōng.

With his unique knowledge of both Western and Traditional Chinese Medicine and Qìgōng, he started the movement for the establishment of the first Qìgōng research organization for the general public—the Beijing Qìgōng Research Association (北京氣功研究會) in 1979, and became one of its founders. He was one of the organizers for the first National Qìgōng Conference (全中國氣功匯報會), July 1979.

In the 1980s, he began to reform Traditional Qìgōng. With innovative applications to Qìgōng, he created Zhìnéng Qìgōng in the early 80's, and in 1989, he opened the first Zhìnéng Qìgōng school in Shíjiāzhuāng, Hébĕi Province (河北省石家莊). Later, he moved the school to Qínhuángdăo (秦皇島), and renamed it "*the Huáxià Zhìnéng Qìgōng Clinic & Training Center*." From 1989 to 1993, the school trained more than sixty thousand students. Dr. Páng has written many articles and has published over fifteen books on Qìgōng.

ACKNOWLEDGMENTS

It has been a great honor for me to have had the opportunity to study with Dr. Páng Míng and to be able to share the wisdom of his teaching and Qìgōng practice with others. The time I spent studying at his Center, *the Huáxià Zhìnéng Qìgōng Clinic & Training Center*—an organization dedicated to exploring the frontiers of human potential through the ancient art of Qìgōng, has had a profound influence on my understanding of Qìgōng. Although the Center has been closed since 2001 due to governmental policies, I am privileged to have been part of it.

I owe a special debt of gratitude to my colleague and editor B. J. Kish Irvine, Ph.D. who spent a considerable number of hours editing and clarifying each sentence of this book. I also want to thank Barbara Benson, J.D. for her valuable time reviewing and proofreading the manuscript. Her comments and suggestions helped to refine the presentation of this book so that its message is easily understood. Finally, I owe my deepest debt to my wife, Eva Lew, M.D. This book would not have been possible had it not been for her support and encouragement.

ACKNOWLEDGMENTS (1st Edition)

How can I thank so many individuals who helped and encouraged me during this project? Nancy Parker spent numerous hours editing my first draft. Yeeming Lǎoshī of China posed for the pictures. B.J. Kish Irvine, Ph.D. proofread the book. With the endless discussions and practice with my brother, Luke Chan, I gained much understanding of Dr. Páng's work. My colleagues, Jīn Lǎoshī and Chen Lǎoshī of China, not only shared with me their experience in teaching and the secret of their success, they also taught me the art of practice. This book never would have been finished had it not been for the support and encouragement of my wife, Eva Lew, M.D. who edited the final draft.

Most of all, I am indebted to all my students. By teaching them, I gained many insights into the art of Qìgōng. They are not only my students; they are my colleagues and teachers.

Please note that this book is based on the writings and teachings of Dr. Páng. It is not a direct translation of his work.

Contents

SERIES PREFACE

After helping Guō Lín Lǎoshī (郭林老師) establish the theoretical aspects of the Xīn Qìgōng (新氣功), Dr. Páng Míng began to reform Traditional Qìgōng in the 1980s. With innovative applications to Qìgōng, he created his own system and called it Zhìnéng Qìgōng (智能氣功); Zhìnéng means intelligent. In 1989, he opened the first Zhìnéng Qìgōng school in Shíjiāzhuāng, Héběi Province (河北省石家莊). Later, he established the first research and training center dedicated to exploring human potential through the ancient art of Qìgōng in the city of Qínhuángdǎo (秦皇島). He named it *the Huáxià Zhìnéng Qìgōng Clinic & Training Center (華夏智能氣功培訓中心).* Zhìnéng Qìgōng has become one of the most popular forms of Qìgōng which has ever been created.

In 1995, in order to introduce Zhìnéng Qìgōng to non-Chinese, Dr. Páng gave approval for my brother, Luke, and me to teach Zhìnéng Qìgōng as Chilel Qìgōng in the Americas and in Europe. Throughout the years, we have shared the arts of Chilel Qìgōng with thousands of people. Although Luke has written a book titled *101 Miracles of Natural Healing* documenting some of the healing powers of Chilel Qìgōng, we do not use teaching manuals in our teachings. Basically, we tailor our teaching to each individual class/workshop. As our students and other teachers began to teach the methods outside of China, standardized non-Chinese text books became necessary. With the support and encouragement from my colleagues and students, I took on the challenges to translate and interpret some of Dr. Páng's writings.

Dr. Páng Míng has written extensively on Qìgōng including a nine-book series on Zhìnéng Qìgōng. The challenges facing me and my colleagues who have translated some of his work into other languages are that he wrote for an audience with a very specific background and his Zhìnéng Qìgōng books in the series are related to one another. A reader who does not have sufficient knowledge in Dàoism, Buddhism, Confucianism and Tàijí Quán may have a difficult time understanding a direct translation of his work. To translate just one book of the Zhìnéng Qìgōng series does not make for easy reading either, because some of the background information is in another book. No one can translate Dr. Páng's books as they are written; all one can do is to interpret them as close to the original as is possible.

The project started out as teaching manuals for instructors in Chilel Qìgōng and has evolved into a series translating some of Dr. Páng's writings. To follow the Chinese tradition of honoring and respecting the teacher, Zhìnéng Qìgōng (known as *Chilel Qìgōng* in the Western world) will be used in the series.

The series, "Guides to Zhìnéng (Chilel) Qìgōng," is an ongoing project; initially, it will consist of three books. The first book in the series is *Zhìnéng (Chilel) Qìgōng: Overview and Foundation Methods,* and it covers the basic information about Zhìnéng Qìgōng and its foundation methods, which work on External Qì for health and vitality. The second book is *Zhìnéng (Chilel) Qìgōng: The Body & Mind Method,* and it covers Zhìnéng Qìgōng's Second Step Gong (intermediate level), which works on the integration of the physical body and mental activities. The third book: *Zhìnéng (Chilel) Qìgōng: Hùn Yuán Wholistic Theory* covers some of the traditional Qìgōng theories and the theories developed and compiled by Dr. Páng Míng.

Although some words such as Qìgōng and Taiji are accepted as common English words, for continuity, I will use only Pīnyīn (official English translations of Chinese words) throughout the series. Because there are no set rules in Pīnyīn to guide whether a certain term should be in one word or two words, for standardization and reference purposes, I will use one word for technical names and two or more words for general terms; for example, 氣功 is a technical name, so Qìgōng will be used, 科學 (science)—a general term, will be kē xué. Also, I will put both Chinese characters and/or Pīnyīn next to the quotations and technical terms in the main text or as a footnote when they first appear. When necessary, I also include "Translator's note" to explain some of the terms or concepts that may be new to some readers. To stay within the context of the original writing, the information in these "Notes" is very brief. Readers interested in in-depth explanations need to do some research on their own or ask their teachers for more information.

Chinese writing is very different from English; for example, in English, the "Translator's note" would be inserted as an endnote or a footnote, but in Chinese, it would be in the main text. Since the series is either a direct translation or interpretation of Dr. Páng's writings, I have maintained the original style of his writing as much as possible. This approach may not agree with standard publishing practices. Any mistakes in the series are mine, not my editor's.

Qìgōng is a living art. It will keep on evolving. As a Qìgōng practitioner, my understanding of Qìgōng will evolve with time. The interpretation presented in the series is my understanding of Zhìnéng Qìgōng at this time. By no means is it the final interpretation or only interpretation. There is a Chinese Proverb that says, "To initiate a discussion, show a brick (your work), someone may answer with a Jade (拋磚引玉)." I hope this series will inspire some of my colleagues to translate some of Dr. Páng's work into not just English, but also other languages.

Hou Hee (Frank) Chan

Roseville, CA

PREFACE

The 2002 first edition of the Body & Mind Method book was an outline of the Body & Mind Method, intended for students to take notes during their classes and not for use as a textbook. In this edition, I expanded and updated the entire book and incorporated it into the Series as the second book. Unlike the first book: *Overview and Foundation Methods*, which is a direct translation of Dr. Páng's writings, this book is my interpretation of his teachings.

This book is divided into three chapters. Chapter One is a brief introduction to Qì, Qìgōng, and How to Practice Qìgōng. Chapter Two is an Introduction to Zhìnéng Qìgōng. Chapter Three is the Body & Mind Method and Tap along the Meridians. Some of the headings in Chapter One and Two may look the same as in the first book: *Overview and Foundation Methods*, but the contents are explained from slightly different angles, most of the information is from Dr. Páng's lectures, not from his books. In Chapter Three, the "How to Practice the Body & Mind Method" section is not in any of Dr. Páng's books, it is also based on his lectures. As I mentioned in the Series Preface, "no one can translate Dr. Páng's books as they are written; all one can do is to interpret them as close to the original as is possible;" interpretation will change with time, but the essence of Zhìnéng Qìgōng will stay the same.

Chapter One:
Brief Introduction to Qìgōng
氣功簡介

The Concept of Qì

Qì and air are the same character in Chinese writing; therefore, it is very easy for people to think of the air we breathe and breathing itself when Qì is mentioned. Some Qìgōng books and practitioners even inaccurately describe or translate Qìgōng as a Breathing Exercise. Although breathing plays a very important role in many Qìgōng systems, not all Qìgōng systems cultivate air (breathing). The Qì in Qìgōng is completely different from the air we breathe. In Chinese culture, "Qì" is a special concept, and all things are related to "Qì". In Qìgōng, Qì has at least the following characteristics.

1. Nature Qì

Qì in nature is the basic material that makes up the Universe and all things in it. It is shapeless and does not have a physical appearance. Normally, it cannot be seen or touched, yet it permeates the whole Universe. They called this shapeless substance Dào, Yuán Qì, or Tàijí, etc. The names may be different, but they generally are referred to as "Qì".

The ancient Chinese believed that this shapeless substance was the source for all things with shape and physical appearance. In other words, all activities in the Universe are the manifestations of this shapeless substance. Zhāng Dài (張戴) of the Sòng Dynasty (宋朝) said: "The Extreme Space does not have shape, it is the Qì's Original Body; it condenses and disperses, resulting in the changing of Qì's temporary appearance/shape." In the Yellow Emperor's Classic of Internal Medicine (黃帝內經), it is said that, "Qì moves, it activates vitalities; Qì disperses, it forms the final shape; Qì circulates, it nourishes; Qì stops, it changes appearance." It means the growth, birth, and death of all things are the manifestations of Qì.

In 1905, Albert Einstein published the theory of special relativity that expresses the fact that mass and energy are the same physical entity and can be changed into each other. It is very similar to the way ancient Chinese describe Qì. It says, "When Qì concentrates, it will form a substance; when a substance disperses, it will become Qì." There are no exceptions for humans. Zhuāngzǐ (庄子 born between 369—286 BC) said, "Man's existence is the result of Qì's condensation; when Qì condenses, man will be alive; when Qì disperses, he will be dead."

2. Human Qì

All things are the manifestations of Qì, therefore, human beings are the manifestations of Qì. The ancient Chinese did extensive research on the Qì inside the human body. They believed and concluded that a human being's Qì is a special substance which is shapeless and has no physical appearance but maintains the physiological functions of the human body. In the Yellow Emperor's Classic of Internal Medicine, it is said that,

"It is activated by Shàng jiāo (上焦), defines the flavors of food, nourishes the skin, replenishes the body, and polishes the hair, as if irrigated by the fog and mist, it is called Qì." Qì is the root of the human's physiological activities. Zhāng jǐng Yuè (張景岳) of the Míng Dynasty said, "Man's life completely depends on this Qì."

According to Traditional Qìgōng theories, a human being consisted of Prenatal Qì and Postnatal Qì. The fetus is formed by the Qì produced by the merging of sperm and egg; this Qì is called Prenatal Qì (先天之氣), it is the root of all future developments. Once the fetus is formed, the substances (nutrition, air, water, etc.) it absorbs from outside the body are called Postnatal Qì (後天之氣). When Prenatal Qì and Postnatal Qì merge as one, it is called Hùn Yuán Qì (混元氣). There are many writings on "Qì within the Body" in Traditional Chinese Medicine ("Qì within the Body" is called Internal Qì; "Qì outside the Body" is called External Qì or "Nature Qì"). Depending on its location and functions in the body, it has different names; for example: it is called Zhēn Qì (真氣), Yíng Qì (營氣), Wèi Qì (衛氣), Zōng Qì (宗氣), Yuán Qì (元氣), Meridian Qì (經絡之氣), Zàngfǔ Qì (Organ Qì 臟腑之氣), Prenatal Qì, and Postnatal Qì, etc. Although there are many names, they are all part of Hùn Yuán Qì. This Qì can power all human life activities. Traditional Chinese Medicine says, "In Yáng Qì, the finer kind nourishes Shén (神 mind activities), the soft kind nourishes the tendons." In other words, the essence (very Yáng) of Yáng Qì is to nourish the mind activities, the soft kind of Yáng Qì is to nourish the physical body. The Qì inside the body cannot exist by itself; it depends on the physical body and is controlled by mind activities. It also nourishes both the physical body and the mind.

3. The interaction and transmutation between Human Qì and Nature Qì

According to Qìgōng theories, the physiological process of the human body is the process of the interaction and transmutation between Human Body Qì (Internal Qì) and Nature Qì (External Qì). If one can successfully obtain Nature Qì to "service" oneself, one will be healthy. If not, one will become sick or die. Practicing Qìgōng strengthens the process of the interaction and transmutation between Human Body Qì and Nature Qì. The process of transforming Human Body Qì to Nature Qì or vice versa needs to go through the process of Qì transmutation. One would say that we convert food to the human body through metabolism; but metabolism is not a simple process. For example, when one eats something (e.g., protein), the digestive system produces enzymes to breakdown the protein into amino acids, then absorbs them into the bloodstream; only then can the protein become part of the body. If one injects protein into the body directly, one may have severe reactions. In Traditional Chinese Medicine it is said that the food one ate must be "Qì-ized" (transmuted by Qì) before it can be absorbed into the body. According to Qìgōng theory, enzyme is the physical (condensed) form of Organ Qì; when it interacts with protein, it "Qì-ized" the protein and transmutes it to become something called semi-Body Qì which is comparable to the Body Qì. This semi-Body Qì has two components, the coarse component is called Wèi Qì (衛氣), the finer one is called Yíng Qì (營氣). When this semi-Body Qì is absorbed into the body, it interacts and transmutes with Body Qì; Wèi Qì will become energy and Yíng Qì become part of the body. In Qìgōng, metabolism is Internal Qì transmutes with External Qì to form a new entity.

Therefore, the concept of Qì in Qìgōng includes Qì in Nature, Qì in the Human and the transmutation between Human Qì and Nature Qì (the human being can use the Nature Qì). Qìgōng practice is mainly to "Qì-ize" Nature Qì for our own use, not to "Qì-ize" physical substances.

The Definition of Qìgōng

The term "Qìgōng" includes hundreds of schools and thousands of methods. As a technical term for a particular system of knowledge, the definition of Qìgōng must include their theories and contents. In the past several decades, there were many schools that established their own definitions of Qìgōng. Although all have merits and reasons for their definitions, none is accepted by everyone. It is because each school has its own theories, techniques and purposes, such as to prevent illness, to strengthen the body, to cultivate virtue, to develop abilities, etc. Therefore, each school describes Qìgōng differently. We use "Qì" as an example—all schools that cultivate Qì agree that Qì is not the air we breathe, but they cannot agree on the essence of Qì. Not even modern science can describe it. Moreover, there are many schools, such as the Cānshān school (參禪) of Buddhist Qìgōng and the "Quiet and Non-engaging" school (清靜無為法門) of Dàoist Qìgōng, that do not even mention Qì. Even with some schools that cultivate Qì, at advanced levels, they no longer require the practitioners to cultivate Qì. For example, in the Nèidān school (內丹派) of Dàoist Qìgōng, once the Dàdān (大丹) is formed, one no longer focuses on cultivating Qì. So if one uses "Qì" and "Gōng" to describe Qìgōng, the description does not include EVERY type of Qìgōng.

Note: Dàdān 大丹 is the dān (ball) that forms by the coherence of Kidney Qì and Heart Qì in the middle Dāntián.

Since Qìgōng has become a popular term, we should use it as a technical word. As in science, technical words have to have special meanings and scope (or boundaries). The special meaning and scope of Qìgōng must contain the essence of each school. With this in mind, Dr. Páng Míng gave the following definition of Qìgōng in 1992:

Qìgōng is a training based on the theories of the Wholism of Life. It is a training that requires the participant to consciously use the mind intent to focus inward to transform, to improve, and to enhance life functions. Mental, posture, and breathing adjustments are the extensions of the inward training. It is a training which enables the participants to transform natural instinctive activities into conscious activities.

氣功是建立在整體生命觀的基礎上,通過主動的向內性運用意識活動的訓練(調心,調身,調息是其外展),改造,完美,提高人體的生命功能,把自然的本能變為自覺智能的實踐.

This definition points out Qìgōng's theoretical foundation, and clearly states Qìgōng's special training methods and training contents. It describes the purposes of the Qìgōng training. This definition includes all of the special characteristics of Qìgōng.

1. It points out Qìgōng's theoretical foundation—the theories of the Wholism of Life (it is also called the theories of "Man and Heaven as a wholistic Entity." Its contents include the following concepts.

   a. The Universe is a Wholistic Entity.
   It contains numerous levels of substance. These substances permeate and transmute each other to form the millions of things in the Universe.

   b. The Human Body is a Wholistic Entity.
   In Traditional Qìgōngs, and Traditional Chinese Medicine, this entity is led by the mind (Shén 神), and the core is formed by the internal organs. They are united by the Qì and the blood in the Meridians to form a Body-Mind Entity.

   c. Man, Society and Nature are a Wholistic Entity.
   The concept that Man, Society and Nature are a wholistic Entity is not only the common theoretical foundation of different schools of Qìgōng; it is the essence of Chinese Ancient Culture. If one looks at this from the progressive point of view, sooner or later, all Qìgōng theories from different schools must progress to this stage. As a matter of fact, the ancient Chinese developed the concept of Man and Nature as one entity through actual Qìgōng practice. Even today, it is still evolving. The development of the concept and the deepening of the Qìgōng practice are unbroken cycles of relationship—they are interdependent on each other. From Qìgōng's historic point of view, the practice before the development of this concept was "Blind Practice;" it belongs to primitive Qìgōng and cannot be compared with modern Qìgōng.

2. It points out Qìgōng's unique training method—Mind Inward Focusing Training. This specific training has two implications.

   a. Normally, one's mind is only conscious about the things outside of one's own internal functions. It is outward focusing. In Qìgōng practice, one's consciousness is focused inward and is united with life functions.

   b. Normal mind activities are expanding outward, from one point to another, and from one to many. In Qìgōng practice, the mind activities are inward and "condensed" to a single point, from many to one and focus on one point only.

   This is the soul of Qìgōng's definition. It is the standard which differentiates physical exercises from Qìgōng. Practicing Qìgōng cultivates inward focusing.

3. It points out that the purposes of Qìgōng are to improve, refine, and enhance the practitioner's life functions. It is to improve the physical body, and to develop intellect and mental clarity. It will also develop the hidden abilities, and enable the practitioner to move from the "instinct state" to the "conscious state."

4. It points out that Qìgōng is a training process that uses a particular method to obtain the goal of improving health and enhancing life functions. Theories and methods are Qìgōng knowledge. If one knows the theories and methodology but does not practice, one still does not understand Qìgōng.

From the above discussion, we can say this "Definition of Qìgōng." which includes theory, method, and purpose, is a complete definition. It includes all of Qìgōng's contents and it also satisfies the guidelines for a definition in the modern sciences. But would this definition be applicable to all schools of Qìgōng? The answer is definitely "Yes." All schools and their methods, no matter in what stage of practice, emphasize using the mind intent. As a matter of fact, all popular Qìgōng in the present day emphasizes using the mind intent. In Traditional Qìgōng, and in Buddhist Qìgōng, the emphasis is on "Clear the mind to see the Xìng (性 essence, nature, soul, humanity)." Dàoist Qìgōng mentions "Cultivate the mind to purify the Xìng." Confucian Qìgōng mentions "Maintain the mind to nourish the Xìng." All of these emphasize the mind practice.

This definition emphasizes the use of inward focusing but it does not mention Qì. Since some schools do not focus on Qì, this definition avoids the unique limitation of Qì in traditional Qìgōng. But for the schools that emphasize Qì, this definition contains the essence of the practice. The mind is Qì's commander—wherever the mind goes, the Qì follows. Thus, using the mind does not exclude Qì, it is embedded within the mind intent.

The Difference between Qìgōng and Physical Exercise

The difference between Qìgōng and physical exercise is based on whether the mind is inward focusing or not. With the exception of body/muscle building, the participant's mind intent in all physical exercise is always outward focusing. Instead of focusing on one's own physical body, in physical exercise the mind is always focused on the external object. Any movement can be either Qìgōng or physical exercise. For example, in dance, when one learns and practices a new routine or a particular movement, one focuses on the body mechanics—how the hands, feet, and the body move in a certain way, etc. This inward focusing is called Qìgōng. On the other hand, when one dances the same routine at a party, instead of focusing on how the body moves, one just follows the music and enjoys the dance. This is called physical exercise. In a broader sense, any movement, as long as one is focused on the body mechanics, is Qìgōng. If the mind wanders and the body moves mechanically, Qìgōng becomes exercise. All cultures have different names to distinguish between the two. In most cultures, they call one "practice" and the other "physical exercise." Thus, Qìgōng practice and physical exercise obviously have different results. They can be explained as follows.

1. Contents

The contents of training are different. Qìgōng consists of the cultivation of will power/self-control, virtue and physical movements. Physical exercise consists mainly of physical movements. Although physical exercise also cultivates will power, it is not initiated by the participant; it is forced on the participants by external factors, such as health issues, competitions, etc. In Qìgōng, the cultivation of will power is initiated by the participant; it is one of the major components of Qìgōng practice. Virtue cultivation is very important in Qìgōng, one cannot achieve high degrees of accomplishment in Qìgōng without virtue ethics. In physical exercise, virtue is non-existence.

2. Physical Movements

The training of the physical body is different. In physical exercise, during the exercise/training, the mind is to service the body movements. Physical exercise focuses on physical movements or on equipment, not in the body itself. It is the body's reflexive action that causes the mind to direct the movements. It is the body which is stimulated, the brain receives and processes the information, the brain gives the orders to the body to move.

Qìgōng focuses on working on the mind (the intent). The body movements are to "service" the mind. In Qìgōng, every movement within the body is consciously directed by the mind. Without stimulus, the brain gives orders to the body to move. Since the movements are not reflexive actions, they are more effective and consume less energy.

3. The Metabolic Change Inside the Body

Physical exercise is mainly muscle movements—it uses a large amount of energy and oxygen to increase metabolism. After exercise, one must rest and replenish nutrition to recover. In other words, in physical exercise, vitality and metabolism are achieved by increasing the production and consumption of energy. In competitive sports, athletes' consumption of energy is no longer for vitality and metabolism, it is for competition purposes; as a result, the consumption and replenishment of energy are out of balance. Consequently, after they retire from competition, many of them have health challenges.

It is different in Qìgōng. Generally speaking, especially for proficient practitioners, the consumption of oxygen and energy will decrease and the metabolism will slow down during the practice. In Qìgōng, vitality and the metabolism are achieved by rearranging and optimizing life processes. A proficient practitioner consumes much less energy than non-practitioners; as he/she ages, he/she is stronger, healthier and younger than most non-practitioners.

4. The Effects on the Abilities

Qìgōng practice increases human sensitivities, and physical exercise increases endurance. Through Qìgōng practice, as the Body Qì becomes sufficient, the sensitivity abilities of the eyes, ears, nose, tongue, and the body will be heightened. It will increase the awareness of cold, hot, numbness, swelling, and pain, etc., in the body. It may also lead to the development of "The Sixth Sense;" such as the ability to see through objects, to see Qì, and to have remote sensing, etc. However, it is different in physical exercise. Due to increased endurance, the abilities to sense are decreased and/or delayed.

How to Practice Qìgōng

As mentioned earlier, there are many schools/systems of Qìgōng, depending on the purpose of the practice. Qìgōng can be cataloged into five schools—Daoist Qìgōng, Buddhist Qìgōng, Confucian Qìgōng, Martial Art Qìgōng, and Medical Qìgōng. Each school consists of hundreds of forms. Although there are overlaps, each school has its own unique characteristics and techniques. Generally speaking, the purpose for Dàoist Qìgōng is attaining immortality, Buddhist Qìgōng is enlightenment, Confucian Qìgōng is cultivating virtue, Martial Arts Qìgōng is self-defense, and Medical Qìgōng is maintaining health. Each Qìgōng form has its own purposes, requirements, and techniques.

Like any kind of modality, Qìgōng requires effort and persistence. It is a very useful tool for anyone who is interested in maintaining good health. One may ask: How can one choose the right kind of Qìgōng? Generally, one should choose a Qìgōng practiced by millions of people and scientifically proven. Moving Qìgōng is more suitable for people with difficulty to concentrate than is sitting or standing Qìgōng. For health purposes, a simple and easy Qìgōng like Chi Lel Qìgōng is better than the complex Qìgōng like Tàijí.

Once the method is chosen, one must follow the requirements, which include mental and physical aspects of the method, knowing the purposes and functions of the movements, and practicing them accordingly. Only through time, can the results be accumulated and the goal be achieved. Qìgōng practice is like a thousand-mile journey; one should take mental and physical conditions into consideration and take it one step at a time. To get results, persistency and determination are needed. Being too eager for success is like pulling the seedling up to help it to grow, which is harmful. Practice according to one's own circumstance and try to practice at the same place, the same time, and include practice as part of daily routines such as brushing the teeth.

Although each Qìgōng form has its own purposes, requirements, and techniques, the following are the common guidelines for most if not all methods.

1. Purpose and Affirmation

Whether we practice Qìgōng for health or enlightenment, we must have a purpose and firmly believe that we can achieve the ultimate goal. Because the grass always looks greener on the other side of the fence, a strong belief in the method and practice can be transformed into will power that overcomes mental and physical difficulties.

Sometimes people give up hope when medical doctors tell them they have incurable diseases. Medicine is just a small part of the total health system. When medical doctors say a disease is incurable, it does not mean that it is incurable in all other ways. Diseases come and go, but man is still around. We have the capability to heal ourselves. In Qìgōng, no two persons are alike in the time and effort needed to achieve results. Thus, it is very important not to give up when results are not evident after a period of practice. Although sometime the mills of Qì grind slowly, they grind very fine. Results can be achieved if belief is combined with effort and persistence.

2. Respect

Respecting the Dào and the teacher is a fundamental principle of Qìgōng. Dào is nature. To respect nature is to respect the environment and all living things. Only by respecting nature can we become part of nature. When we become part of nature, we will receive information and vitality from nature.

In Qìgōng, the Dào also encompasses methodology, purpose and virtue. To practice Qìgōng is to cultivate the Dào. By working on techniques alone, we can only achieve perfection of our skills. By working on techniques, following the principles, and having virtue, we can then cultivate the Dào. One of the principles in Zhìnéng Qìgōng is living in a state of complete physical, mental, and social well-being. When we have mental or physical setbacks, we need to address the issues instead of blaming others or becoming dejected and giving up. By believing in ourselves, we can face challenges and receive satisfaction in overcoming them. This is respecting the Dào of Qìgōng.

To respect the Dào of a certain Qìgōng, we should practice that Qìgōng wholeheartedly. We should be very careful in choosing the kind of Qìgōng to practice. Some Qìgōngs may not be worthy of respect. For example, some Qìgōngs say that there are three thousand six hundred side doors and eighty four thousand side roads and that they are the only path leading one to the Dào. How do we know what is the right path? What is the standard for comparison? Generally speaking, good Qìgōng improves physical and mental health without interfering with other people's well-being; otherwise, the Qìgōng is not good. On an individual basis, a good Qìgōng is one that can help the individual achieve his/her goal.

Can we practice different kinds of Qìgōng at the same time? Each Qìgōng has its own characteristics, purposes, requirements, and techniques which will create a certain rhythm in the body with practice. If more than one Qìgōng is practiced, the rhythms produced by one may interfere with another. Chaos may occur. This also may hamper improvement. One may reach water a lot faster by digging one well instead of ten. Committing to one Qìgōng is respecting the Dào of that Qìgōng.

Confucius once said, "Among three persons, one can be my teacher." What is a teacher? A teacher is anyone who can help us make progress toward our goal. If someone has expertise in one area, learn from him/her. If another person makes a mistake, learn from his/her experience, and avoid the same mistake. Time is limited, so we should tap into the vast resources of fellow practitioners.

As a teacher, we should not take respect as a given right. A teacher must earn the respect from his students. We should always ask ourselves "Am I good enough to be a teacher?" Good includes two parts. One is proficiency. Do we practice and know the methods well enough to teach? A teacher must walk the walk before talking the talk. The other is virtue. Do we teach for the good of the students or for the good of ourselves? It is unethical to withhold secrets and mislead students. To respect others is to respect ourselves.

3. Ardor

Whether we achieve the Dào or not depends entirely on ourselves. The Dào comes from within and cannot be given. The methods may be excellent and the teacher may share all secrets, but if we do not practice, they are useless. The methods are the gates and paths leading to the Dào. Teachers can point out the correct gates and paths to take, but we still have to walk down the road. How?

a. Be assiduous and persevering

Once the gates and paths are identified, we must follow them carefully. In other words, we must follow the mental and physical requirements of the method. We need to know the purposes and functions of the movements and practice them assiduously and with perseverance. Only through time can results be accomplished and the Dào be achieved. As they say in the United States, the only way to Carnegie Hall is to practice, practice and practice.

How much and how hard should we practice? Everyone is different. Mental and physical conditions need to be considered. A practice schedule should be a regular part of the daily routine like brushing the teeth. Practice up to maximum ability, but do not be obsessed. Do not compare yourself with others, only with progress in your own practice. Find out what makes the improvements or setbacks. There is always room for growth. Results take time and effort to obtain. Once the schedule is set, stay with it. Never practice to a point where it takes a few days for the body to recover. This will harm the body. Listen to the body. Know when to stop. When the body is getting better, discomfort may appear. Stay with the practice; otherwise, one may go backward. Be patient.

b. Progress gradually

Qìgōng practice is like a thousand-mile journey; take one step at a time. To get results, persistence and determination are needed. Everything happens in its own time. The rule of thumb is to progress gradually, from simple to complex and from one to many. After a proper practice, one should feel that the body is rejuvenated, the mind is relaxed, and that there is harmony with nature.

One of the common mistakes made by many practitioners is to consider learning new forms to progress. There are many levels of practice within one form. It is not how many forms that are known, it is how well they are known. Every trail leads to the mountain top. Just do it, one practice at a time. As long as we follow the principles, we will arrive at the goal.

4. Relaxation, Quietness and Being Natural

a. Relaxation

Relaxation consists of two parts, physical and mental.

Physical relaxation

The body is relaxed but not collapsing, poised but not stiff. Instead of using force to maintain the posture, one uses Qì and mind intent; therefore, body postures are poised, and maintain a certain degree of tension without being stiff. The perfect example for achieving this requirement is when a baby reaches for something. The baby's natural body posture is what is called "relaxing without collapsing."

One of the most common misconceptions about relaxing is to "not use any force." To maintain our body posture without collapsing, some force is needed. "Force" in this case means unnecessary force. If maintaining body posture takes ten pounds of force, then using ten pounds is not using force; using 10.1 pounds, however, is using force and 9.9 pounds is collapsing.

Mental relaxation

How can we maintain this kind of relaxation? When the physical body begins to relax, the mind intent has to expand. As the mind intent expands throughout the body, the trapped force or excess tension will be released. Qì follows the mind. In the moving Qìgōng forms such as the Body & Mind Method of Zhìnéng Qìgōng and internal martial arts, the mind has to penetrate/permeate into every movement. Whether Qì is present or not will depend on the penetration and expansion of the mind. When the mind is excited, it is very difficult to have a relaxed body.

One of the most effective methods to relax is called the Three-Line Relaxation Method or the Sections Relaxation Method. In Zhìnéng Qìgōng, we use the Sections Relaxation Method for preparation most of the time. Students follow the teacher's instructions to relax each section of the body, from head to toes, and then continue by expanding the mind (head touches sky, feet stand on earth, etc.). Sometimes, the Sections Relaxation Method is combined with the Sound Vibrating Method. For example, when the teacher says, "relax the head," students concentrate on the head, mentally relax it, and at the same time pronounce "sōng 鬆."

b. Quietness

Normally, quietness refers to the mind in a tranquil state. Quietness has two meanings. One is that the mind does not have a single thought; the other is that the mind concentrates on one thing only—a thousand thoughts are substituted with one. It is not easy to maintain a single thought without any interruption for a long period of time (i.e., forty-five minutes), let alone not having one single thought. The quietness that Zhìnéng Qìgōng is looking for can be found in concentrating on doing the movements without distractions. One of the techniques for concentrating is to give instructions for the body to follow—to call out the form. If one can follow the instructions without distractions, one achieves the requirement of quietness.

c. Be Natural

Being natural refers to following the natural rhythms of the body. Nothing is forced. A person's daily activities are accomplished by the integration of body and mind. The aim of practicing Qìgōng is to purify the body movements, to strengthen beneficial ones, and to eliminate harmful ones. In the beginning, Qìgōng requirements seem awkward. Awkwardness does not mean unnatural. We have acquired numerous bad habits over the years that strengthen some abilities and weaken others. This creates physiological imbalance that can be harmful to the body. Many movements in Qìgōng are designed to correct habitual movements.

Returning to the natural uninhibited stage may cause an unnatural feeling in the beginning. Everyone starts from a different point. What is natural for one person may not be natural for another. We should listen to our own bodies and find the most comfortable way to practice. When we believe we are practicing to the best of our abilities, our minds will relax and be natural. For example, if someone has limited mobility in the upper body and can only perform half of a movement in the prescribed way, and as long as he/she respects the body's limitations, he/she has met the requirement to be natural. Visualizing a non-moving part moving can lead Qì through that area, causing illness to gradually disappear. If someone always shows off in front of others, he will not be able to consolidate Qì.

Qìgōng is an inward cultivation. We should not compare ourselves with others, especially the disadvantaged ones. If we do not feel comfortable with our own practice and fear that other people are watching us, we are not being natural. Ideally, one does not pay attention to the others in a group practice. Once the eyes are closed, each person is the only person in the world. Everything around him/her does not exist anymore. He/she and nature have become one. Accepting our limitations and working hard to improve them is what being natural is all about.

5. Nourishment

Qìgōng requires two things, practice and nourishment.

Nourishment includes good nutrition and adequate rest. When health improves from one stage/level to another, the demand for Qì in quantity and quality greatly increases. During this time, we may feel tired and drained. The reason is that once new channels for Qì open up, we do not have enough Qì to fill them. Only when we accumulate enough Qì will that feeling disappear. For example, assume the volume of Qì one needs to maintain life functions is ten liters and an extra ten liters is needed each time the health improves from one stage/level to another. When stage/level one begins to fill up, we feel energized and have plenty of Qì. But once the health improves from stage/level one to stage/level two, twenty liters of Qì is needed and we still have only ten liters. So we may feel tired and have less energy. It is not a sign of regression, but an indication of improvement. During this stage, practice and nourishment are very important. We should continue to practice with intensity and have plenty of rest and proper nutrition.

Zhìnéng Qìgōng recommends a balanced diet with dietary supplements, if necessary. In order to survive in adverse conditions, wild animals and plants absorb and retain vast amounts of universal Qì. So "wild" food (animals, vegetables, fruits, etc.) is better than farm raised; organic food is better than regular food, fresh food is better than canned food. When choosing food, select a variety of sources and flavors. According to Traditional Chinese Medicine, different flavors and foods nourish different inner organs. For example, foods with sour flavor nourish the liver. Wheat, onions, lamb and almonds nourish the heart. Too much or too little of one food can lead to illness.

In Qìgōng methods, traditional moving Qìgōng is considered practice, while stillness Qìgōng is considered nourishment. Zhìnéng Qìgōng incorporates practice and nourishment into the movements. In Zhìnéng Qìgōng, nourishment means Qì circulating uninterrupted. We get sick when Qì is blocked in one area of the body, depriving the area of proper Qì nourishment. No matter how much rest and nutrition we get, as long as Qì is blocked, illness remains. Only by opening all the Meridians can the body then get the proper nourishment.

From the very beginning, the goal of Zhìnéng Qìgōng practice is to merge ourselves and nature into one, and to facilitate releasing Internal Qì and absorbing External Qì. When we use the mind intent to activate Qì, it is practice; when we absorb universal Qì into the body, it is nourishment. Each open and close sequence contains one practice and one nourishment. We consider the Lift Chi Up and Pour Chi Down Method as practice and the Three Centers Merge Standing Method as nourishment. In contrast, the Body & Mind Method is practice, and the Lift Chi Up and Pour Chi Down Method is nourishment.

In Zhìnéng Qìgōng, practice and nourishment are considered to be one—different, yet inseparable. Generally speaking, open and release movements are practice, and close and absorb movements are nourishment. On a deeper level, the process of closing/opening is practice, and the split-second before opening/closing is nourishment. Breathing in/out is considered practice, while the pause between inhaling and exhaling is nourishment.

A bow with too much tension becomes rigid; with too little tension it becomes slack. In either case, the bow is useless. Only when the proper degree of tension exists will the bow become useful. If we understand this principle, then we will find that every Qìgōng method has both practice and nourishment. When practice is combined with nourishment, health improves quickly.

6. Focus and Observe Simultaneously

This concept also is called "Stop and Examine Simultaneously" (Dìng huì shuāng yùn 定慧雙運). Focus (Dìng) refers to the ability to eliminate distracting thoughts, to let the mind focus/stop in one area, and to enable the mind to relax. It is the most common method most practitioners use at the initial stage of Qìgōng practice. After one achieves Dìng (the mental conditions are relaxed and balanced), one proceeds to examine Huì (慧). Huì refers to the inner observation and preservation of the changes inside the body, such as numbness and painful feeling, sensations of Qì flow, the open and close of the acupuncture points, and the changes of mindfulness, etc.

With total focus inside the body (this is called Dìng inside the body), one observes and perceives, and does not analyze or anticipate (this is called Huì). The better one observes, the deeper the mind intent will permeate inside the body. With practice, one will gradually develop a special perceptive ability and lay the foundation for the training of internal Qì phenomenon observation. Observation/examination (Huì) is not logical thinking or analyzing, it means to use the mind directly to observe/examine the internal structures/systems and the state of internal movements. No matter what kind of changes or reactions one may observe and perceive, once aware of them, the mind just follows them, no analyzing, anticipating, or directing.

Although Focus (Dìng) and Observation (Huì) have different meanings, they cannot be separated during the practice. They do not contradict but complement each other. During the practice, it is not only normal but essential to use both Focus and Observation alternatively. For example, when distracting thoughts occur, one would use Focus to stay concentrated; with concentration, one can proceed to Observe. During Observation, the feeling one has or the things being observed may stimulate the brain and cause distractions. Then, one will have to use Focus again. As a matter of fact, during Observation, the mind and Qì are merged as one; the better the merger, the easier to maintain the concentration. Therefore, Observation is Focus, the deeper the observation, the better the Focus; the deeper the Focus, the finer the Observation. Whether there is progress in the practice or not depends upon the application of Focus and Observation.

7. Time and Place

We need to work out a schedule according to our own circumstances. Ideally, we should practice at the same place, same time, and for the same length of time every day. Do not be too ambitious; be realistic. Once the schedule is set, stay with it. Even when we feel sick, stay with the practice. This is the time when we need Qì the most. After a long day at work, practice can rejuvenate our tired body and mind. We can overcome most temptations and excuses to quit by staying with a realistic schedule.

Practicing Qìgōng not only cultivates the Qì, but more importantly, cultivates the mind. If we continue to practice in adverse circumstances, we can increase our mental abilities to deal with mundane daily activities. Daily practice also is habit forming. By practicing in the same place, a Qì Field is created by attracting Qì into that space every day. Moreover, we may notice our small pets coming to where we practice and sitting near us. They are attracted to the strong Qì in the area. If our minds remain relaxed, these animals may actually protect the Qì Field.

In order to advance to higher levels, practicing only in a fixed time and place is not enough. We need to incorporate Qìgōng into daily life and practice all day long. There are two ways to practice. One way is to practice in a set place, at a set time, and with set routines. This is called doing a "gong." The other way is to apply Qìgōng principles into daily activities. For example, before picking up a book to read, close the eyes for a few seconds and concentrate on the lower Dāntián. When reading, continue to pay attention to the lower Dāntián. By connecting the Dāntián with every movement, we are practicing Qìgōng. We also should move with the proper body postures at all times, not just during practice. While walking, suspend the head from above, relax the shoulders, drop the elbows, push the Mìngmén out, relax the whole body, and pay attention to the Dāntián. This is walking Qìgōng. Recall that Qìgōng requires the mind to be calm and relaxed. The best way to train is by applying Qìgōng principles to the chaos of daily life. If we can remain calm and centered during adverse circumstances, we are practicing the highest level of Qìgōng. One of the key points in Qìgōng is to merge mental with physical activities; perform every movement mindfully. For example, to erect the palms: first, the brain thinks of erecting the palms (mental activity); then, it issues the command to erect the palms. Next, the body begins to move (physical activity), and the palms are erected. When the mind is concentrated on the movement of erecting the palms, it is merging mental activity with physical activity. Qìgōng practice is flexible. Routine work can be very boring, sometimes becoming a hazard. If we can put our minds into the routine and be conscious of our body movements all the time, we are practicing Qìgōng.

Different Ways to Practice Qìgōng

Traditionally, Qìgōng practice is divided into three major ways to practice.

1. Jīng Practice

In this practice, Shén and Qì concentrate on the posture; it is Shén and Qì that service Jīng/body. This technique uses the mind intent to concentrate on the postures to achieve the integration of consciousness with the physical body; through the integration, Qì is also concentrated in the physical body. With this type of practice, the abilities of the physical body will be strengthened; consequently, Shén and Qì are also strengthened. But in this practice, Shén is only strengthened on the posture level, and its function is expressed in the abilities of the posture, such as running faster, being stronger, etc. Most martial art Qìgōngs use this method at the beginning and intermediate stages of practice.

2. Qì Practice

The focus is on Qì, and Jīng and Shén to service Qì. Shén plays a vital role in this practice, but it is not the focal point. One needs Shén to practice Qì; it is Shén that concentrates toward Qì. The posture belongs to Jīng, but the purpose of the practice is not to strengthen the body (postures), it is to strengthen Qì; and Jīng services Qì. In this practice, the body would not become bulky or overly muscular; and may even look weak. The truth is that the body (posture) is more refined and is extremely strong, it is steel wrapped in cotton.

One of the major branches of Dàoist Qìgōng, Dān Dào Qìgōng (丹道氣功), uses this approach. Normally, Dān Dào Qìgōng focuses on Prenatal Qì. It begins with Breathing, then progresses to "Change Jīng into Qì" (練精化氣). From the beginning to the end, the practice focuses on Qì. Once the body has accumulated enough Qì, the Meridians will open up; then the practitioner will concentrate Qì and proceeds to change the physical state of Qì. At the highest level, the physical body will become the Qì body.

3. Shén Practice

The focus is on Shén (mind intent, consciousness). Jīng and Qì are not important in this practice, they service Shén. The whole practice is within the mind intent; in other words, one practices with the mind only. It seems very easy, all one has to do is "think" about it. But in reality, it is easy to think about something, but to be able to merge the focus with mind intent, and to have body and Qì serve Shén simultaneously is extremely difficult. Shén practice ignores the physical body and Qì, and focuses on cultivating Shén only; therefore, the Qì activation is relatively slow. It is very difficult to achieve high levels of cultivation. The Zen branch of Buddhist Qìgōng (佛家禅宗) uses this approach.

Although focal points are different, the Jīng, Qì and Shén practices overlap one another. It cannot be said that Jīng practice is pure Jīng practice nor that Qì practice is pure Qì practice. Shén plays a vital role in all practices; therefore, there are practices which are a combination of Shén and Qì, and Shén and Jīng.

4. Shén and Qì Practice

The main characteristic of this practice is that the practitioner focuses on both Shén and Qì; Shén and Qì complement one another; they utilize and help each other. There are four steps to this practice.

a. Shén Thinking Qì

This practice requires the mind to merge with Qì by thinking about Qì. It is like thinking about a loved one; one always is aware of, pays attention to, and thinks about Qì. As we all know, Qì is formless and invisible in normal circumstances. Formless and invisible do not mean that it is empty or non-existing, it is a unique substance that is in an existing and a non-existing state, it is called Xūwú (虛無) in Qìgōng.

The Qì in traditional Shén Thinking Qì practice is Internal Qì. But most practitioners would not be able to feel or be aware of it in the beginning stage of practice. How do you think of something that is non-existing and cannot be felt? The method that Zhìnéng Qìgōng uses is to think about External Qì first. The technique is to think blue sky or to think about the vastness of outer space. One important point is that the blue sky is not empty but is filled with formless, odorless, colorless Qì. Think blue sky, actually means to think of this Qì. Normally, this substance is very difficult to feel. The feeling of Qì that one experiences while practicing comes from Internal Qì being scattered around the body. Therefore, one needs to have an existing and non-existing image of Qì. But it is not the image that one is looking at, it is the feeling of the image. If one keeps thinking of that existing and non-existing image, sooner or later, one would have a feeling of the image.

If one still has difficulty thinking of Qì, the next step is to practice Lā Qì[1] (拉氣). (Lā Qì: hands open/separate to shoulder width, close back to almost touching each other and repeat). Do Lā Qì whenever there is chance/time. Once there is feeling during Lā Qì, proceed to think of the body, and do Lā Qì with the body. With practice, the body will begin to have a Qì sensation; then one thinks about that Qì sensation.

---

[1] Lā Qì: For details, refer to page 125, Zhìnéng (Chilel) Qìgōng: Overview and Foundation Methods

Strictly speaking, sensing things should belong to the next stage—Shén Observing Qì. When one is thinking of Qì, one is also observing Qì, and gradually, one will sense Qì. When the mind is very focused in "Thinking Qì," it becomes "Observing Qì." Therefore, the separation between "Shén Thinking Qì" and "Shén Observing Qì" is not clear cut. As the mind becomes highly concentrated, the volume of concentrated Qì will increase; consequently, one will have Qì sensation. When "Shén Thinking Qì" becomes proficient, Qì will be concentrated into a "light ball" or "Qì ball." When that happens, one has to dissolve that ball; otherwise, the attention will be on the image of the ball, it is no longer Qì.

When using the External Qì method, besides Nature Qì, one can think of the Qì that surrounds the body. One can practice thinking of the surrounding Qì during daily routines such as walking. The technique is to use the mind intent to enlarge oneself, become bigger and occupy bigger space. Imagine oneself as a giant engulfed with a layer of Qì. When walking, imagine you are holding that layer of Qì with the hands; hold on to that Qì and do not let it drop or dissipate. Hold on to that Qì and do not let it drop or dissipate means to pay attention to and think about that Qì. At the beginning, one may not be able to hold on to the Qì, but if one can imagine carrying that layer of Qì all the time, it would not take too long before one is able to hold and sense Qì. Also, other people may be able to sense that layer of Qì when a proficient practitioner is close by. When one is aware of this layer of Qì and connects it with the body, the Internal Qì and External Qì will gradually merge as one.

b. Shén Observing Qì

Shén Observing Qì means to observe, to see or to feel Qì; and Shén Observing Qì also can be a special perception of Qì. Seeing Qì can be either with the eyes open or closed. But for beginners, squinting the eyes makes it easier to see Qì, which can be either Internal Qì or External Qì.

Normally, one begins with observing External Qì. With squinting eyes, one can see Qì as a thin layer of foggy mist engulfing an object such as the sun, moon, trees and flowers, etc. For the beginner, it is the best to begin with observing the Qì from the trees. In the early morning, look at the trees. With practice, one will be able to see the trees' Qì as light grey or white mist. Next step is to see the flowers' Qì, and then the Qì in the space/air. Once one is able to sense the existence of Qì, one should merge Shén and Qì according to the form's requirement. This can strengthen Qì's functions.

Instead of observing Qì in the external objects, one can also observe the Qì surrounding the body. Because Qì in and around the hands is very strong and obvious, one should begin with observing the Qì around the hands, first by squinting the eyes, and then with eyes open. After the hands, the next step is to observe the Qì surrounding the body. Qì contains much life information, once one can see Qì, one will gradually be able to sense that information.

Once one can see External Qì, the next step is to see Internal Qì. Observing the Internal Qì is more difficult, requiring proficiency in observing External Qì first; it is because different kinds of Qì (organ Qì, Meridian Qì, etc.) interact with one another inside the physical body. These types of Qì are affected not only by the changes in the physical body, but also by the mind's activities. Traditional Qìgōng emphasizes "Tranquil Observation." Through tranquil observation, one's mindfulness can engulf the whole body and one may sense a hazy Qì being either inside or outside the body. This Qì being can be either slightly larger or smaller than one's own physical body. The larger being is the sensation one feels and sees when the Internal Qì is scattered around his/her own body; the smaller being is the sensation one feels and sees when the Internal Qì is in the skin and membranes.

c. **Shén into Qì**

In Shén observes Qì, Shén is the observer and Qì is the target. They are separate. In this step, it requires that Shén gets inside Qì. There are two ways to achieve Shén into Qì. Traditionally, in Qì Practice, when one cultivates "Change Jīng into Qì" up to a certain point, Qì in the body becomes so sufficient that the lower Dāntián and middle Dāntián would merge as one. One would see a hazy object below the heart. This hazy object is the Qì changed from Jīng. If one can observe the object with supreme concentration, gradually, Shén will be into Qì. This Qì is Internal Qì.

Another way to achieve Shén into Qì is via Shén Observing Qì, but the practitioner must be able to observe Qì. With the eyes closed, one begins with observing the Qì engulfing the body, then slowly expands outward to the surrounding Qì; the surrounding Qì expands outward continuously, gradually letting go of the mind intent and focusing on Qì only. At the beginning, Shén Observing Qì is Shén in one side and Qì in another, they are separated; now Qì is surrounding the whole body. It is Shén inside Qì. This Qì is External Qì.

d. **Shén and Qì become one**

In the Shén into Qì stage, Shén and Qì are still separate. In this stage, while observing External Qì, Shén expands, engulfs and permeates both Internal and External Qì; Shén and Qì then become one. In other words, Qì is cultivated to a point that it becomes Shén. It is a very high level of practice that very few people can do.

5. Shén and Xíng Practice

The main characteristic of this practice is that the Shén and body postures complement each other; they use and help each other. There are three steps for this practice.

a. Shén Thinking Xíng Stage

In this stage, mind activities are integrated with the body movements. Mind activates and directs every body movement. In other words, the mind gives very clear commands to the body on what and how to execute movements. Every movement is divided into small segments; the sequence of the segments is observed and followed. Most important, the mind has a very clear picture of the sequence of the movement and every segment is executed; therefore, one must have correct postures in practicing Shén Thinking Xíng.

Generally speaking, if one's mind gives a movement command to one's body to execute, it is called Shén Thinking Xíng. Shén Thinking Xíng is a process, a process of merging mind intent and body movements. This seems very simple, yet it is not easy to do. Most practitioners can only maintain Shén Thinking Xíng for a very short period of time. If the mind cannot concentrate or wanders slightly, it fails the requirement of Shén thinking Xíng. Once one masters this stage, distracting thoughts will cease to exist.

b. Shén Observing Xíng Stage

In this stage, Shén is seeing or feeling the body movements. Normally, one begins this stage of practice only after he/she has achieved a certain degree of proficiency in Shén Thinking Xíng, but one can begin with this stage first. The way to do it is to practice in front of a mirror and observe one's own posture. The first step is to observe the body posture first, then the movements; the next step is to observe the body posture during the movements. When one is able to be aware of the body during the movements, one proceeds to Shén Observing Xíng practice.

Shén Observing Xíng can be divided into two steps.

1) Shén observing external body postures

With the eyes closed during practice, Shén is "observing" one's own body movements as if watching someone else practicing. Shén can be observing movements from the front of the body. Shén can also look into the Dāntián area to observe a small self doing the practice. Once Shén is able to observe the whole sequence of movements, the mind has achieved a high level of self-control.

2) Shén observing internal Xíng

Once we have achieved a certain proficiency in observing external body postures, Shén's abilities to observe and penetrate will allow us to see through the body. For example, Shén can see and feel the movement of Qì inside the body when the body moves. With practice, we can see the circulation of Qì inside our bodies and the exchange of Qì between ourselves and nature. One important point is that we can only observe, not analyze. In traditional Qìgōngs, this is called "tranquility and reflection." Tranquility means that the mind is calm. Reflection means that the mind only observes and reflects changes in the body like a reflecting pond — the calmer the water, the better the reflection.

c. Shén into Xíng Stage

It is a very advanced practice that very few people can do because it requires Shén into every part of the body including cells. The most common practice is while observing the internal body, Shén fixes on a particular point and observes the surrounding areas from that point. When one can be aware of the surroundings and all their activities simultaneously, Shén is into the body.

The reason for dividing Shén and Qì practice and Shén and Xíng practice into different stages is to improve understanding of the overall practice. In actual practice, the stages overlap one another. Shén and Qì practice and Shén and Xíng practice also overlap one another. The point of focus differentiates the stage and the practice.

Chapter Two: Zhìnéng Qìgōng

智能氣功

The Characteristics of Zhìnéng Qìgōng

1. Zhìnéng Qìgōng has a system of special theories: Hùn Yuán Wholistic Theory

The Zhìnéng Qìgōng theoretical system consists of Wholistic Theory (整體論), Hùn Yuán Theory (混元論), Human Hùn Yuán Qì Theory (人的混元氣), Consciousness Theory (意識論), and Morality Theory (道德論); collectively, they are called Hùn Yuán Wholistic Theory. Traditional Chinese Medicine and most Qìgōng schools divide Human Qì into different kind of categories such as Zhēn Qì (真氣), Yíng Qì (營氣), Wèi Qì (衛氣), Zōng Qì (宗氣), Yuán Qì (元氣), Meridian Qì (經絡之氣), Zàngfǔ Qì (臟腑之氣), etc. Zhìnéng Qìgōng defines Human Qì which consists of Prenatal and Postnatal Qì as Human Hùn Yuán Qì. Zhìnéng Qìgōng further divides Human Hùn Yuán Qì into Body Hùn Yuán Qì (軀體混元氣), Organ Hùn Yuán Qì (臟真混元氣) and Yí Yuán Ti Hùn Yuán Qì (意元體混元氣) and devises a series of methods to cultivate them. For example, Lift Qì Up and Pour Qì Down Method and the Body & Mind Method focus on Body Hùn Yuán Qì; the Five Element Method and the Central Meridian Hùn Yuán Method focus on Organ Hùn Yuán Qì; and the Central Line Hùn Yuán Method focuses on Yí Yuán Ti Hùn Yuán Qì.

Depending on which level (kind) of Hùn Yuán Qì the practitioner is cultivating, different theories are applied to the methods accordingly. According to Hùn Yuán Wholistic Theory, the interactions between humans and nature which cause changes are transmutation processes. The Internal-External transmutation process is to transmute Human Hùn Yuán Qì with Nature Qì into one, which can be used by the body. The methods to cultivate Body Hùn Yuán Qì follow this principle. For example, Lift Qì Up and Pour Qì Down Method uses the mind intent and movements to activate the body's Open-Close functions. The Open-Close functions merge the Internal Qì (Human Hùn Yuán Qì) and the body surrounding Qì with Nature Qì and transmute them into one.

The Hùn Yuán Wholistic Theory states that there are five levels of Hùn Yuán Qì (Hùn Yuán Element Stage (混元子層次), Primal Hùn Yuán Qì Level/Stage (初始混元氣層次), Ten Thousand Things Level (萬物混元氣層次), Human Hùn Yuán Qì (人混元氣層次) and Yì Yuán Tǐ (意元體混元氣層次). Each level's substances have their unique characteristics. For External Qì, most Qìgōng Schools cultivate and use the Ten Thousand Things Level Hùn Yuán Qì, Zhìnéng Qìgōng's primary focus is on cultivating and using Primal Hùn Yuán Qì, and secondarily, on Human Hùn Yuán Qì. There are three reasons for that approach.

a. The Hùn Yuán Element exists in an extremely brief time, and then it becomes nonexistent. The Primal Hùn Yuán Qì exists in every part of the Universe and permeates every level of matter. It is the most basic, formless and inexhaustible substance; and it is the energy source and the raw material for transmutations between different types of matter. Ten Thousand Things Level Hùn Yuán Qì (substances), such as flowers, trees, etc., all have their own characteristics. Although some of their characteristics are similar to the Human Organ Qì, it is similar, but not the same. For example, in order to absorb the vegetables Qì into the body, one must break down the complex Qì (vegetables Qì) into simple Qì that is comparable the Human Qì; it is a very complicated process and requires a lot of energy. The Primal Hùn Yuán Qì is the raw material that can be changed into the Human Body Hùn Yuán Qì. All one has to do is use the mind intent to connect with it and bring it into the body; there is no additional refinement needed. It is very straight forward and simple.

b. Most Ten Thousand Things Level Hùn Yuán Qì that one absorbs into the body lacks vitality. For example, most of the food that one eats is cooked, live vegetables become cooked vegetables and their vitalities may not be as strong. Occasionally, one may not be able to get all the necessary Qì from them and imbalance may occur.

c. Each person's Qì is different. The Hùn Yuán Wholistic Theory states that the human body consists of Prenatal and Postnatal Q, and is divided into Jīng (physical body), Qì, and Shén (consciousness/mind), which are the manifestation or the different appearances of the Hùn Yuán Qì. Since the Primal Hùn Yuán Qì is the purest and most basic, it can be used by everyone.

Most Qìgōng manuscripts refer to the Primal Hùn Yuán Qì as Nature Qì or Língyáng Qì (靈陽之氣 efficacious Yáng Qì). In Dàoist Qìgōng, the practitioner first focuses on the Lower Dāntián to cultivate Jīng; up to a certain degree, he dissolves the Jīng into Qì. Then, the practitioner will cultivate Qì into Shén. When the Lower Dāntián and Middle Dāntián merge to form a unified Dāntián, Shén and Qì merge to form a Dàdān (大丹) which is also called Zhēnyīn (真陰). The final step is to cultivate Shén into Xū (虛 man and nature become one). "Cultivate Shén into Xū" means to bring in Língyáng Qì and merge it with Zhēnyīn to dissolve the Dàdān.

From the very beginning, Zhìnéng Qìgōng emphasizes collecting the Língyáng Qì. In order to pull the Qì in, one must have a solid foundation; without a foundation, one cannot pull the Qì in or hold on to it. Since the Zhìnéng Qìgōng practitioners do not have the same foundation as the Dàoist Qìgōng practitioners, Zhìnéng Qìgōng uses a different approach to achieve "man and nature become one." Zhìnéng Qìgōng uses mind intent and mindful body movements (movements merged with mind intent) to pull in the Língyáng Qì and merge it with Internal Qì; starting from the outside (outer level) first and gradually moving inward. The focus point of the mind intent is different in each method; for example, the Lift Qì Up and Pour Qì Down Method is mainly external and focuses on External Qì. The Body & Mind Method is internal and focuses on muscles and bones. The Five Element Method is also internal and focuses on the organs. The Central Meridian Method is the center of the body and focuses on the Central Meridian. The Central Line Method focuses on the center line, and Return to One Method is to shrink the center line into one point and then dissolve it to achieve Man and Heaven become one.

There are many schools of Qìgōng in China; each has its theories and perspectives; therefore, their training methods are different. The school based on Yīn/Yáng theories uses balanced Yīn/Yáng as the measuring point to regulate and balance the body's Yīn and Yáng to eliminate illness and to strengthen the body. Some systems are based on Sāncái (三才 Man, Heaven and Earth) theories. The Sāncái in the human body are Jīng, Qì, and Shén. The human being is an entity formed by the integration of the three into one. Through 2,000 years of practice, Dàoist systems have found that the methods based on Sāncái theories are very effective ways to improve health. Some systems are based on the Five Elements, which in the human body, are the five internal organs. When the five organs functions are normal, the body is healthy. Some systems are based on the Bāguà (八卦). The Bāguà, in the human body, is the eight Extraordinary Meridians, which are directly related to the circulation of Qì and blood in the Meridians. They can also regulate the twelve Meridians of the body. When the eight Extraordinary Meridians functions are normal, the body is healthy. Some schools use a more complicated system such as the twelve Meridians. In this system, they use different methods, according to the special characteristics of each Meridian, to strengthen the different Meridian functions. The most complicated one is based on the Ten Thousand Things Level, which uses different methods for different illnesses. From the Yīn/Yáng theories level to the Ten Thousand Things level, the theories and methods become more complicated with each level.

The Hùn Yuán Wholistic Theory states that all these levels (Yīn/Yáng, Bāguà, etc.) of Qì are the manifestations of the Primal Hùn Yuán Qì. Zhìnéng Qìgōng is based on the Primal Hùn Yuán Qì level, its theories and methods are very simple; practitioners can just follow the requirements of the methods to practice and to absorb the Primal Hùn Yuán Qì into the body. The Hùn Yuán Qì in the body will automatically regulate and balance the Yīn/Yáng, the internal organs (Wǔháng 五行), the Meridian's Qì and the blood (Bāguà 八卦). If the Yīn or Yáng is deficient, the Hùn Yuán Qì will replenish it. Whichever organ or Meridian is deficient, the Hùn Yuán Qì will automatically regulate, balance, and replenish it. Any illness can be returned to normal. For this reason, in healing, there is no need for diagnosis or different treatment methods for different illnesses, nor any need to consider the status of the body's Yīn/Yáng, the Five Elements, and the Bāguà etc.

Each school of Qìgōng bases its theories and methods on the appearance (or level) of Qì. We can use the metaphor of a tree to describe and explain the theories and methods they use. A tree's vitality is indicated by the withering or the flourishing of its leaves and branches. The Ten Thousand Things level system focuses on the condition of the leaves to work on the tree. The Yīn/Yáng, the internal organs (Wǔháng 五行), and the Meridian (Bāguà 八卦) systems focus on the state of the large and small branches. The system based on Primal Hùn Yuán Qì focuses on the trunk of the tree. If the trunk is strong and healthy, the branches and the leaves will flourish. Although the basis for the theories is different, each has its own merits. One should not use Zhìnéng Qìgōng's theories to measure the merits or short comings of other systems, nor should one use other systems' theories to explain Zhìnéng Qìgōng. The characteristics of Zhìnéng Qìgōng's theories and methods are simple and straight forward to the core. Integrating other theories, such as Yīn/Yáng, the Five Elements, etc., with Zhìnéng Qìgōng will deviate from the basic foundation theories of Zhìnéng Qìgōng.

2. Zhìnéng Qìgōng has a complete system of methods

The Zhìnéng Qìgōng system consists of three types of practice: Moving Forms (動功); Stillness Forms (靜功); and Spontaneous Forms (自發功). These three types of practice follow the process from elementary to advanced, from External Hùn Yuán to Internal Hùn Yuán, and to Central Hùn Yuán.

The Zhìnéng Qìgōng Moving Forms consist of three stages and six progressive methods. The three stages are: External Hùn Yuán; Internal Hùn Yuán; and Central Hùn Yuán. The six progressive methods are the following.

a. The First Step Gōng: Lift Qì Up and Pour Qì Down Method (捧氣貫頂法). It belongs to the External Hùn Yuán stage.
b. The Second Step Gōng: The Body & Mind Method (形神庄)—the practice to merge the body and the mind.
c. The Third Step Gōng: The Five Elements Method (五元庄)—the practice to merge the inner organs.
   Both the Second and the Third Step Gōng belong to the Internal Hùn Yuán stage.
d. The Fourth Step Gōng: Central Meridian Hùn Yuán.
e. The Fifth Step Gōng: Central Line Hùn Yuán.
f. The Sixth Step Gōng: Return to One.
   The Fourth, Fifth and Sixth Step Gōngs belong to the Central Hùn Yuán stage.

The progressions of the above methods are arranged according to the physiological activities of the human being. The skin, muscles, blood vessels, inner organs, skeleton, and cells, etc., all have membranes. For people who have not practiced Qìgōng, the Hùn Yuán Qì inside of the body mainly circulates along the membranes; therefore, exchanging Qì with nature occurs mostly on the membranes and the skin.

The first step Gōng, Lift Qì Up and Pour Qì Down Method, is to cultivate the External Hùn Yuán. Its purpose is to strengthen these innate functions and to ensure the venues for exchanging Qì with nature will remain open and uninterrupted. This will transmute the Hùn Yuán Qì in the skin and the membrane and the Hùn Yuán Qì in nature into one. This process mainly uses the mind intent and occurs mainly outside of the body; therefore, it is called External Hùn Yuán. Through this method, one can activate releasing Internal Qì and absorbing External Qì functions—one will be able to absorb more External Hùn Yuán Qì into the body. This not only increases the amount of Hùn Yuán Qì inside the body, but also improves the quality and instills in the practitioner the ability to use External Qì for healing. Because the membrane's function is strengthened, sensory functions will be improved. Extraordinary abilities such as seeing Qì, see-through, and perceiving information, etc., can appear. However, in the External Hùn Yuán stage, Qì mainly circulates in less dense areas of the skin and the membranes. The strength and quantity are not as strong; consequently, the functions of the extraordinary abilities that develop are very limited. Nevertheless, when practicing External Hùn Yuán successfully, one is already assured of normal life functions and there is sufficient Qì to strengthen health, and to prevent and cure illness.

The Internal Hùn Yuán stage includes the second step Gōng—the Body & Mind Method, and the third step Gōng—the Five Elements Method. The Body & Mind Method focuses on the integration of the physical body and mental activities. For the Hùn Yuán Qì to be able to gradually permeate from the surface layers to deep inside the body, it requires a high degree of integration between the physical body and the mind intent. The Body & Mind Method mainly cultivates the Body Hùn Yuán Qì. Its purpose is to merge the Meridians' Qì and the blood into one by opening the venues between the five layers of the physical body (skin, muscles, tendons, blood vessels, and skeleton). This will strengthen the Internal Qì's nourishing the body abilities and broaden the degree of depth and the extent of the nourishment. When the Hùn Yuán Qì is sufficient in every part of the body, the functions will be stronger, and then the body will be healthier.

The Body & Mind Method stretches the tendons and loosens up the joints, ligaments, and bones; therefore, it is the most strenuous of all of the six methods. Practicing this method, one can permeate Qì deep into the muscles and the skeleton, increasing their sensitivities. As a result, one can feel/be aware of his/her condition. Although the Body & Mind Method also activates some Inner Organ Qì, one needs to practice the Five Elements Method to cultivate the Inner Organ Qì. It is important to understand that when practicing the Body & Mind Method successfully, one's health will exceed the norm.

The Five Elements Method cultivates Qì in the heart, liver, spleen, lungs, and kidneys. In this method, one not only cultivates the Inner Organ Qì, more importantly, one also cultivates the emotions and mental activities associated with the inner organs. Traditional Chinese Medicine considers the five organs as corresponding with the five emotions: the heart corresponds with joy; the liver with anger; the spleen with pensiveness; the lungs with worry/sadness; and the kidneys with fear. These five organs also are connected with the five mental activities: the heart with the mind; the liver with anima; the spleen with consciousness/intent; the lungs with the soul; and the kidneys with will.

Practicing the Five Elements Method will make the Inner Organ Qì sufficient, strengthen the organs' functions, and regulate the emotions and mental activities associated with the inner organs. It also strengthens one's ability to circulate Qì both inside and outside of the body. Through the Body & Mind Method, one integrates the skin, muscles, tendons, blood vessels, skeleton, and Meridian Qì and blood into one; and integrates the Inner Organ Qì, and the emotions and mental activities associated with them into one.

The Internal Qì integrates/merges the Meridians and the inner organs within the body and the physical body with hundreds of bones and ligaments, the four limbs, the five sensory organs, and the seven orifices into one, forming the Internal Hùn Yuán. At this point, the Internal Qì will be sufficient, the mind is serene and peaceful, the tendons are soft, the bones are strong, the body is healthy, and the physical body and mental activities are harmonized.

The ability to control one's own body is very limited for non-Qìgōng practitioners. For example, inside the body, there are many involuntary muscles such as the large and small intestines, inner organs, etc., that are not easily controlled by the mind intent. Through the practice of the Internal Hùn Yuán, one can increase the ability to control different parts of the body. For example, up to a certain degree, one can control the speed of the heartbeat, the blood pressure, and the movements of the intestines, etc. The practice of the Internal Hùn Yuán also can strengthen the ability to control one's own mind. Due to the Body Qì continuing to permeate deeply inside the body, this practice will greatly increase the degree of integration between man and nature. On this foundation, Qì continues to permeate into the body, and that is the beginning of practicing the Central Hùn Yuán.

Note: Since Fourth, Fifth, and Sixth Step Gōngs, Stillness Forms, and Spontaneous Forms have not been taught by Dr. Páng, their introduction will be omitted.

3. Zhìnéng Qìgōng contains many special/secretive practice techniques

Zhìnéng Qìgōng methods were a collection of many special techniques from Confucian, Dàoist, Buddhist, Medical, Martial Art, and Folk Qìgōngs. They were organized into one system. Dr. Páng studied with nineteen teachers. He had learned many techniques from these teachers which took them decades to refine, and were not easily taught to outsiders. These techniques may not be the essence of the methods, but they are the keys and the shortcuts to the practice. The arts such as Qìgōng, martial arts, and acrobatics, etc., have many techniques that normally were not taught to outsiders.

Zhìnéng Qìgōng contains many techniques that are simple and important. For example, in the section that describes the requirement of proper Qìgōng postures, it divides the body into fifteen sections—from the head to the toes—to describe the correct postures and the best way to accomplish them. Many of these techniques were secrets and were not taught to outsiders. Without the special techniques (pointers), it may take the practitioner years of searching to come up with the answers.

Zhìnéng Qìgōng methods are adopted from various traditional Qìgōng methods, which are very complicated and take years to learn. Dr. Páng Míng modified the methods and rearranged them into a series of movements. In the critical junctions, he added the special techniques to enhance the forms. For example, the Lift Qì Up and Pour Qì Down Method is the combination of the Six-direction Collecting Qì Method, Five Elements Collecting Qì Method, the collecting Qì from Heaven, Earth and Man Method, Yīn Yáng Collecting Qì Method, and the Permeating Qì Relaxation Method. The Lift Qì Up and Pour Qì Down Method becomes a form specialized in collecting Qì. The Body & Mind Method uses Nèi Gōng (内功) as a foundation, and adopted the martial art techniques from Tàijí Quán (太極拳), Mín Shān Tàijí Quán (岷山太極拳), Tàijí Quán Shí Sān Dān Fǎ (太極拳十三丹法), Tōng Bì Quán (通臂拳), Yì Jīn Jīng (易筋經), and Éméi Shí'èr Zhuāng (峨嵋十二庄), etc. The Body & Mind Method is a form specialized in stretching the tendons and loosening up the ligaments and bones. The Five Elements Method is basically from Yì Jīn Jīng(易筋經), Hùn Yuán Gōng (混元功), and Éméi Zhuāng Fǎ (峨嵋庄法), etc. The Five Elements Method also uses ancient secret-sound vibration techniques and is a form specialized in opening up Qì Channels in the inner organs.

4. Zhìnéng Qìgōng uses three teaching systems

The three teaching systems refer to teaching through the mind (intuitive transmission), verbal instructions, and physical demonstrations. The Ancients chose different teaching methods to accommodate the students with different abilities. Extraordinary students were taught by intuitive transmission, good students were taught by verbal instructions, and average students were taught by physical demonstrations. Extraordinary, good, and average refer to the differences in physical and mental conditions, and in the ability to comprehend the teaching.

a. Teaching through physical demonstrations

Teaching through physical demonstrations means to show the posture and the movement in a correct way. Zhìnéng Qìgōng follows Qìgōng theories, Chinese and

Western medicine theories, and some modern science theories to arrange every movement in the practice series comprehensively and rationally. Every movement is very precise and has its purposes. Therefore, the teachings focus on the body postures and movement first. Correct postures are the keys to obtain the intended results. To teach physical movements, one must use physical demonstrations. Some students may not be able to comprehend the theories, but with repeated demonstrations and practices, everyone should be able to master the essence of the movements and be able to achieve the correct postures. Because these movements and practice methods are primarily effective practicing techniques, by simply following the requirements of the forms, one activates the Qì inside the whole body, and nourishes and regulates the Meridians, the Qì, and the blood.

b. Teaching through verbal instructions

During the physical demonstrations, when the teacher explains the essence of the movements, the correct postures and the theories behind them, these explanations become verbal instructions. The true verbal instructions involve both teacher and student, they are not just the teacher's explanations, the student must be able to understand and absorb the explanations. For example, when the teacher says "relax," the student should experience the relaxation. If the student treats it as a word, it is not verbal instruction; when hearing the word "relax," the student's body follows the instruction to relax, then it is verbal instruction. When the teacher explains something, the student should apply the explanations/theories to the body, and let the theories become actual applications. For example, when the teacher is explaining a certain movement, the corresponding part of the student's body should move accordingly. Therefore, during verbal instruction the teacher explains, and the student listens/receives and practices to cause changes in the body.

In Zhìnéng Qìgōng, all methods are based on the Hùn Yuán Wholistic Theory, teaching through verbal instructions also means to teach Qìgōng theories. Teaching the theories not only helps the students to understand the principles of the methods, but more importantly, it builds one's Qìgōng awareness/ consciousness. Allowing this Qìgōng awareness to play a leading role in one's physiological activities will strengthen one's ability to comprehend the practice. The more one can comprehend Qìgōng theories, the more Qìgōng knowledge will be engraved into the brain. Once Qìgōng awareness is established, during practice or daily activities, one will use this awareness, either consciously or unconsciously, to direct life activities. This will cause one's physiological activities to follow Qìgōng's requirements to evolve. This is a very important point. Before Qìgōng awareness is able to direct the physiological activities, the Qìgōng practice will only be able to strengthen the body and eliminate illness. The body will not be able to achieve the evolution of an advanced Qì function; therefore, Zhìnéng Qìgōng emphasizes that the theories are the methods, and the methods are the theories. They are integrated as one. This is especially important when one's practice reaches the advanced level.

c. **Teaching through intuitive transmission**

In the old days, teachers with high abilities taught the students whose physical and mental conditions were very healthy, and with a high degree of comprehension through intuitive transmission. They did not need to speak and used only their consciousness for the students to receive and understand the teachings. It is called "teaching through intuitive transmission." However, the one who had the ability to use this teaching method was extremely rare; most of them used the method called "Verbal instruction (teacher), receive through the mind (student) (口傳心受)."

Instead of depending on the abilities of the teacher, Zhìnéng Qìgōng uses a different approach to teach through intuitive transmission. It is mainly done by Organizing the Qì Field. "Organizing the Qì Field" refers to the teacher using his/her mind intent to gather and mobilize the natural Hùn Yuán Qì and the Qì of every participant, and to unite and transform them into one "Field." The first step of "Organizing the Qì Field" is the organizer/teacher synchronizing every participant's mind intent. After synchronization, the organizer merges the natural Hùn Yuán Qì and the group Qì into one "Field;" once the Field is formed, the final step is the organizer/teacher issuing instructions for the group to perform a task, such as to practice the form, to perform healing, etc. In a Qì Field, all mind intent and movements are synchronized; with unified movement and mind intent, the group power will greatly improve the results.

Zhìnéng Qìgōng's "Organizing the Qì Field" is a unique, new teaching and healing method. It was developed and restructured by integrating modern scientific knowledge with the combination of two techniques used by Qìgōng teachers. One of the techniques is the way ancient teachers taught and led their students in practice. The other technique is the way modern Qìgōng teachers arrange patients in a circular position for better healing results. Zhìnéng Qìgōng combines the two techniques (intuitive transmission and arranging the group in a certain way) into one through "Organizing the Qì Field," and it has become one of Zhìnéng Qìgōng's teaching characteristics. Since Organizing the Qì Field is done mentally, and the participants have the corresponding responses to the teacher's mind intent, it falls into the category of teaching through intuitive transmission. But it is not at the same level as the accomplished teacher's intuitive transmission; it belongs to the elementary stage of intuitive transmission.

5. Zhìnéng Qìgōng does not use special consciousness activities

Qìgōng is about mindfulness; there are many ways to use consciousness activities in practice. For example, there are Orbital methods, focusing on Dāntián methods, observing/visualizing things inside or outside of the body methods and emptiness and tranquility methods. Zhìnéng Qìgōng uses mind intent merges with the body posture method; it is called "Shén Xíng (mind and body) combined" in Traditional Qìgōng. In this method, the mind can merge with either dynamic or static postures; Zhìnéng Qìgōng mainly merges with the dynamic postures.

Note: The Orbit (Yùn Zhōu Tiān 運週天), Yùn 運 means to circulate along, Zhōu Tiān 週天 means orbit. These types of Qìgōng are called Orbital Qìgōng. There are three types of orbits in traditional Qìgōng. The most common type is when Qì and Shén circulate along a certain Meridian route (loop); another type is when Qì and Shén circulate along a certain route inside the inner organs; and the last type, such as the Belt Meridian Orbit, is when Qì and Shén circulate in a particular route.

"Do not use special consciousness activities" means the mind does not engage in any activity that is not related to the practice. Zhìnéng Qìgōng primarily requires the practitioner to focus consciously on the execution of the movements, and to follow the movements' requirement to focus the mind intent on each of the relevant areas during the practice. Besides these focusing requirements, there are no specific mind activities in Zhìnéng Qìgōng.

Just concentrating on the practice is not that easy for beginners. Most beginners are not able to finish a form without distractions. To use the mind to direct the movement is much more difficult. Zhìnéng Qìgōng uses verbal instructions to direct the movements to help the practitioners to concentrate. For example, at the beginning of the Push & Pull movements, in the practitioner's mind, the idea of Push & Pull movements merges with the concept (verbal command) of Push & Pull movements. Later, the concept of Push & Pull gradually disappears; at the end, it becomes an idea. When the idea (command) and movement are fully synchronized, one can truly "focus consciously on the execution of the movements."

Zhìnéng Qìgōng does not focus on emptiness/nothingness, nor does it use special activities. It embeds the non-engagement into the engagement. It is simple and straight forward, direct to the core. This applies to all stages of practice. In addition, it requires practitioners to do their best to merge the mind with every movement in their daily routines such as walking, standing, sitting, and reclining. When the body and the mind integrate, the Qì also is integrated, and at the same time, Jīng, Qì and Shén are all activated. By paying attention to the integration of the body and mind all the time, it is much easier to progress to a higher stage.

6. Zhìnéng Qìgōng uses the "Inducing Qì" method to activate Qì

In Qìgōng, the first stage of practice is to cultivate and activate Qì. There are many methods to activate Qì's concentrate/disperse and circulate functions to achieve smooth Qì flow in the body. The method Zhìnéng Qìgōng uses to activate Qì is the inducing/attracting Qì method. It contains three kinds of techniques.

a. Using the mind to induce/attract Qì

Generally speaking, there are two ways for the mind to activate Qì, one is "Mind Leading Qì" and the other is "Mind Inducing/attracting Qì." Many traditional Qìgōng practices use "Mind Leading Qì Method," Zhìnéng Qìgōng uses "Mind Inducing Qì Method."

The cultivating methods are different in Leading Qì and Inducing Qì, and the outcomes also are different. Leading Qì occurs when the mind intent focuses on a particular area and concentrates Qì in that area. After the mind intent and Qì are united firmly, the practitioner uses the mind intent to lead the Qì to circulate in a particular route and to activate the Qì functions. Inducing Qì is to focus on the mind's movement, not Qì. As the mind moves from point A to point B, by focusing on the mind's movement, Qì will automatically follow and moves from point A to point B; consequently, Qì functions are activated.

Qì follows mind movement is not a Qìgōng phenomenon; it is something that exists in everyone. It is formed by daily routines. As a newborn baby, Qì runs naturally in the body, and his/her movements and Qì are not connected. As a toddler, his/her mental activities and movements are connected but not highly integrated, therefore, movements are not as precise. For example, when the toddler reaches out to touch something, many times the hands are not in the right position. As a person gets older and the brain matures, the mental activities will firmly connect with the body via the nervous system; this enables the mind activities to merge with the Qì activities. It is a gradual process and occurs naturally. As a toddler, one learns to walk, to move, etc., the mental activities gradually merge with body movements. When the mind moves, the body follows. Because the mind and the body are connected by Qì, when the mind moves, Qì and body follow; this is mind induces Qì.

Why does Zhìnéng Qìgōng use "the Mind Inducing Qì Method?" It is because "Leading Qì" uses the mind to lead the Qì to circulate in a fixed route. If the route is incorrect, the Qì will circulate in the wrong area. This is called "Stray fire, into the Devil." "Stray fire, into the Devil" is a special Qìgōng technical term. For example, when practicing Meridian Orbit Qìgōng, the practitioner uses breathing to activate the Dāntián Qì until the Dāntián becomes hot. This process is called "Ignite the fire." When the fire is cultivated up to a certain degree, the mind and Qì merge as one, and the mind is used to lead Qì to circulate along the Conception Meridian and the Governor Meridian. It is called "Let go of Qì, follow the Meridians." While leading the Dāntián Qì upward, if the mind travels in a different path, instead of moving along the Conception and Governor Meridians, it is called "Stray fire (out of control)." When the Qì circulates along the wrong path, Shén is deprived of Qì nourishment, hindering the brain's functions and causing the nervous system to malfunction, and not be able to be self-controlled. This is called "Into the Devil."

"Mind Inducing Qì" directs the mind intent to the destination where one wants the Qì to go, and then lets the Qì follow its own inherent route to that place. This way, the Qì will not create any deviation—will not get lost or "Into the Devil." We use an out-of-towner looking for the Zhìnéng Qìgōng Center as an example to illustrate the difference between "Leading Qì" and "Inducing Qì." "Leading Qì" is to have someone leading the way to the Center. If that person does not know the directions and/or gets lost, it is "Stray fire." If he leads the out-of-towner to a dangerous area where no one is supposed to go, then it is "Into the Devil." "Inducing Qì" is someone putting a huge flag on the roof of the Center. Once the out-of-towner gets off the train, all he has to do is walk toward the flag, and he will find the Center.

Traditional Chinese Medicine and Qìgōng theories consider the rhythm of life process to be the following: up, down, open, and close. Human beings and nature maintain balance through the function of open and close. Human beings and nature exchange Qì constantly and continuously—this includes the Hùn Yuán Qì within the physical object and the materials that make up the Hùn Yuán Qì: physical matter, energy, and information. Zhìnéng Qìgōng's first step Gōng, the Lift Qì Up and Pour Qì Down Method, is based on this rhythm to bring forth the "mind and Qì integration, using the mind to induce Qì." The mind intent synchronizes with the movements to activate the integration of Body Hùn Yuán Qì with Nature Hùn Yuán Qì. When the hands do the open/close movement, the mind intent opens and closes simultaneously, and all pores and acupuncture points of the whole body will follow suit. The Hùn Yuán Qì inside the body is able to go out, and the outside Hùn Yuán Qì is able to come into the body. In the push and pull movement, as the hands push out and the mind visualizes the horizon, the Internal Qì is induced to go out. As the hands are pulled back, the mind visualizes inside the body, and External Qì is induced to come inside the body. This strengthens the exchange between human beings and Nature Hùn Yuán Qì, and the connection between human beings and nature.

b. Using the movements to induce Qì

In the section titled "Zhìnéng Qìgōng does not use special consciousness activities," we mentioned that Zhìnéng Qìgōng primarily requires the practitioner to focus consciously on the execution of the movements, and to merge the mind intent with the movement. In this section, we refer to the movements themselves; the body moves and posture changes can activate the Qì movements. Of course, to move the body and change the posture, the mind has to focus on the body. In Martial Arts Qìgōng, it is said that "the mind focuses on the posture, and Qì follows the movement of the posture." It means that once the posture moves, the Qì will follow.

The Qì that is activated by movements is different from the Qì activated by the mind. "Movements inducing Qì" means to use the physical movements to activate the Meridian Qì. "Mind Inducing Qì" is to use the mind intent to activate/induce Hùn Yuán Qì and Dāntián Qì, but not the Meridian Qì. In daily life, the norm is that when the body moves, the Qì will follow. Some of that Qì is induced by the mind, some by the movement. The Qì induced by the movement is Meridian Qì. The twelve Meridians and eight Extraordinary Meridians in the body connect with the corresponding organs and with various parts of the body. When activity increases in a certain part of the body, it will activate the corresponding Meridian Qì. Therefore, it increases the Qì flow in that particular Meridian, and strengthens the functions of various parts of the body.

However, to regulate and change the Meridian Qì is a slow process; on the other hand, regulating the Hùn Yuán Qì is a fast process. Therefore, Zhìnéng Qìgōng's approach to cultivate Meridian Qì is different from traditional Qìgōng. Orbital methods such as the Macrocosmic Orbit Method use movements, internal visions, and mind intent to concentrate on the Meridian route, and to merge with the Qì inside that Meridian; then the mind intent is used to lead the Qì to circulate. Consequently, the Meridian route, functions, and Qì volume will be increased and strengthened. This type (regulating and changing the Meridian Qì) of practice will hold the Qì in the Meridian and prevent it from expanding outward.

Zhìnéng Qìgōng combines two approaches to strengthen the process of regulating and changing the Meridian Qì. One approach is to use movements to strengthen and activate the Meridian Qì. For example, in every section of the Body & Mind Method, which is based on the rhythm of inherent life processes, the characteristics and the corresponding acupuncture points of each Meridian are given full attention. The Body & Mind Method emphasizes the movements in the tips of the limbs and the small joints. For instance, in the section on "Erect Palms, Separate Fingers and Open Meridians" in the Body & Mind Method, because the tips (ends/beginnings) of most of the Meridians are located in the fingertips, moving each finger will activate the whole Meridian and increase its Qì flow. With increased amounts of Qì in the Meridians, the Qì flowing out from the acupuncture points will increase. One important point is that we use the Movement Inducing Qì Method, focusing on the movements, and not on the Meridian or Meridian Qì.

The other approach is to focus on the body posture to induce Hùn Yuán Qì to the area. We will use the same movement as an example. After separating the fingers, as the palms push out, the mind merges with the movement and also pushes out. The Hùn Yuán Qì inside of the body will follow the mind to go out. Furthermore, when the movements activate the Meridians and increase the volume of Qì flow inside the Meridians, the corresponding part of the body will have an expanding sensation. This expanding sensation will reflect back to the mind and will cause the mind to focus on the area: the mind moves, the Qì follows. The Hùn Yuán Qì will go to the corresponding areas. This process is called: "Mind merges with the body, use the body to induce Qì, use Qì to activate the mind." Since the movements in the Body & Mind Method are designed to activate the Meridian Qì, the Hùn Yuán Qì will concentrate in the Meridian. With movement and concentration, the in-out and expansion-contraction functions of Meridian Qì and Hùn Yuán Qì will be strengthened.

In Zhìnéng Qìgōng, basically every movement goes through this process: when the mind moves, Qì moves (it is mind inducing Qì), and when Qì moves, the body moves (it is Qì inducing posture). When the body (posture) moves, Meridian Qì is activated—this is postures inducing Qì. With the increased amount of Qì, the area will have sensations, and these sensations will create attention—attention in an area will bring in more Qì. It is an endless loop.

c. **Using sound to induce Qì**

In addition to body parts, such as the mouth, tongue and throat, etc., a sound producing practice involves movements in the chest/abdomen; therefore, it has Movement Inducing Qì effects. But its effects on Meridian Qì are not that strong. In conjunction with breathing, Sound inducing Qì vibrates Qì in the body. When the head vibrates, the intention is to vibrate Shén; the chest area vibrates to vibrate Qì, the stomach area vibrates is to vibrate Jīng, etc. When the lower abdomen or navel vibrates, this vibration can affect the Body Hun Yuán Qì. When the Shānzhōng area vibrates, it affects Organ Qì. When the Head vibrates, it affects the mind. Therefore, sound has a huge influence on Qì functions in the body. Different movements have different results. If the sound causes movement or vibration to open outward, Qì will follow and open outward, and vice versa. Generally speaking, when pronouncing the sound with the mouth open, Qì disperses outward and with the mouth closed, Qì closes inward.

According to classical Qìgōng theories, sound inducing Qì relates to the types of practices which use mantras, incantation, and chanting, etc. The sounds (syllables) were passed down by ancient teachers, and include the following: The Six Syllable Rhyme (Liù Zì Jué 六字訣), Ā 呵, Sī 嘶, Hū 呼, Xī 唏, Xū 嘘, Chuī 吹; the Six-Syllable Sanskrit Mantra (Liù Zì Dà Míng Shén Zhòu 六字大明神咒), Ǎn 唵, Má 嘛, Ní 呢, Bā 吧, Mī 咪, Hōng 吽; and The Yellow Emperor's Classic of Internal Medicine (Huáng Dì Nèi Jīng 黄帝内經), Gōng 宫, Shāng 商, Jiǎo 角, Zhēng 徵, Yǔ 羽, etc.—all of these use chanting (pronunciation) to activate the Qì inside the body. Different sounds can vibrate Qì in different parts of the body. Zhìnéng Qìgōng uses the "sound inducing Qì" method in the third step Gōng—the Five Elements Method.

Zhìnéng Qìgōng uses "mind inducing Qì," "movements inducing Qì," and "sound inducing Qì"—all three different methods strengthen the inherent rhythm of life processes. They are safe, reliable, and have no side effects.

7. Zhìnéng Qìgōng belongs to an Open System

Qìgōng can be divided into two systems: Open System and Closed System. In the Closed System, the practitioner uses his own Jīng, Qì, and Shén in the practice. The practitioner avoids contacts with the outside world to eliminate distractions and excitement. In the advanced stage, such as Open the Heaven's Gate stage, the body opens up and merges the Qì inside the body with Nature Qì. The environment is very important in the Closed System; most practitioners live and practice inside temples or in isolated areas. Qīngxiū pài (清修派) of Dàoist Qìgōng and Zhǐ guān fǎmén (止观法門) of Buddhist Qìgōng belong to this system. In the Open System, the practitioner emphasizes merging the Qì in the body with Nature Qì; this system requires the practitioner to connect himself with the environment (nature and society). The practitioner uses Nature Qì to cultivate his Jīng, Qì, and Shén. Zhèngyī pài (正一派) and Yīnyáng pài (陰陽派) of Dàoist Qìgōng, and Chánzōng (禅宗) of Buddhist Qìgōng belong to this system.

Zhìnéng Qìgōng belongs to the Open System. The "Open" in Zhìnéng Qìgōng includes Qì Open, Shén (Mind) Open, and Xíng (Body) Open. "Open" means to relax/open the physical body (Xíng 形), Qì, and the mind (Shén) outward and to connect with nature. But Open does not mean that once Jīng, Qì or Shén opens outward, the process is finished. Open means to open outward, but the practitioner's mind should still be connected to the body; like flying a kite, the kite goes out but is attached to the body. One of the reasons we are tired after spending some time looking at things is because when we look at things, Qì goes out through the eyes. Therefore, no matter whether it is Qì Open, Xíng Open, or Shén Open, one cannot let go of all of them, i.e., one of them must be attached to a part of the body—for most practitioners, that part of the body is the Dāntián.

The purpose of the first step Gōng, Lift Qì Up and Pour Qì Down Method, is to practice "Qì Open," letting the Internal Qì move outward and absorbing the External Qì inward. It also includes the practice of "Shén Open." In this way, it connects the body with Nature Qì, and allows the body to absorb much more of the inexhaustible nature Hùn Yuán Qì. Compared with the closed system which only cultivates one's own Qì, the open system increases the sources of Qì, and enhances the improvement of the body and the mind. With the continuing practice of the next several step Gōngs, one can reach a high level of accomplishment where man and heaven are merged as one. This is called "Qì Open."

The human being is a product of nature and is also a part of society. Therefore, "Open" includes both open to nature and open to society. In other words, we must be part of nature and society. The Shén (mind) is the control center (commander) of the human being; therefore, among Xíng (physical body), Qì and Shén, the opening of the Shén is the most important. The most fundamental aspects of "Shén Open" are to be able to abide by the laws of nature and the morals of society.

Cultivating virtue is the essence of Zhìnéng Qìgōng. It requires the practitioners to cultivate ethics between man and nature, and to abide by the morals of society during daily activities, such as working, studying, etc., and to eliminate "self-righteousness." It also requires the practitioners to achieve the following: "be comfortable with the change of the four seasons; be accustomed to cold and hot; be harmonized with exultation and anger; be peaceful with living conditions; balance Yīn and Yáng; and nourish the rigidness and the softness." It means that under any circumstances, one must be able to keep the emotions stable and be composed, as well as maintain the balance with nature and society.

The ancients said "Nourish Qì in a quiet place, train the mind in a noisy place." In other words, practice cultivating Qì in a quiet place where there is no disturbance from other people. Practice training the mind in a disturbing and noisy environment, which trains the mind's self-control abilities to reach where one will not "deviate due to emotions." This is an advanced practice method. From the first step Gōng to the highest level of practice, Zhìnéng Qìgōng requires the mind to be open as described above.

In "Xíng Open," Xíng normally refers to the Acupuncture Points, such as Láogōng, Mìngmén, Navel, Tiānmén, Yǒngquán, etc. If the practitioner does not know the locations of the Acupuncture Points, he can use the pores in the skin. "Xíng Open" is not physically open, it is the mind intent opening from the Acupuncture Points; consequently, the Acupuncture Points will follow and open. In Zhìnéng Qìgōng, "Xíng Open" is done unconsciously. For example, the Lift Qì UP and Pour Qì Down Method has both "Shén Open" and "Qì Open"; its open and close movements are synchronized between Shén and Qì. The synchronized movements automatically activate the function of "Xíng Open." "Xíng Open" also means that daily activities and Qìgōng practice merge as one: a Qìgōng practice integrates with daily activities, and daily activities integrate with Qìgōng practice.

In the beginning stage of practice, "Open" (all Xíng, Qì, and Shén Opens) means that there is a "string" attached to the body; later, "Open" is accompanied by absorbing Qì inward. The absorbing can be done in two ways: one way is from outside to press inward; the other way is from inside to pull inward. The destination or origin point in the body can be the Upper Dāntián, Middle Dāntián or the Lower Dāntián. The main purpose for the "Open" is to absorb and to concentrate Nature Qì into the body. The key for the Open System is absorption. For example, the reason we practice "Shén Open," is to have our mind go out to merge with the environment and to bring Nature Qì back into the body. In order to do that, we have to hold on to the Shén; otherwise, the Shén will wander away. To hold on to the Shén, the mental state has to be stable; therefore, the purpose of practicing "Shén Open" is to cultivate mental wellness and stability, so that the external environment (both nature and society) would not be able to affect our emotions, focus, or pull our Shén away (get distracted). With stabilized mental conditions, in "Shén Open" practice, Shén and Qì in the body would not go away, and the Nature Qì will be brought into the body. This way, the practitioner can use the Nature Qì to cultivate his Jīng, Qì, and Shén.

"Organizing a Qì Field" for teaching and healing demonstrates the characteristics of "Open System" methods. In an organized Qì Field, everyone's mind and Qì are open and interacting with each other. With all movements and intentions in unison, the resonant effect will form a powerful Qì Field. This Qì Field is formed by the participants in the field; in turn, this Qì Field will strengthen everyone's practice, and will improve the healing results. "Organizing a Qì Field" for teaching and healing will benefit from improved results. One can benefit oneself and others at the same time. Based on these theories, the practices, and the applications, Zhìnéng Qìgōng has established a complete series of methods in an "Open System."

8. Zhìnéng Qìgōng uses External Qì for healing without depleting one's own Qì

In most Qìgōng practices, in order to use External Qì for healing, one must activate the Dāntián Qì first. The practitioner must cultivate Dāntián Qì until it becomes sufficient before he/she can emit Qì for healing. There is a risk it may harm or deplete his/her own Qì. In the past, people who practiced the Closed System specifically avoided sending Dāntián Qì outward. They feared that it would interfere with their progress.

Zhìnéng Qìgōng cultivates Hùn Yuán Qì. While cultivating one's own Hùn Yuán Qì, one simultaneously activates the Nature Hùn Yuán Qì to work for one's own health. The first step Gōng, the Lift Qì Up and Pour Qì Down Method, is a collecting and permeating

Qì method. Its purpose is to collect the Nature Hùn Yuán Qì, and to pour and permeate it into the body to achieve good health and healing. If one changes the target and pours the collected Qì into another person, one is emitting the External Qì to facilitate healing; therefore, emitting External Qì for healing is the most elementary practice in Zhìnéng Qìgōng. Because one uses the Nature Hùn Yuán Qì instead of his/her own Dāntián Qì, this practice will not deplete his/her own Qì.

The process of emitting External Qì to heal others is also a process of training one's own ability to activate Nature Hùn Yuán Qì. The state of mental and physical health and the ability to activate Internal and External Qì are the indicators of one's level of proficiency in practice. If one can easily activate External Qì, it is an indication that his/her mind's ability to govern Qì is relatively high.

When emitting Qì to oneself or just to one other person, if one focuses on himself/herself or on that person, it only trains the mind's ability to activate Qì for one person's healing. When organizing a Qì Field for healing, whether it is for ten or for more than a hundred people, the mind must include all of these people and unite everyone's Hùn Yuán Qì with the Nature Hùn Yuán Qì to form "the Field." This intention will greatly strengthen the ability to activate the Hùn Yuán Qì; therefore, emitting External Qì for healing can help increase one's ability to achieve a higher level of practice, which has been confirmed by years of field practice in Zhìnéng Qìgōng.

All over China, many Zhìnéng Qìgōng teachers were physically infirm or unhealthy before they began their practices. After they regained their health through practicing Zhìnéng Qìgōng, many of them went on to other places to teach and to spread Zhìnéng Qìgōng. In utilizing the Qì Field for teaching and healing, their bodies became healthier and healthier, and their practice continued to improve. Some of them were even able to heal broken bones in just a few minutes by emitting Qì. In using External Qì for healing, Zhìnéng Qìgōng has the above-mentioned differences compared to other systems. These differences in theories and methods constitute some of the characteristics of Zhìnéng Qìgōng.

9. Zhìnéng Qìgōng practice reactions are noticeable (refers primarily to uncomfortable feelings)

When practicing Zhìnéng Qìgōng, one can accumulate Qì quickly. The effects are very obvious—one's health improves continually, and the changes are noticeable. In the process of improving to a healthier state, the body will discharge the accumulated matter that is no longer beneficial to life activities. This accumulated matter can be either mental or physical, or both. When that happens, the practitioner may experience some discomfort or pain in the corresponding area. This is called a practice reaction or a Qì reaction. The following are common types of Qì reactions.

a. **Reactions from discharging disease and toxins**

Some diseases cannot be eliminated or returned to normal directly inside the body, because the toxins need to be discharged quickly; therefore, various reactions will occur when the toxins are discharged from different channels of the body. Some discharges come out from the lower excretory system, through diarrhea, blood and/or pus in the stool, cloudy urine, increased and smelly menstruation, etc. Some discharges come out from the upper excretory system, through coughing, phlegm, vomiting, runny nose, bleeding from the nose, and increased eye secretion, etc. Some discharges come out from the body and the limbs, through fever, perspiration, rashes, sores, and beriberi, etc. All of these symptoms are an indication of the discharge of toxins and/or disease.

The most common Qì reaction is diarrhea. An illness occurring due to a high fever would normally have a high fever Qì reaction, sometimes reaching up to 40°C (104 °F) or even 41°C (105.8 °F). (If the high fever is a Qì reaction, the patient's mind will stay clear and alert; and he would not experience dizziness or unconsciousness). When a Qì reaction occurs, one should not panic, nor stop the practice.

One may ask "In a situation when one cannot distinguish if the symptom is an actual illness or if it is a Qì reaction, what should one do?" Zhìnéng Qìgōng does not treat illness based on symptoms or diagnoses. The practice alone will have a healing effect on any kind of illness; therefore, even with an illness, with persistent practice and trust in Qìgōng, the illness can be cured. If one's mind is restless and/or anxious, and he/she suspects that it is an illness rather than a Qì reaction, and doubts Qìgōng's healing effects, then it is appropriate to take some medications. The medications should be for mitigating the symptoms, not as an antidote. For instance, in diarrhea, one should take lots of fluid instead of medicine that stops the diarrhea; for coughing, use medicine that dissolves the phlegm—not to stop coughing. Taking moderate amounts of a tonic will be beneficial to all Qì reactions.

It is extremely important to consult your physician and to seek medical advice to eliminate the possibility that the symptoms are due to actual illness. DO NOT assume all symptoms are Qì reactions.

b. **Reactions from Qì working on an illness**

After practice, the part of the body which has illness/lesions may feel worse than before the practice. This experience is called "reactions from Qì working on lesions." This is a unique phenomenon that happens when the Qì inside the body becomes sufficient with practice; the practitioner's health gradually returns to normal, but he/she is not yet fully recovered. It occurs most often in patients with chronic illnesses.

When an illness has existed for a long time, the body adapts to the disease, and forms a temporary pathological balance. With practice, Qì builds up and works on the illness. The functions, including sensory abilities, of the affected areas will gradually recover. As the sensitivities improve, the symptoms will become more obvious. This can create the illusion that the disease is getting worse.

We will use a bone spur in the cervical vertebrae as an example. The spur affects the nerves—at first, lifting the arms up will be painful. After several years, a pathological balance will be formed. The spur has not gotten any smaller, but the pain is no longer there; the arms can move freely, but the range of movement is smaller. Qìgōng and Traditional Chinese Medicine explain the phenomenon in this way—the human body has numerous large and small Meridians. A healthy person has, let's say, ten Meridians in the shoulder for Qì and blood to circulate through. After a spur has grown, three of the Meridians are obstructed and blocked. If one moves the arm in the same way as before, Qì will be blocked in a certain area. When that happens, pain will occur. If the Meridians are blocked for a long period of time, some areas in the arms/shoulders will be depleted of nourishment from Qì and blood; therefore, the functions will diminish and weaken, and the sensation of pain will disappear. When Qì becomes sufficient with practice, it will burst open the blocked Meridians. The arms'/shoulders' functions will begin to recover. Before the functions reach a normal state, with the improvement of the functions of sensation, more pain and discomfort will be felt. Therefore, "reactions from Qì working on an illness" are actually the indications of the improvement and recovery of the body functions. As Qì becomes more plentiful with continued, persistent practice, the pain will disappear.

Another situation may occur when a disease is in a latent stage, or where an old illness has not yet completely been cured. Although the disease was gone, its residual information is still there. In these cases, reactions may appear with practice. This reaction is an indication of progress in the purification process.

c. **Reactions from progress**

As physical and mental health gradually improve with practice, healthy people may also experience Qì reactions. In the process of moving from being unhealthy to healthy, the body needs to discharge the pathological ingredients of the illness. When physical and mental health improve from a lower level to a higher level, the body also needs to discharge the impurities that are not in accord with a higher, healthy state; therefore, Qì reactions may occur. Each time one moves up to a higher level of health, one's body must go through a purification process.

To illustrate the point, we will use flour as an example. Flour can have several qualities—unsifted, regular, and finely ground. Unsifted flour corresponds to unhealthy people, regular flour corresponds to normal people, and finely-ground flour corresponds to very healthy people. From an unsifted quality to reach normal quality, it requires the use of a normal quality flour sifter to sift out the bran. From normal quality to reach the finely-ground quality, it requires that a sifter designed for finely ground flour sift out the substandard, coarse flour. Sometimes, the reactions from progress can be as severe as, or even exceed the reactions from discharging disease and toxins.

Zhìnéng Qìgōng is not the only system that has Qì reactions—the differences are how these reactions are manifested. In the Dàoist closed system, the reaction called "Reborn" (leave the embryo, change bones) occurs after forming Dàdān, but before the Qì is open. The reaction is very intense and lasts about seven to fifteen days. During that time, the practitioner will experience a high fever and unconsciousness for seven days and nights; all joints and ligaments are very painful, and bleeding occurs from the seven apertures (mouth, ears, nose and eyes). In the past, they described the extent of the agony as: "In a scale of 1 to 10, even if you are as strong as a "10," at this point, you will be weaker than "1"." Because very few practitioners can achieve the level of forming Dàdān, very few have experienced this kind of reaction.

Zhìnéng Qìgōng is an open system. In the process of opening the body, Qì, and the mind, it requires the practitioner to readjust himself/herself to maintain the balance between him/her and nature. After short periods of practice, Qì reactions from progress may appear. When one reaction disappears, with the improvement of health, a new reaction may appear. One small reaction is followed by another small one, and finally one can also achieve "Reborn."

One of the common Qì reactions in Stillness Qìgōng is mental Qì reactions. During the practice, one may experience strong emotions, such as happiness, sadness, anger, etc., and uncontrollable releases such as laughing, crying, etc. If the reaction does not bother the practitioner, he/she should continue the practice. He/she should not encourage or discourage the reaction, and should just observe it, and behave like a mirror—reflecting things in front without any judgments or opinions. If he/she feels uncomfortable, he/she should finish, and stop the practice session. If he/she still has uncomfortable feelings after the practice session, then do some physical forms such as Wall Squatting, the Body

& Mind Method, etc. Normally, a few hundred Wall Squats should fix the problem.

When the various reactions, as described above, appear, one should stay calm, and also should recognize that it is a temporary phenomenon in the process of improving one's health. It is very important to have the correct attitude and to be joyful. One should constantly send wellness information, and remind oneself that the illness is disappearing, or that one's health is improving. This can accelerate Qì to work in the right direction. Contrarily, with fear and worry, one sends bad information to oneself that the illness is worsening or that the practice is on the wrong track. Instead of leading Qì to progress toward wellness, this unhealthy information may lead the Qì to head in the wrong direction.

One should not treat Qì reactions lightly. There is a very fine line between Qì reactions and an illness getting worse. The symptoms described in this section may be caused by worsening conditions, or by incorrect postures, and/or by incorrect mind intent. One should check with the teacher and seek medical advice by consulting a physician. The first rule of any activity is to "Do No Harm."

Zhìnéng Qìgōng's Three Stages of Practice

In the "Characteristics of Zhìnéng Qìgōng" section, we mentioned that the Zhìnéng Qìgōng practice consists of three stages: External Hùn Yuán; Internal Hùn Yuán; and Central Hùn Yuán. What is Hùn Yuán? In the Chinese language, Hùn Yuán can be either a noun or a verb. As a noun, it means "(two or more substances) transmuted as one." Because everything is Hùn Yuán entity, the word "Hùn Yuán" is omitted from the writing most the time, for example, Hùn Yuán Qì becomes Qì, Body Hùn Yuán Qì becomes Body Qì and Nature Hùn Yuán Qì becomes Nature Qì, etc. As a verb, it means "to transmute two or more substances into one; or to transmute a large substance into two or more smaller substances." The Hùn Yuán in the three stages of practice is the process of transmuting Body Hùn Yuán Qì and Nature Hùn Yuán Qì into one. Zhìnéng Qìgōng continues to use the word Hùn Yuán to remind the practitioner that Hùn Yuán is both a process and an end result.

1. External Hùn Yuán Stage

This is the beginning stage for practitioners to strengthen their normal physiological activities.

a. What is External Hùn Yuán?

External Hùn Yuán is a technical name. It refers to the transmutation of Nature Hùn Yuán Qì with the mind intent. It enables Nature Hùn Yuán Qì to be easily absorbed and used by the body. Because the process of transmutation normally occurs outside of the body, it is called External Hùn Yuán. It has three meanings.

1) The mind intent merges and transmutes with Nature Hùn Yuán Qì. It means the mind pays attention to xū kōng (虛空 space).

   Note: xū kōng: Xū 虛 is a special Chinese word with no equivalent in English. The closest translation is "nebulous." It has a meaning of existing yet not existing—empty yet not empty. It describes something that does not have a physical form nor occupies space. For example, although one can see and walk around in an empty room which is filled with light smoke, one cannot say the room is empty, because it is not, it is xū. Kōng 空 means empty. xū kōng normally refers to space/sky. It means to be immense and plenty—it is empty yet not empty.

   When the mind goes out to xū kōng, the Upper Dāntián Qì will go out with it. As the mind stays with xū kōng, the Upper Dāntián Qì will merge and transmute with the xū kōng's Primal Hùn Yuán Qì. This will allow the Primal Hùn Yuán Qì to receive the life information from the practitioner and to synchronize with human Hùn Yuán Qì. When the mind comes back to the body, this transmuted Qì will follow and will be absorbed into the body, and it can be put to use easily. Therefore, it is very important that the space (xū kōng) cannot be empty. In the mind, the space is empty yet not empty; something exists yet does not exist there. If one practices in a confined space, one can use imagination to dissolve the surrounding area into xū kōng. If one does not have the solid concept or image (area should be vague) of the surrounding area or is not hindered by the surrounding area, one can easily absorb the Nature Hùn Yuán Qì and put the Nature Hùn Yuán Qì to use.

2) The mind intent merges and strengthens the Hùn Yuán Qì that is surrounding/engulfing the body. The exchange of Qì between Human and Nature normally occurs in this area. For the non-Qìgōng practitioner, this layer of Qì is approximately 50 cm deep; normally, it is deeper for the Qìgōng practitioner. When the mind thinks about the surrounding Qì, the mind opens up (expands outward) and the body (normally the pores in the skin) would also open up. Mind opens outward will induce Body Hùn Yuán Qì to open outward; as the mind expands, so will the Body Hùn Yuán Qì. When the mind thinks about the surrounding Qì, the consciousness will merge with the surrounding Qì; the merged Qì will have the characteristics of Body Hùn Yuán Qì and can be absorbed into the body. When we practice External Hùn Yuán, basically, we are working on the surrounding Qì. When the Body Qì opens outward, Qì (Body Qì and Nature Body Qì) will begin to merge in the surrounding area; and the surrounding Qì layer will become denser and deeper. As the mind withdraws inward, the merged Qì will follow. This will create room for the Nature Qì to enter the surrounding area and to begin the merging process again, starting from the area farthest from the body to that which is the closest. If one has difficulty visualizing or feeling the surrounding Qì, one can use the following process: open, think space; withdraw (close), think inside the body. When the mind intent opens toward the space/horizon, there should not be any fixed route, just think space. But when withdrawing the mind intent inward, the visualization should be more detailed; for example, the route should be from space, to horizon, to the surrounding area, and to inside the body; this way the Nature Qì and surrounding Qì will merge as one and follow the mind intent to enter the body.

3) The mind intent merges with the skin's permeating functions. The skin, which includes pores, Acupunctures points, the digestive tract, and the respiratory tract, refers to any contact area with the external world. All the openings in the skin are venues for Qì to go in and out of the body. If we pay attention to the skin all the time, it will strengthen the skin's function/abilities to release Internal Qì and to absorb the External Qì.

b. The Effects of Practicing External Hùn Yuán

The following list describes the effects of practicing External Hùn Yuán:

1) strengthens the connections between the body and nature;
2) absorbs the External Hùn Yuán Qì to replenish the body Hùn Yuán Qì; and
3) accelerates the process of improving the body functions from a normal stage to a superior stage. For example, one can be aware of the existence of External Qì, etc.

One may ask "How can it be possible to achieve these kinds of results by practicing External Hùn Yuán?" According to modern science, the normal physiological activities of any living thing—no matter whether it is a single cell or a complex human body—needs to maintain the balance of a series of physiological functions within the body. This balance is maintained by exchanging material, energy, and information between the living thing and its surroundings.

In Qìgōng Science, metabolism is the process of a living entity's releasing Internal Qì, absorbing External Qì, and the transmutation of these two forms of Qì. These processes occur mainly in the surrounding membrane—in a cell it is the membrane; in a human it is the membrane and the skin. The membrane's Qì functions directly relate to physiological activities. When the function exceeds a certain limit, it creates illness. Normally, a living entity depends on a natural balancing mechanism to return its function back to normal. It will die once the balancing mechanism is no longer working. All of these Qì functions occur inside the body automatically and follow their own rhythm.

Qìgōng Science discovered this physiological process and observed that the mind intent can influence this process. Following the nature of this process, the entity develops certain Qìgōng methods to strengthen the processes of releasing Internal Qì, absorbing External Qì, and transmuting these two forms of Qì. Consequently, it will strengthen the metabolism. Also, it will gradually change the process from an automatic to a mind intention.

2. Inner Hùn Yuán Stage

This stage leads the mindful (mind intended) physiological process into deeper level stages.

a. **What is Inner Hùn Yuán?**

Inner Hùn Yuán is distinguished from External Hùn Yuán. It means the mind intent merges with the Body Hùn Yuán Qì inside the body, enables it to permeate inside the body (body and internal organs), and merges the skin, muscles, tendons, bones, meridians, and the inner organs as one. In Zhìnéng Qìgōng, the intention of the Body & Mind Method is to merge with Physical Body Hùn Yuán Qì, and the intention of the Five Element Method is to merge with Organ Qì. In strict Inner Hùn Yuán practice, the practitioner's mind stays within the body. All Zhìnéng Qìgōng methods have "from inside moving/opening to outside, from outside moving/entering to inside" processes. Therefore, Zhìnéng Qìgōng methods cannot be purely External or Inner Hùn Yuán. For example, in External Hùn Yuán stage, in the pushing outward movement, the mind goes outward, and in the pulling inward (toward the body) movement, the mind withdraws inward. The Qì follows the mind intent going in and out of the body, it is the mind that induces Qì and belongs to External Hùn Yuán; but as the mind moves inward and stays within the body, it will merge with Body Qì inside the body and becomes Inner Hùn Yuán. In the Inner Hùn Yuán stage, if the mind awareness wanders away from the body, it will merge with Nature Qì and becomes External Hùn Yuán. In Inner Hùn Yuán practice, one mainly focuses on the body.

Although the Inner Hùn Yuán practice is based on the foundation of External Hùn Yuán practice, some practitioners may find it easier for them to begin with it. In Zhìnéng Qìgōng, beginners may find External Hùn Yuán practice is more suitable for them due to the fact that Inner Hùn Yuán practice is much more strenuous. Which method to choose is based on the ability of the practitioner and the results that he/she can achieve. For most practitioners, it is recommended to start with the very basic level of practice and to progress one stage at a time, from the outer layer to the inner layer of the body.

b. **The Effects of Practicing Inner Hùn Yuán**

The following list describes the effects of practicing Inner Hùn Yuán:

1) Strengthens the abilities of directing and controlling Qì, and can lead Qì to all parts of the body.

   Normally, humans exchange Qì with nature through the surface of the body, Qì naturally follows skin/pores' open-close motions to circulate in and out of the body; and the mind intent (focus) in and out of the body plays a very important role in the Qì activities. Due to fact that humans seldom focus inside the body (muscles, tendon and bones); therefore, normal mind activities have minimal effects on the Qì circulation inside the body. Qì movements inside the body are normally caused by the circulation of Qì in the Meridians and blood circulation in the vessels. In order to improve the results of mind intent to induce Qì into the inner body, one must strengthen the ability to merge the mind intent with Qì and the ability to direct the Qì. With practice, one will gradually be able to direct/move the Qì including Qì in the organs. Since Meridian Qì does not follow the mind intent, the Qì that follows the mind intent to permeate inside the body is Nature Qì. During the practice, we focus on a certain part of the body; consequently, the mind intent will merge the Body Qì in that area. When the merged Qì becomes stronger with increasing volume, it will permeate inside the body. When the mind intent relaxes, Qì will follow to relax outward.

2) Strengthens self-control and the mind's abilities, and stabilizes the emotions.

In the beginning, Inner Hùn Yuán practice is strenuous for most practitioners. For example, most practitioners cannot hold the arms at shoulder level for more than ten minutes; in order to hold on to the practice, one must have self-control. When the body hurts or has Qì reactions, one must stabilize his/her mind and emotions. As the degrees of difficulty increase in the practice, one will be able to strengthen his/her self-control abilities.

3) Develops a certain degree of the "feeling" ability—one can feel the changes in Internal and External Qì.

When practicing Inner Hùn Yuán, one needs to focus and concentrate on a certain area; gradually, the bond between the mind intent and that area will be stronger. With the stronger bond, one may develop the ability to feel, see, and observe Qì in the body and the changes inside the body.

4) Achieves the first stage of the mind and the body in harmony and in a healthy stage.

Although most practitioners are in generally good health, to achieve the first stage (the mind and the body in harmony) of wellness is not that easy. Being healthy is not just about the physical body, it also should be about mental health. Only after one achieves Inner Hùn Yuán, then can one achieve the first stage of wellness.

5)Strengthens the transmutation process between the Body Hùn Yuán Qì and the Internal Organ Hùn Yuán Qì.

3. Central Hùn Yuán Stage

Because this is an advanced stage which very few practitioners can achieve, this stage will not be described.

Chapter Three:

The Methods

功法

The Body & Mind Method

形神庄

Introduction

The definition of the Body & Mind Method

The Body & Mind Method (Xíng Shén Zhuāng 形神庄) is a technical name for the second method of Zhìnéng (Chilel) Qìgōng. In Chinese writing, Xíng means "physical body," Shén means "mind activities or consciousness," and Zhuāng means "body postures" in this context. This title means to practice the postures of Jīng (Xíng), Qì and Shén. In Zhìnéng Qìgōng, Xíng Shén Zhuāng means the training to merge consciousness with body postures to achieve the body-mind merging as one wholistic entity through the technique of the body postures following the mind's commands. This method is called Xíng Shén Hùn Yuán (形神混元 body and mind merged as one).

> *Note. To distinguish the difference between humans and all others, the human physical body is called Jīng, not Xíng; however, the physical appearance or the body postures of a person is called Xíng.*

The Body & Mind Method works on Xíng Shén Hùn Yuán of Internal Hùn Yuán

In Qìgōng practice, if one cultivates External Qì, it is called External Hùn Yuán. If one cultivates Internal Qì, it is called Internal Hùn Yuán. External Hùn Yuán refers to the transmutation of Nature (External) Qì with the mind intent; it enables the Nature Qì to be easily absorbed and used by the body. Because the process of transmutation normally occurs outside of the body, it is called External Hùn Yuán. Inner Hùn Yuán means the mind intent merges with the Qì inside the body, enabling it to permeate inside the body and internal organs) and to merge as one with the skin, muscle, tendons, bones, meridians and inner organs.

At the beginning stage, Xíng Shén Hùn Yuán requires the mind and body activities to merge as one. In normal physical exercise, although body movements are directed by mind intent, the mind intent is not focused on the body's movement but on the destination of the movement. This is outward-mind intent. The Body & Mind Method requires Shén to fully concentrate on the body area performing the movement, and gradually enables Shén to permeate into the muscles, tendons and bones. Since Qì follows Shén, Qì will follow and permeate inside the area that Shén permeates thus changing the distribution of Qì inside the body. On the cellular level, Qì is usually concentrated in the membranes. As Shén concentrates, the volume of Qì will increase. When Shén permeates into the body's structures, Qì will follow. Gradually, the Internal Qì increases to a point when intracellular Qì and membrane Qì become indistinguishable and become known as Internal Xíng Shén Hùn Yuán.

Characteristics of the Body & Mind Method

1. High Degree of Difficulty

Most movements in the Body & Mind Method are based on Martial Art Qìgōngs and Traditional Moving Qìgōngs. Including the Opening movements, it consists of eleven sections, but there are no strong links between them; therefore, they all can be practiced individually. These movements, when isolated or broken down into small sections, are mostly straight or square with a few circular movements, and are relatively simple and straight forward. Because this method is designed to correct body postures and the imbalance of Qì caused by daily life, these movements may feel awkward compared to habitual movements. This method also exercises areas such as small joints and back muscles that are normally ignored during daily routines. In the beginning, if one practices the form correctly, one may feel that the movements are unnatural. In order to have correct posture, some of the movements require using force, and one may feel sore and tired after practice. But they are necessary steps one must take to loosen up the tendons and ligaments, and to open up the Meridians.

2. Movements are Balanced and Comprehensive

The Body & Mind Method emphasizes body movements. Its structure is very comprehensive and is designed to move every part of the body. It is divided into three sections.

- Body: head, neck, chest, back, ribs, stomach, hip bones, and tail bone.
- Upper limbs: shoulders, elbows, wrists, palms, and fingers.
- Lower limbs: hip joints, knees, ankles, feet, and toes.

The movements balance both the left and right sides, the front and the back, and the upper and lower parts body. They work on extension and contraction of muscles and tendons, and on the mobility and flexibility of the joints. Following mind intent, we exercise almost every part of the body. Practicing this method will balance Qì and beautify the body.

3. Uses Posture Inducing Qì Method

"Shén concentrates in Zhuāng (movement), and Qì follows Zhuāng's movement (神注庄中, 氣随庄动)" is the basic principle of traditional moving Qìgōng. Because Qì follows mind intent, "Shén concentrates in Zhuāng" is called "Mind Inducing Qì." The Qì being induced by the mind intent is Body Hùn Yuán Qì or Nature Hùn Yuán Qì. "Qì follows Zhuāng's movement" is called "Movements Inducing Qì." The Qì being induced is Meridian Qì.

In general, each body movement consists of two kinds of Qì movement—fast and slow. When a command is given to execute a certain movement, the mind focuses on the areas involved in the movement. At the same time, Hùn Yuán Qì (the merged external and internal Qì) concentrates in that area. This process is called "intent arrives, Qì arrives (Yì dào, Qì dào 意到, 氣到)." This is a fast process, occurring in a split second. Meridian Qì circulates to its own rhythms, which is subjected to the influence of body movements and internal organ activities. As the body moves and the posture changes, these movements will activate Meridian Qì and will alter its distribution. Consequently, Meridian Qì in the moving areas of the body will increase. This is a slow process and is called "Movement inducing Qì." The fast and slow Qì movements work to complement each other in order to maintain the body's vitality.

The Body & Mind Method activates Qì by the following process: (1) "mind intent induces Qì; (2) Qì induces body postures; (3) postures induce Qì; and (4) Qì activates the mind." In other words, mind intent induces Qì to concentrate on the areas involved in the movement. The merged mind intent and Qì produce body movements. The movements activate Meridian Qì and cause Qì and blood to concentrate in the moving areas of the body; and this concentration will create an expanding and circulating feeling. This feeling attracts the mind's attention to the area, and consequently, Hùn Yuán Qì follows the mind's attention and concentrates in that area.

4. **Activates Meridian Functions**

According to Meridian theory, all internal organs and limbs are connected through the Meridian channels. Each Meridian contains Qì circulating in distinctly characteristic fashion and each connects with one another at different parts of the body. For example, the hands and fingers are connecting points for Hand Yīn Meridians and Hand Yáng Meridians. The head is the connecting point for Hand Yáng Meridians and Foot Yáng Meridians. The feet are the connecting points for Foot Yīn Meridians and Foot Yáng Meridians. The chest and stomach are the connecting points for Foot Yīn Meridians and Hand Yīn Meridians. Moreover, each human being needs to exchange Qì with nature constantly, and External Qì enters the body mainly through the tips of the hands and the feet. In Meridian theory the tips of the limbs are the roots and the head and internal organs are the ends of the Meridians. Because the exchange points between the Meridians, the exchange points between Internal and External Qì, and the beginning and ending points of the Meridians are all located at the tips of the limbs, the Body & Mind Method emphasizes exercising the limbs to activate all major Meridians. Once the Meridian Qì is activated, it would connect the inner organs' Qì with the membrane Qì, and will unite the whole body as a unit.

5. **Merges the Body and Mind, Uses both Tension and Relaxation**

   Due to a high degree of complexity, it is very difficult to practice Body & Mind Method as required without using force in the beginning. Once force is used, it is very easy to become rigid and tense, which violates the principles of relaxation and flexibility in Zhìnéng Qìgōng. To resolve this conflict, the Body & Mind Method uses a method called "use both tension and relaxation simultaneously." There are two stages in this method.

   a. In the beginning of practice, do not be afraid to use force. The body may be tense, but the first priority is to obtain the proper posture. It is possible to begin to relax only after we have learned and become familiar with the new routine. As the body moves, muscles and ligaments will contract and expand, creating tension in some parts of the body. When that happens, the mind gives the body the command to relax. While maintaining the correct posture, using the mind to relax the body is called "Xíng is tense, Shén is relaxed."

   b. Parts of the body are tense and the rest of the body is relaxed. This condition requires that during the practice, the moving area exerts a certain degree of tension to obtain the proper posture; while maintaining the proper posture, the non-moving part is totally relaxed. Tension is not brute force or unnecessary force, it is the right amount of strength required to perform the movement. Learning how to use the right amount of force is part of the training. Once we develop internal strength, we will automatically become relaxed.

6. **Angular Outside, Circular Inside**

   The Body & Mind Method contains numerous straight and angular movements. When changing from one posture to another, the angles are very obvious. Although this kind of movement is very effective in activating Meridian Qì, it lacks finesse and smoothness. It also contradicts the principle of "circular and flexible" movements. In practice, the Body & Mind Method uses two techniques to solve this problem.

   a. **Angular outside, circular inside**. For example, in the bending the elbows movement, the elbows form a very obvious 90-degree angle outside the body between the upper arm and forearm. In the inner side of the angle, however, the mind intent forms an outward expanding circular force. This outward expanding circular force creates the "angular outside, circular inside" posture.

   b. **Use both straightened and bent movements.** In straight movements, the posture should be straight yet not completely straight. Do not straighten the posture to the limit. The joints are relaxed and are not locked in order to maintain their flexibility and to prevent over extension. A proficient practitioner can add undulating motion to the straight movements.

7. **Contains both large and small movements**

   The Body & Mind Method exercises every part of the body. It contains both large and small movements. For example, "Bend Body, Arch Spine." and "Return Qì to One" sections are large movements. "Erect Palms, Separate Fingers" and "Spring Leg, Move Foot to Draws Taiji" sections are small movements. In addition, each section consists of large and small movements. For example, shoulder, elbow, and knee movements are large; wrist, finger, ankle and toe movements are small. Waist movement is large; vertebrae movement is small, etc. Generally speaking, the body movements that can be easily observed are considered large; the internal movements, which are more difficult to observe, are considered small. In addition to the physical movements, the Internal Qì function also has whole body and localized functions.

   The reason why the Body & Mind Method consists of both large and small movements is twofold:

   a. In daily routines and exercises, most people have a tendency to focus on large movements and neglect small ones. The Body & Mind Method specifically corrects this mistake. Small movements require agility and precision. Focusing on them develops a high degree of concentration. Consequently, tranquility can be achieved.
   b. Small movements are very effective in activating Meridians to improve the circulation of Qì and blood.

8. **Whole Body Behaves as One Unit, Stillness in Motion**

   The structure of Body & Mind Method is designed to be practiced one section at a time, from the top to the bottom of the body. But the essence of the method is that the mind is focused on the whole body in every movement. For a proficient practitioner, there is no isolated movement, the whole body is involved in every movement. For example, in the "Crane's Neck" movement, in the beginning, one uses the first thoracic vertebrae as a stationary point to draw a circle which will loosen up the cervical vertebrae. Then the thoracic followed by lumbar vertebrae will begin to move. As one progresses, the legs, ankles and all the way to Yǒngquán (on the sole of the foot) will move with the head movement. When that happens, it is called "whole Body Behaves as One Unit."

   "Stillness in Motion" means to remain concentrated and serene throughout the practice. The methods one can use include focusing on the movement, and paying attention to the acupuncture points or being aware of the Qì flow in the body. In the beginning, most practitioners should focus on the posture/movements. In addition to focusing on every posture in every movement, one should be aware of both the internal and external body. With practice, one will become aware of the acupuncture points and the changes of Qì flow in the body during each section.

The Form

1. Preparation: Wújí zhuāng 無極庄

Stand straight with the inner sides of both feet slightly touching each other. The body is centered, and the hands relaxed naturally with the fingers pointing to the ground. The knees and arms are straight but not locked. Look at the horizon; then slowly withdraw vision inward and gently close eyelids. The whole body is relaxed. To relax and balance the body, shift weight to the balls of feet, use Bǎihuì to lead the body to rock back and forth slightly a few times. Fig. 1-1.

Fig. 1-1

a. Physical Preparation

1) Head

Requirements

The head remains relaxed and centered at all times. It cannot drop forward or backward nor lean to the left or to the right. To satisfy these requirements, the head needs to be pulled upward as if suspended by a string in mid-air. To be precise, the head is centered because Tóu kūnlún (頭崑崙 located approximately 1 cm behind the center point of the line connecting the tip of the ears) is pulled upward as if it is suspended by a string. It is called "the head is suspended in midair (頂頭懸)" in Qìgōng.

Method

After the head is centered, tuck in the chin toward the Adam's apple, withdraw the Adam's apple to Yùzhěn (玉忱), and continue to move upward to Bǎihuì, and from Bǎihuì (百會) pull the head upward (at the same time, relax the eyebrows and facial muscles). Or, the tip of the nose points to the chin, the chin points to Huìyīn (會陰), the mind intent circles around Huìyīn and goes upward along the inner side of the spine to Yùzhěn, continues to the Bǎihuì, and Bǎihuì pulls the body upward. Using either method will automatically straighten the cervical vertebrae and will give the practitioner a suspended feeling.

Another technique to practice the correct head posture is to put a small marble on the Tóu kūnlún (there is a dip there) and walk around. The marble would not drop if one can maintain the correct posture. After repeated practices, one will be able to maintain the head in a centered position.

The key is to relax while adjusting the posture, one cannot use force when pushing or pulling upward.

Purpose

The head plays a vital role in centering the body. If the head is not centered, one can easily feel malaise and the body will not be able to achieve the proper posture or balance. A centered head induces Qì upward to nourish the brain. If the head leans backward, Qì in the Governor Meridian (Dū mài 督脈) will have difficulty in moving upward, causing stiffness and numbness in the neck area. If the chin does not tuck in, Qì in the Conception Meridian (Rèn mài 任脈) will not be able to move downward easily, resulting in dizziness and high blood pressure.

2) Eyes

Requirements

The eyes are either completely closed or have a slit opening, the eyeballs remain level (as if looking at the horizon), withdraw the vision inward, and then move/focus the withdrawn vision to the practicing area (lower Dāntián).

Method

The eyes look straight forward all the way to the horizon, where the sky and the earth meet. During the looking-forward process, one should remain focused and ignore any object between the eyes and the horizon; the mind intent goes out with the eyes to the horizon. Once the mind intent and the eyesight are fixed on the horizon, slowly withdraw the mind intent and the eyesight inward; and close the eyelids (beginning with the outer corners) slowly and evenly.

There are two options in this movement, one is to close the eyes completely and do not let the light come inward. This option would help the participant to concentrate. The second option is that the eyes are not closed completely, and there is a slit opening between the eyelids. This slit between the eyelids will allow the Qì in the body to connect with Nature Qì and to constantly absorb Nature Qì into the body. Besides helping the participant to concentrate, this option can help in activating the Qì functions.

The most important part of the closing-eyes movement is the slow, even movement, and that one must focus on the outer corners of the eyes. Once the eyelids are closed, one cannot roll the eyeballs. Closing the eyes and withdrawing the vision inward is a very useful technique to concentrate the mind.

Purpose

a) In Traditional Chinese Medicine, the eyes are considered the outlet for the liver (目為肝之竅), and the gateways for the soul (Hún 魂). Closing the eyes slowly and evenly is an important way to concentrate the mind and to pacify the soul. When startled during Qìgōng practice, especially during a meditating state, one can be easily agitated, annoyed, and begin sweating—this is what Traditional Chinese Medicine called "startled, Qì is in chaos (驚則氣亂)." When that happens, do not stop the practice nor open the eyes; slowly rotate the eyeballs to the left to the maximum (do not turn the head), back to the center, then rotate to the right. After four repetitions, one should be able to calm down and return to the meditating state.

b) The eyesight can direct Qì. Traditional Qìgōng uses the expression that the "Eyes are the forefront of the mind (目為心之先鋒)." It means that wherever the eyesight goes, Qì would follow. The eyes are the connecting points between Yīn Qiāo Mài (陰蹺脈) and Yáng Qiāo Mài (陽蹺脈); they are also the points where Wèi Qì (衛氣) goes in and out of the body. That is the reason why all Qìgōng practitioners need to place emphasis on adjusting their eyes. Martial Art Qìgōng requires angry eyes and the raising of the eyebrows (怒目揚眉); the purpose is to move the Wèi Qì to the outer body to strengthen the bones and muscles for combat. For health purposes, the practitioner is required to withdraw his/her eyesight inward; the purpose is to confine Wèi Qì inside the body to nourish the internal organs for longevity.

3) Mouth

Requirements

The lips are slightly touching each other, the upper and lower front incisors are touching yet not touching; the bicuspids are touching as if biting something; the tip of the tongue touches the upper palate (beginners can touch the gum line).

Method

Relax and close the lips; use the nose to breathe and do not let any air come out of the mouth. Withdraw the Chéngjiāng xué (承漿穴 the depression under the lower lip) and tense the Rénzhōng xué (人中穴 under the nose, about midway to the upper lip) slightly; the upper and lower front teeth slightly touch each other, and the bicuspids are touching as if biting something. The tip of the tongue touches the area between the teeth and the upper palate. If the tip of tongue touches the hard palate, one may feel sluggish or sleepy.

Purpose

Closing the lips and touching the tongue to the upper palate are intended to connect the Governor and Conception Meridians, and to allow the Qì to circulate through these meridians to complete a circle. If the tip of the tongue touches the gum line, it will connect the Qì in the skin and its membrane. The tip of the tongue touching the upper palate (the area between the soft and hard palates) will connect the Qì in the Governor and Conception Meridians. When there is sufficient Qì in the Governor Meridian, the area between the eyebrows may vibrate if the tip of the tongue is still touching the gum line. If that happens, one should move the tip of the tongue to touch the upper palate.

4) Neck

Requirement

The neck should be relaxed and straight, and cannot lean forward.

Method

Tuck the chin toward the Adam's apple, the Adam's apple withdraws toward the Yùzhěn, the Yùzhěn pushes up toward the Bǎihuì; use the Bǎihuì to pull up the head. If there are too many curvatures in the cervical vertebrae, one must intentionally push the Yùzhěn toward the back to induce Qì upward.

Purpose
This position of the neck is intended to minimize the curvature in the cervical vertebrae and to induce Qīng Yáng Qì (清陽氣) to the brain. If the neck leans forward, it would cause numbness in the neck and the head, and would block the Qì flow in Yùzhěn. Tensing the back of the neck would cause the Qì to be stuck in the chest area. If the Adam's apple is not withdrawn inward, the Qì in the chest area will not be able to go downward.

5) Chest and Back

Requirement
Hollow and expand the chest; the chest is relaxed and withdraws inward to release the tension and pressure in the chest area. Pull up the back and drop the upper arms to straighten up the spine.

Method
a) Hollowing the chest means to slightly withdraw the triangular area formed by the nipples and the xiphoid process of the sternum. The correct way to hollow the chest is to protrude the chest first, followed by relaxing the chest. Take a deep breath, the tips of the shoulders move outward and upward to expand the chest cavity, and then slowly exhale, dropping and relaxing the shoulders and the chest downward. The key to hollowing the chest is to expand it at the same time. If one hollows the chest too much, the chest cavity would collapse and cause breathing problems and one would have an uncomfortable feeling in the ribs. The way to avoid that from happening is to expand the chest. After the inhalation, the armpits and the shoulders move upward and outward to pull open and to expand the chest to the sides, and then naturally relax shoulders.

b) Pulling up the back is done to straighten the spine. Pulling up the back is very important; if it is not done correctly, the back may be cold and numb, and it may increase calcium deposits in the cervical vertebrae. The correct way to pull up the back is to use the Bǎihuì and the Dàzhuī (大椎 the first thoracic vertebra) to pull up the cervical and the thoracic vertebrae while the tailbone goes downward to stretch and straighten the spine.

Purpose
The heart and the lungs are located in the chest cavity. The heart regulates the blood's circulation, and the lungs regulate the Body Qì. Hollowing and expanding the chest can enlarge the thoracic cavity and allow the heart and the lungs to settle comfortably inside the body to ensure that Qì and blood circulate smoothly. Relaxing the chest and the back allows the Governor and Conception Meridians to

connect easily and ensures the normal functions of the inner organs. Dàzhuī xué is called "climbing the Heaven's ladder (Shàng tiān tī 上天梯)" and means that Qì is having great difficulty going up; pulling up the back can help the Qì to move upward. The chest area is the junction point for the six Yīn Meridians. Relaxing the chest and pulling up the thoracic vertebrae maintains the smooth connections between the Yīn Meridians, which connect the inner organs, to ensure their normal function. When the chest is protruding outward, it would cause Qì to move upward along the Kidney and Conception Meridians, resulting in Qì and blood concentrating in the head, and may lead to high blood pressure. Pulling up the back and dropping the upper arms can loosen up the Gāohuāng xué (膏肓穴); once that meridian point opens up, Qì can reach the heart, the lung and the abdomen's membranes. Pulling up the back is very important; if it is not done correctly, the back may be cold and numb, and it may increase calcium deposits in the cervical vertebrae.

6) Shoulders

Requirement

The shoulders should be relaxed, and the armpits should be empty.

Method

The shoulder joints are relaxed and naturally hang loosely. The upper arms are turned outward and inward slightly to create an empty space in the underarm area. Another way to relax the shoulders is to take a deep breath, then exhale, relax the inner organs and the ribcage, let go of tension, and drop the shoulders. While dropping the shoulders, the shoulders should expand outward from the spine, and embrace to the front as if hugging a tree.

Purpose

Relaxing the shoulders eliminates blockage and allows the Qì to circulate smoothly in the arms; and it opens the Jíquán xué (belongs to the Heart Meridian), and allows Qì to reach the elbows and the wrists.

7) Elbows

Requirement

The overall requirement is that the elbows are dropping downward yet hanging by an imaginary string.

Method

Relax and naturally drop the Tiānjǐng xué (天井 SJ-10) and Xiǎohǎi xué (小海 SI-8); but the mind intent cannot be too intense, otherwise, the shoulders and the elbows become heavy and not flexible. While dropping the tips of the elbows downward, imagine a string is pulling up the Qūchí xué (曲池 LI-11) and Zhǒuliáo xué (肘髎 LI-

12). With the mind intent on these four acupuncture points, it will strengthen the Qì and blood circulation in the arms.

Purpose
The purpose is to maintain that the upper limbs' Qì and blood moves smoothly. The upper limb acts like a bow with the wrists and the shoulder joints as the ends and the elbows as the center—a relaxed elbow will ensure an agile limb.

8) Wrists

Requirement
The requirement is to sit the wrists.

Method
To relax the wrist, focus on Shénmén xué (神門 HE-7) and relax it downward as if the wrist is sitting down. The fingers move upward to create a folding/bent position between the hands and the forearms.

Purpose
The purpose is to maintain the Qì functions in the upper limb to act as one unit, so that the Qì can easily circulate.

9) Palms and Fingers

Requirement
Cup the palms and naturally extend the fingers.

Method
Withdraw the centers of the palms slightly; the hands are slightly cupped as if holding a very large and very delicate Qì bubble, which if held too tightly will burst—held too loosely, it will drop. Round the body, relax the shoulders, drop the elbows, and sit the wrists.

Purpose
The purpose is to maintain the Qì functions extending all the way to the finger tips. With the fingers naturally extended and the finger tips slightly curved inward, one can collect the Qì surrounding the hands into the body. There are six Meridians (three Yīn and three Yáng hand Meridians) in the upper limbs. By relaxing the shoulders, emptying the armpits, dropping the elbows, sitting the wrists, and extending the fingers, the Qì will circulate smoothly in these Meridians and the Qì can reach the finger tips.

10) Abdomen

Requirement

The abdomen should be withdrawn inward.

Method

Withdrawing the abdomen does not mean to tense up the abdominal muscles, it means to use the mind intent to pull the navel toward the Mìngmén. The tips of the hipbones move toward Zhāngmén xué (章門穴) straighten up the lower back, and the rib cage moves slightly upward and backward.

Purpose

This is an important step to help in concentrating the Qì in the Dāntián, and to increase the pressure in the Dāntián area to move the Qì to circulate inside the body. This position also moves postnatal Qì into the kidneys and changes it to prenatal Qì. If the navel is relaxed and the abdomen is dropped downward, it may cause a "Happy Buddha Tummy" (big belly).

11) Waist

Requirement

Relax the lumbar vertebrae, tendons and muscles in the waist area. The waist (lumbar vertebrae) remains straight throughout the practice. The Mìngmén pushes toward the back when standing, and pushes toward the front when sitting.

Method

Pull up the head (see section on the head) and drop the tailbone to lengthen and straighten the spine, following the instructions in the section on the abdomen. Push the second, third, and fourth lumbar vertebrae toward the back.

Purpose

The purpose of this requirement is to strengthen the kidneys' functions, and to maintain the flexibility of the body. If the stomach is protruding toward the front and the Mìngmén is pressed inward, it would hinder the Qì in the Dāntián and block the Qì movements in the back of the body, and also would prevent Qì from moving upward which would result in back pains, dizziness, swelling between the eyebrows, and bloating in the abdomen.

12) Kuà (跨)area

Requirement

Relax and loosen both hip joints and the sacroiliac joints.

Method

In Wújí zhuāng one does not bend the knees nor physically fold the Kuà. The participants use the mind intent to relax the knees and the hip joints, and to have a sitting-down feeling. The Kuà refers to the angle of the hip joints between the thighs and the abdominal area of the body. When the legs and the upper body form a straight line, the Kuà is open; when the upper body (or abdomen) touches the thighs, the Kuà is closed. When the thighs and the upper body form an angle, the Kuà is folded.

Rounding the waist area will open the sacroiliac joint and will prevent the stomach from protruding outward and the Mìngmén from pressing inward. The way to round the waist is to use Mìngmén. From Mìngmén, one expands outward along the hip bones to the sides and continues outward, and then scoops the tips of the hip bones to the front to that they join each other in front of the navel (forming a circle). Then use the mind intent to bring that joining point back to the Mìngmén.

Purpose
The purpose is to relax and loosen the hip joints to allow the lower limbs to move freely, to relax and loosen the sacroiliac joints to enlarge the Dāntián area, and to create a bigger space for the storage of Qì.

13) Coccyx

Requirement
The requirement is to relax the coccyx (tailbone) downward.

Method
Fold the Kuà, the hips slightly sit down, pull up the Huìyīn, perineum, between genitalia and anus, use the mind intent to have the tailbone be the third leg which goes all the way toward the ground to support the body. When relaxing the coccyx downward, one must pull up the Huìyīn; otherwise, the anus muscles may drop.

Purpose
The coccyx can move and activate the body's Yáng Qì. Once the coccyx loosens up, it is easier for the Qì to circulate and to return to the Dāntián.

14) Crotch *(*Dāng 襠)

Requirement
The Dāng is pulled up and rounded.

Method
Pull up the Huìyīn which includes the muscles in the anus and genital area; round the crotch area (thighs are not squeezing each other and the Huìyīn area is round); and turn the upper knees slightly inward. The proper posture of the Kuà and the coccyx will help in the rounding of the Dāng.

Purpose
The Huìyīn is the starting point for the Conception, Governor and Chōng (冲脉) Meridians. A correct Dāng posture will prevent the Huìyīn from being pressed or squeezed by the buttocks and the thighs. In order to allow the Qì to circulate smoothly, all areas need to be relaxed, except the Huìyīn which needs to maintain a certain tension to prevent it from being squeezed. Thus, this position of the Dāng ensures the smooth circulation of Qì flow in the Conception and Governor Meridians. Pulling up the Dāng also prevents Qì leaking from the anus and genitals.

15) Knees

Requirement
The knees are relaxed and scooped inward.

Method
With the lower legs fixed (do not turn or move), rotate the kneecaps inward, and then upward toward the Huìyīn. The knees are relaxed and are not locked.

Purpose
The lower limbs can maintain flexibility when the knees are relaxed. The knees scoop inward to help in rounding the Dāng, and to create a force which spirals downward from the back of the hips to the inner thighs and to the feet. Whether the Qì and blood are connected with the feet or not is determined by whether the knees are relaxed or not; relaxing the knees allows Qì and blood to reach the toes.

16) Feet

Requirement
The feet are placed flatly on the ground with the weight evenly distributed.

Method
Adjust and center the body, curl the big toes slightly downward to induce Qì downward. Lower the body weight from the Bǎihuì, to along the ears, the shoulders, the sides of the body, and the outside of the legs to the centers of the feet (Yǒngquán 涌泉); then evenly distribute the weight from the toes to the heels. Pull up the knees and loosen the joints of the feet; gradually, one will be able to have the feet flatly on the ground (Yǒngquán touches the ground).

Purpose
The purpose is to loosen up the joints in the feet which will allow the Body Qì to reach the toes. Once the Yǒngquán is able to touch the ground, it will connect the Body Qì with the earth Qì.

b. Mental Preparation

Before practicing the Body and Mind Method, there are Eight Essential Guidelines to review mentally. These Eight Essential Guidelines mainly emphasize using the mind intent. Generally speaking, there are two ways to follow the guidelines, one is external practice and another is internal practice.

In external practice, the purpose for the guidelines is to unite the practitioner with the Universe's vastness/emptiness. With the body relaxed, the mind can observe this unification in a relaxed and tranquil state. Through this observation, one further adjusts his/her body posture, mental condition, and the Qì functions in the whole body, and enters into the practice state.

In internal practice, the mind intent stays within the body. The top of the head is the sky, the bottom of the feet is the earth, and the body is the universe. To achieve this kind of internal feeling, the mind intent must go from within to without. For example, when thinking of the blue sky, the mind intent must start from within the body expanding outward toward the blue sky; the process cannot begin from outside the body. Also, the body does not have skin (boundary); there is no separation between the body, the blue sky, and the earth. The body and the universe are one.

The Eight Essential Guidelines of Zhìnéng Qìgōng

頂天立地	dǐng tiān lì dì	Head touches sky, feet root to the ground.
形鬆意充	xìng sōng yì chōng	Body relaxes and mind expands outward.
外敬内静	wái Jìng nèi Jīng	Outward expression is respectful and internal feeling is tranquil.
心澄貌恭	xīn chéng mào gōng	Mind is clear and appearance reverent.
一念不起	yī niàn bù qǐ	Not a single thought is raised.
神注太空	shén zhù tài kōng	The mind expands and merges with space.
神意照體	shén yi zhào tǐ	Mind intent observes the body from space.
周身融融	zhōu shēn róng róng	Whole body is nourished with Qì.

Because external practice is much easier than internal practice for most practitioners, and the application of the Eight Essential Guidelines is the same for both practices, we will use external practice to explain their meanings.

Head touches sky

The Bǎihuì, located on the top of the head, pushes upward. The blue sky is above the head. When pushed upward, the Bǎihuì will touch the xū kōng in the blue sky. Do not analyze how high the sky is. Because the color blue has vital information of ten thousand things, when the Qìgōng practitioner visualizes the blue sky's vastness/emptiness, it will activate the practitioner's vitality.

Feet root to the ground

When the feet step downward, they will reach the xū kōng inside the earth. One cannot think about standing on the ground, on the floor, or on the concrete. To imagine all of these materials will confine the practitioner's mind, and the Body Qì will stay at the surface of solid materials. As human beings, we are standing on solid earth, and the earth is enveloped by air. In one of his writings, Wáng Bīng (王冰) of the Táng Dynasty said that the reason the earth can stay afloat in space is because it is supported by Qì. The earth is supported and lifted by Qì; the earth is just a small particle in the space. The practitioner must imagine himself/herself as the earth and be surrounded by Qì and emptiness. In doing so, one can merge the Body Qì with universal Qì though the mind intent.

Only through such imagination can we have a foundation to practice "Man and Heaven Merge as One." We can use an example of an egg to illustrate this idea. There is a yolk and egg white inside an egg. If we are inside the yolk, then we and the yolk will be engulfed by the egg white. We live on the earth—the earth is engulfed by Qì and emptiness. If one can imagine that one is the yolk, then it is very natural to merge with the egg white to become one. When one can imagine and use this concept, one would not be confined to just sky and the earth. One would naturally merge with the vastness/emptiness as one. (One can also imagine one's head is above the clouds, the feet are in the earth).

Although we do not mention Yīn and Yáng nor Heaven and Earth Qì in practicing Zhìnéng Qìgōng, we live on the earth and connect with the earth. When we practice, we collect the most Primal Hùn Yuán Qì from outside the body. The earth also contains this level of Primal Hùn Yuán Qì—all things in the earth are evolved from Hùn Yuán Qì. So when we merge with the heaven and the earth before practice, we merge with the most basic/available material. That is why we need to "touch sky, stand on earth" at the very beginning of the practice.

Body relaxes, mind expands outward

The body relaxes means that the physical body is relaxed. Mind expands means that the mind intent expands outward.

The ***"body relaxes"*** requires relaxing the skin, the muscles, tendons, blood vessels, bones, and the internal organs. This is based on relaxing the mind first, and follows with the mind's intentions. One can use the mind's imagination to help loosen up and open the pores in the skin, and relax the capillaries in the muscles. This intention can help Qì's in and out function.

Mind expands has two implications:

a) The mind intent permeates the physical body. It means following the relaxation intention—the mind is aware of each section of the body which is relaxing (normally the mind intent occurs first, leading, and directing each body section to relax). When the mind intent is strong, Qì is abundant. This concept means that the mind is the leader and that Qì follows the mind. When the mind arrives, Qì arrives.

b) The mind intent expands to the space outside of the body. This requires the mind intent to permeate the space between heaven and earth in six directions (up and down, left and right, and front and back). It is usually done with the help of the imagination, such as imagining that one becomes a giant with his/her head touching the sky, and the feet touching into the earth. The whole body balloons outward to fill up the whole space; or one can imagine that one's mind intent fills the space between heaven and earth. In other words, it is the mind's intention to expand to the point that it can engulf the heaven and the earth. This will help to merge one's mind intent with the Universe Hùn Yuán Qì.

The ***"body relaxes and the mind expands"*** are complementary to each other. This relationship between the two is very obvious when the mind permeates and expands within the body and the body is physically relaxed. The physical body will become sluggish when it relaxes without expanding the mind intent; to have the mind intent but not a relaxed body, one will become stiff and tense. Only by using both at the same time can one achieve the soft and agile state of "relaxed but not sluggish, tense but not stiff."

Being able to achieve ***"Body relaxes and mind expands"*** is a key step in practicing Qìgōng. Besides, it can produce a peaceful and tranquil mind, and a smooth flow of Qì. It can also strengthen the practitioner's permeating abilities. The process is to relax physically, permeate with mind intent, and fill the body with mind intent (松透, 充). With a relaxed body, the mind intent permeates into the body; in the meantime, Qì will follow to fill the body. When the mind intent permeates the body, the awareness of the body will increase, and one will be able to feel his/her internal conditions.

Outward expression is respectful and internal feeling is tranquil

Respectful (Jìng 敬) means to be quiet in a respectful way, not being sluggish, and being careful. It means to treat people and things with high esteem. ***Tranquil*** (Jìng 靜) means single minded and concentration. Most Qìgōng practitioners know the important part that "tranquility" plays in Qìgōng, but most ignore the "respectful" part. In fact, a respectful mind set is very helpful in achieving tranquility. For example, would you have any distracting thoughts at the moment you meet the person you highly respect and adore? It is undeniable that these indescribable feelings, the blood running, and the heart pounding sensation are produced by the reverent mind.

According to Qìgōng theory, a respectful mind can lead to concentration (tranquility). It can stimulate vitality. There are many writings and descriptions about this concept in the book "Guǎnzi 管子"—such as the following: "be respectful and let go of distractions, Jīng will come automatically (敬除其舍，精將自來); "appearance is respectful and reverent, Jīng will be centered by itself (嚴容畏敬，精將自定); and "people with a respectful outside and tranquil inside, will return to the primal virtue/soul (外敬而內靜者，必反其性)," etc. Chéng Yīchuān (程伊川) of the Sòng Dynasty said that "the best way to achieve Dào is through respect. Respect can lead one directly to Dào (入道莫若敬，敬以直內)."

As described above, one must have a respectful mind to practice Qìgōng. Ancient Qìgōng masters required students to respect the teachers. In fact, through the process of respecting the teachers, the students strengthened their own cultivation. Zhìnéng Qìgōng is against worshipping any individual; it does not require the students to respect the teachers in this ancient way. However, each practitioner should respect Qìgōng Science, and respect his/her own practice. Only with respect and avoidance of slacking off, can one practice meticulously, and get into the Qìgōng State (Qìgōng tài 氣功態) quickly.

Mind is clear, appearance is reverent

Clarity "chéng (澄)" means clear and transparent. Reverent "Gōng (恭)" means an attitude of adoration. There is a slight difference between "Gōng" and "Jìng (敬)." "Jìng" is mainly an internal feeling. "Gōng" is the physical expression of that feeling. This statement is the extension of "Respectful outside and tranquil inside." "Chéng" is the extension of quiet (tranquility). The mind is as quiet as still water—clear and transparent. It indicates that the mind does not have any thoughts; it is as transparent as water, and as clear as a mirror. Thus, it will strengthen the mind's observing abilities. Reverent "Gōng" is an extension of respect "Jìng." which allows (extends) the inner respectful feeling to become external expressions. This will put both mental and physical conditions into a respectful state. In turn, this will bring one into a deeper Qìgōng State.

Not a single thought is raised. The mind expands and merges with space

These two statements have the same meaning. Based on the previously mentioned "be respectful and be tranquil." This statement requires the practitioner to concentrate, and to be empty of distracting thoughts. But it is not to say that one does not think of anything, or does not get involved. Due to the fact that most people cannot achieve the state of "not a single thought arises." it requires the practitioner to merge the mind intent with space/emptiness. It means to focus on the space/emptiness. This not only follows the principle points of Qìgōng practice (inward mind activities), but it is also a high level Qìgōng practice technique. In order to have a deeper understanding of this concept, we can explain it in the following way.

Zhìnéng Qìgōng belongs to an Open System, and requires that the practitioner merge the body and the mind with his/her surroundings. Through mind intent, one uses these two statements to merge the body with nature to become one entity. It is a very effective technique. In traditional Qìgōng, the highest-level practicing technique is to "use xū kōng (space) as a stove, the body as the pot, and the mind intent as the herb." Regular methods use the following techniques: the body as a stove, the mind as the pot; or stomach as a stove, and the head as the pot; or use the lower Dāntián as the stove, and the middle Dāntián as the pot, etc.

Use xū kōng as the stove and the body as the pot means to use the Hùn Yuán Qì in the xū kōng to purify the practitioner's body and mind. With practice, the mind activities (the herb) become purer and purer. The key part of this type of practice is that the mind intent cannot stay within one's own body—it must stay outside. This way one can easily absorb the External Hùn Yuán Qì for one's own use, and slowly merge nature with one's own body. This is what the Ancients called "Outside the body yet store inside the body (外其身而身存). " This is the technique ancient practitioners used to achieve "Man and Nature become One."

Of course, the way that the Zhìnéng Qìgōng practice of External Hùn Yuán uses "no distracting thoughts, think space." and the mind intent merges with xū kōng technique is not the same as the high level technique mentioned by ancient practitioners. (In reality, very few ancient practitioners were successful in using the emptiness as a stove and the pot technique to cultivate Qì). The purpose for focusing the mind intent on space is to merge it with the blue sky. When it merges with the empty and unobtrusive space, it can put the mind into a non-distracting, non-doing, unoccupied, and tranquil state, and a state of clarity.

Mind intent observes the body from space. The Body is nourished with Qì

As the mind is focusing on space, the practitioner brings back his/her awareness from the xū kōng to observe and to examine the body. Because when the mind and space merge, they will merge with the Hùn Yuán Qì in the space to become one. Thus, when one brings his/her awareness back to observe the body, the Hùn Yuán Qì will automatically go into the body. This xū kōng Hùn Yuán Qì will fill, strengthen, and harmonize the body Hùn Yuán Qì. The whole body will have a feeling of warmth and relaxation.

In order to bring back one's awareness more effectively from the xū kōng, and to bring in more Hùn Yuán Qì, one can say one of the Mantras "kōng, qīng, lái, lǐ (空青來裡)" or "Ǎn, lán, lái, lǐ (唵藍來裡)." The purpose of using these words is twofold. First, the purpose is to use the sound vibration to achieve the result. The second purpose is to use the meaning of the words to lead the Qì in the xū kōng into the body. It will help to bring one's awareness from the xū kōng back into the body while saying these words. (kōng 空 means emptiness, qīng 青 means green color, lái 來 means come, and lǐ 裡 means within, Ǎn 唵 has no meaning, lán 藍 means blue color).

Overall, the Eight Essential Guidelines are a very good Qìgōng method by themselves. They contain a complete practicing process in their contents. With the body and mind adjustments, one begins with a non-practicing state, and enters into the practicing state, into a concentration state, and into a man and nature harmonized and integrated state. If one can achieve this state, it is considered that one has reached a good proficiency in his/her practice in traditional Qìgōng. However, Zhìnéng Qìgōng requires the practitioner actively to improve his/her mind and body. It considers this process too passive. One should create ways to harmonize with nature. So one must continue the practice while retrieving the mind from space and merge it with the body—in this way one would maintain the practice as "one within the Qì," "the Qì within one," and the "man and nature as one" state.

2. Opening 起式

Movements

Rotate the hands backward and then downward, press the earth to collect Qì. Then push forward 15 degrees and pull back to the beginning position. Repeat 3 times. Fig. 2-1, Fig. 2-2, Fig. 2-3, Fig. 2-4.

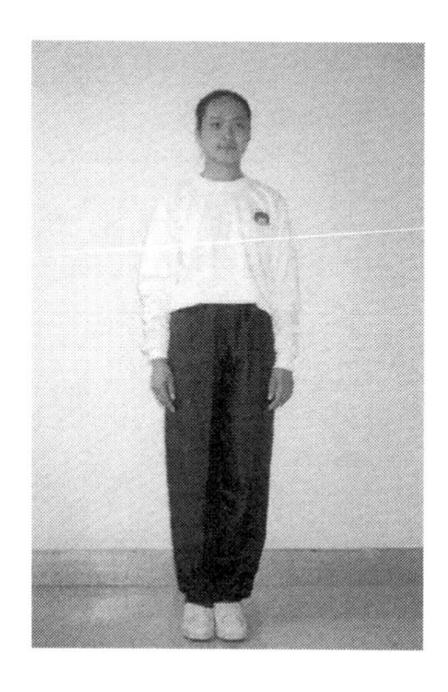

Fig. 2-1

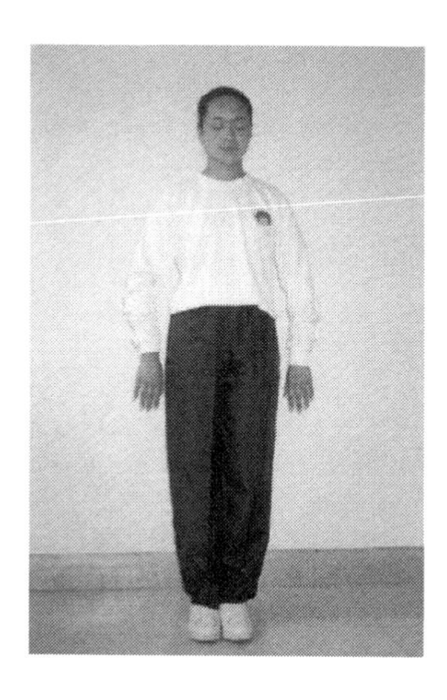

Fig. 2-2

Fig. 2-3

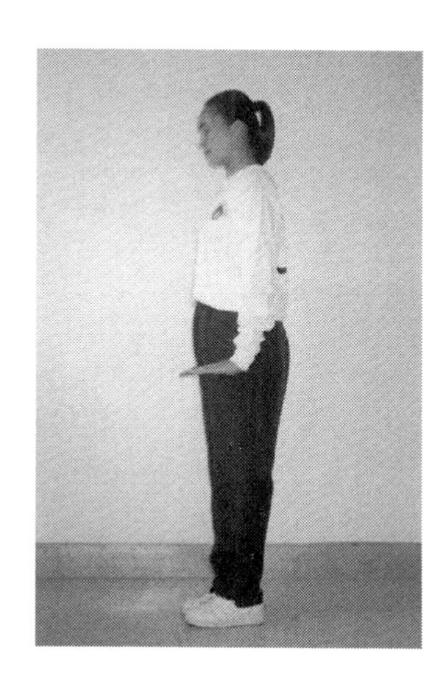

Fig. 2-4

Relax wrists and turn palms to face each other. The hands lift Qì upward to the navel level and deliver it to the Dāntián through the navel. Fig. 2-5, Fig. 2-6.

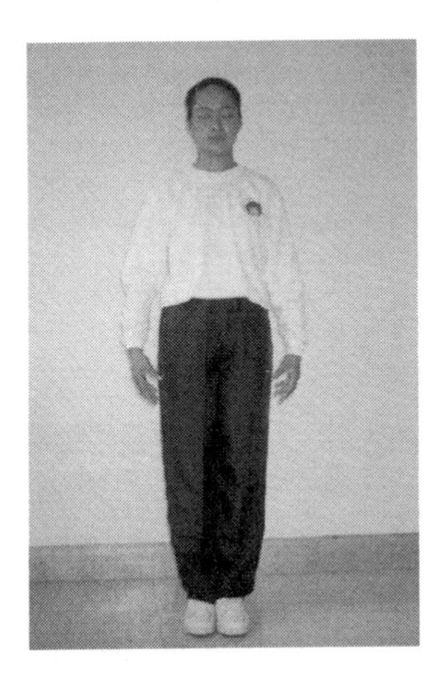

Fig. 2-5

Fig. 2-6

Turn palms down and circle them around to the side. Fig. 2-7, Fig. 2-8.

Fig. 2-7

Fig. 2-8

Continue to turn and scoop Qì to the back. Point to Mìngmén and deliver Qì to the Dāntián through Mìngmén. Fig. 2-9, Fig. 2-10.

Fig. 2-9

Fig. 2-10

Move the hands upward and forward to the underarms; with the tips of the middle fingers lightly press Dàbāo and deliver Qì inside. Rotate elbows backward until fingers point to the front. Fig. 2-11, Fig. 2-12.

Fig. 2-11

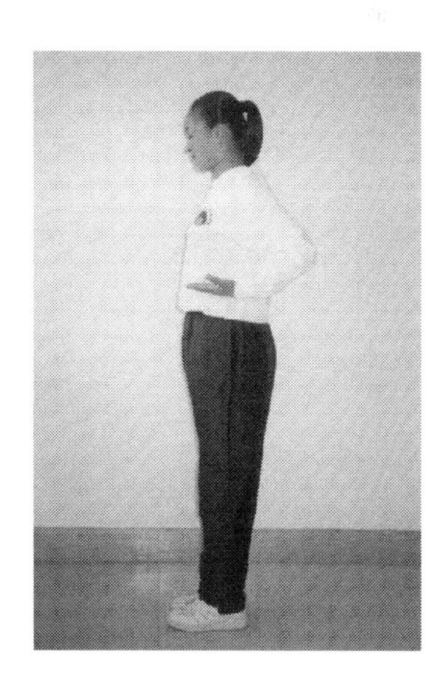

Fig. 2-12

Extend the hands forward with palms up to shoulder level and width. Slightly bend the middle fingers to reflect Qì into the head through Yìntáng (between the eyebrows). Rotate the arms 45 degrees until palms are facing each other diagonally; then circle the arms around to the sides forming a straight line. Fig. 2-13, Fig. 2-14.

Fig. 2-13

Fig. 2-14

Rotate the arms to turn the hands down, then up to scoop Qì upward. Lift hands upward in a circular motion until the hands are above the head. Put hands together and lift upward farther. Then lower the hands to the chest level forming a praying position. Fig. 2-15, Fig. 2-16.

Fig. 2-15

Fig. 2-16

Details

Opening posture/sequence

Rotate the palms upward and press down to pull Qì. The movement requirements are the following:

1) Starting from the sides of the body, and leading with the little fingers, turn the centers of the palms backward, using the wrists as pivot points, move the palms and fingers upward toward the front. When rotating the palms, one must rotate the arms and shoulders as one unit, turn the hands and arms about a quarter of a circle. Fig. 2-1, Fig. 2-2.

2) When doing the push and pull movements during the press downward to Lā Qì movement, beginners can use a straight front and back approach—push forward fifteen degrees, and then pull back to the beginning position. Once one becomes proficient, this push-pull movement can be performed as if drawing an arc along an elliptical route. Also, it should be performed with slightly up and down movements. This would cause the centers of the palms to protrude outward and to cup inward, creating one movement of tension and one of relaxation. Fig. 2-3.

3) When the hands push forward, the centers of the palms protrude outward and press downward. As the hands push to the maximum, cup and relax the centers of the palms. Protrude the centers of the palms outward when pulling back; cup and relax the centers as the hands move back to their original positions. This will create a "protrude-cup, protrude-cup" rhythm as the hands move back and forth. Fig. 2-4

4) When the hands press down, the mind intent presses down into the xū kōng underneath the ground. The mind intent leads the Body Qì outward and into the xū kōng to merge with the Qì in the xū kōng. Relax the body. Cup the hands slightly when pulling back, absorbing the earth Qì as one draws this small ellipse. If one examines only the movement, it is a push and pull movement, but it actually uses the small protrude-cup motion to achieve the result of one open and one close movement. Following the open and close movement, the body expands outward and contracts inward. Fig. 2-4, Fig. 2-5.

5) After three push and pull movements, relax the wrists and rotate the palms. Do not neglect this movement and do not perform it mindlessly. This movement requires leading with the small fingers. From a facing the ground position, the palms turn a quarter of a circle to return to the original position with the centers of the palms facing the thighs. Fig. 2-5.

   Also, the shoulders and the arms should return to the original position at the same time. In this way, the body Qì will be whole and not concentrated in the hands. When the hands relax downward, one must imagine the hands going deep inside the xū kōng beneath the earth to hold and move Qì upward. When holding and lifting the Qì ball, which has a huge Qì tail which is still connecting to the xū kōng from the earth, the hands must be carefully held and must treasure the Qì ball. Fig. 2-6.

6) When the hands cup inward slightly to face the navel, the mind intent is to deliver the Qì ball into the navel. This way, one delivers uninterrupted Hùn Yuán Qì from the earth into the navel. One must think deep inside the body, all the way to Mìngmén. In this way, the Hùn Yuán Qì from the earth will permeate the Dāntián. The Dāntián Qì will be sufficient. Fig. 2-7.

7) Then, still leading with the small fingers, rotate the centers of the palms downward, rotating the arms at the same time. Circle the hands around the body at navel level. The rotating palms and the circling around the body movements should be even and continuous, avoiding rigid, angular movements. This rotating movement is done to move along the surface of the earth. The hands pressing the earth and touching the horizon will put the body between heaven and earth, and will enable the body to absorb the Hùn Yuán Qì in heaven, the earth, and in the xū kōng all at the same time. Fig. 2-8, to Fig. 2-9.

8) Circle the hands to the back to shoulder width, turning the palms to face Mìngmén, and at the same time, bend the elbows outward slightly—this way, the hands can be at the same level as the Mìngmén. When turning the palms to face Mìngmén, one should think deep inside the body through to Mìngmén. Fig. 2-10.

9) The next movement is the hands reaching under the armpits, and the middle fingers pressing Dàbāo (located between the sixth and seventh ribs, directly under the centers of the armpits). This is a key area. There are fifteen major collateral points (络穴). Every collateral meridian has a collateral point. Dàbāo is the Spleen Meridian's major collateral point. To cultivate Hùn Yuán Qì, we must open all the collateral meridians. Pressing this point helps to open the collateral meridians. When we press Dàbāo, we must concentrate and focus on the middle fingers pressing inward as if the middle finger tips are touching each other inside the body. This focus can make opening the meridians easier. When that happens, one would have a special sensation running through the whole body, all the way into the inner organs; sometimes, it would run from the inside toward outside the body, and sometimes from the outside running inward. The collateral Meridian Qì runs smoothly and harmoniously. Fig. 2-11.

10) To press Dàbāo, one may use the finger tips to draw a small circle from the back toward the front, and then press. When the arms extend outward, the hands are in a position as if holding something—this position is to receive the Qì from heaven. Use the mind intent to connect the arms (as if the arms are connected with something). Fig. 2-11 to Fig. 2-12.

11) When in this position of pointing to the Yìntáng movement, beginners can cup the palms slightly. Once one becomes proficient, one can point the tips of the middle fingers to Yìntáng to deliver the Hùn Yuán Qì ball in the hands to the Yìntáng—the smaller the pointing to the Yìntáng movement, the better. The middle finger tips join each other at Yìntáng as if they are connected by two threads. This way, inside the Yìntáng will have a bloated, tense, and vibrating feeling; sometimes even the base of the ears would have this vibrating sensation. The Qì will enter the head to open the Upper Dāntián (上丹田). It will increase the sensibilities of the Meridian points inside the head, and will be very beneficial for opening the Heaven's Eye (between the eyebrows). It also will help with the development of acuity. Fig. 2-13.

12) The force for the elbows and the arms pushing outward is from the shoulders; therefore, it is the shoulders leading the elbows to push open. The centers of the palms rotate slightly upward and push outward diagonally. For beginners, just pushing outward diagonally is sufficient. After some practice, one can experience three kinds of forces. The first force occurs when the back and the ribs expand outward—one feels as if he/she is not able to move. The second force occurs when the shoulders and the elbows open sideways—one feels as if there is an attracting force between the arms, and cannot open the elbows. The third force occurs when one feels that the space between the arms is full of Qì as if there is a huge Qì Ball expanding outward. Fig. 2-14.

13) Circle the arms around the body along the horizon with the fingers pointing toward the sky (horizon) and pushing outward. With this movement, one can connect the Internal and External Qì, and unite them as one. Fig. 2-14.

14) When the arms almost form a straight line, leading with the small fingers, rotate the arms a quarter of a circle downward to turn the centers of the palms facing toward the ground. Rotate and move the arms and palms upward from the sides in an arching motion, and continue to turn until the palms face the sky. This movement must be round and continuous to maintain an uninterrupted Qì flow. When rotating the palms, the mind intent is at the horizon. Following the rotation of the palms, one moves/scoops the Qì, and holds and lifts it upward along the edge of the blue sky. The body should be straight yet relaxed. The hands are in a position as if holding something. One would feel physical exertion and heaviness between the arms in the chest. This is the result of holding the heaven and earth Qì, and also is an indication of sufficient Qì in the arms. In the process of holding Qì upward, the arms also are gathering Qì from xū kōng to the center of heaven—the mind intent needs to direct this Qì to concentrate at the center of the highest point along the edge of the sky—it is also called the center of heaven (天心). Following the movement of the hands to close toward the center of heaven, the gathered Qì will descend and enter the head. Use the mind intent to direct it into the body. Fig. 2-14, Fig. 2-15.

15) Lower the hands and the arms—when the wrists almost reach the top of the head, move the hands to the front of the face, and continue to move downward. Relax the shoulders, level the elbows, round the shoulder blades, and open the armpits—the armpits must remain empty. Continue to lower the hands until they are in front of the chest forming a praying-hands position. The wrists and forearms cannot be lower than the chest with the thumbs at about Shānzhōng (Xiphold) level. The upper arms and the body form a forty-five degree angle, as if supported by a Qì balloon inside the elbows and arms. This position is called praying hands in front of the chest. This posture not only can maintain the Qì in the arms circulating in a circular fashion, it also is very helpful to obtain concentration—many religions use this posture as a form of greeting. Fig. 2-15, Fig. 2-16.

Purpose

This opening sequence seems very simple; it actually goes through the Heaven Route (天盤), the Earth Route (地盤), and the Man Route (人盤). Heaven, Earth, and Man are three routes—it is also called the "Three-Route Posture (三才式)." From rotating the palms to Lā Qì to pointing to the navel to deliver Qì to the lower Dāntián is the Earth Route. Pressing Dàbāo to deliver Qì to the middle Dāntián, and turning the palms to point to the Yìntáng to deliver Qì to the upper Dāntián is the Heaven Route. Closing the hands on top of the head to deliver Qì to Bǎihuì and Tiānmén (located at the top of the head), the hands form a praying-hands position in front of the chest—this belongs to the Man Route which will connect both the upper and lower Dāntiáns. Zhìnéng Qìgōng collects Hùn Yuán Qì. It does not work on heaven Yáng Qì (天陽) and earth Yīn Qì (地陰), but we can use different ways to understand and experience these types of Qì.

Opening movements merge Heaven Qì, Earth Qì, External Qì and Internal Qì into one; and activate whole body Qì functions. Because most of the movements lead with the little finger which belongs to the Heart Meridian, the movements activate the Heart Meridian to nourish the heart and help concentration. When in the praying position, the fingers' Meridians touch one another and enable Qì to circulate as a loop. The Center of the palms (Láogōng 劳宫) facing each other can balance the Qì functions in both left and right sides of the body. Holding the hands in front of the chest in praying position is very spiritual and helps one to concentrate. The beginning movements activate the body Shǎo yáng Qì (少陽清氣). The middle fingers touch Dàbāo and rotate the elbows backward to activate the five Organs Qì. Putting the hands together and lowering the palms to in front of the chest can help concentrate Shén (mind intent). The thumbs pointing to Shānzhōng can help in balancing Qì and blood. The opening posture/sequence adjusts the mental state and activates Qì functions.

3. Crane's Neck and Dragon's Horns 鶴首龍頭氣沖天

Movements

a. Crane's Neck

Fig. 3-1

Preparation: separate and lower hands along the rib cage. Then rest hands on the waist with thumbs slightly pressing Jīngmén 京門 at the tip of the 12th ribs. Crane's Neck: Tuck in the chin, and push and pull the cervical vertebrae backward and upward. Lean the head backward while pulling up the chin and Bǎihuì. Fig. 3-1 to Fig. 3-3.

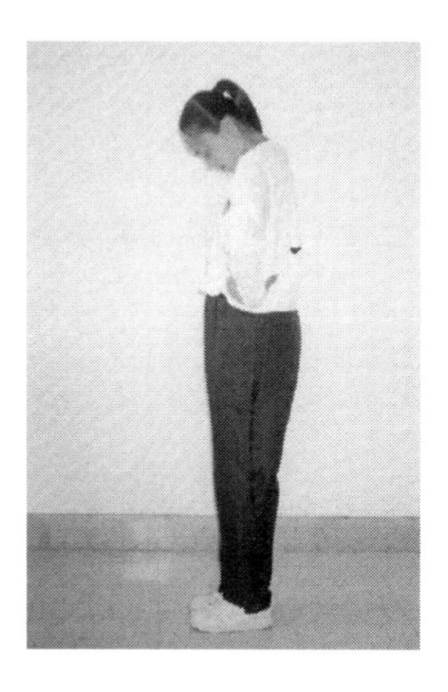

Fig. 3-2

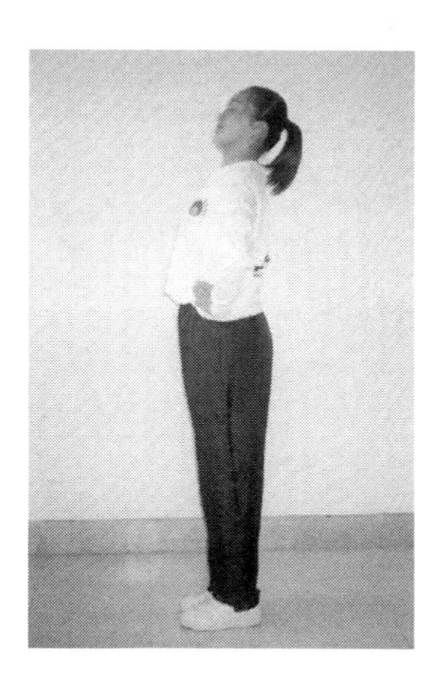

Fig. 3-3

Relax the cervical vertebrae and move the chin from upward to forward, downward, inward, and along the chest upward to complete the circular motion, returning to the beginning position. Fig. 3-4 to Fig. 3-7. Repeat nine times.

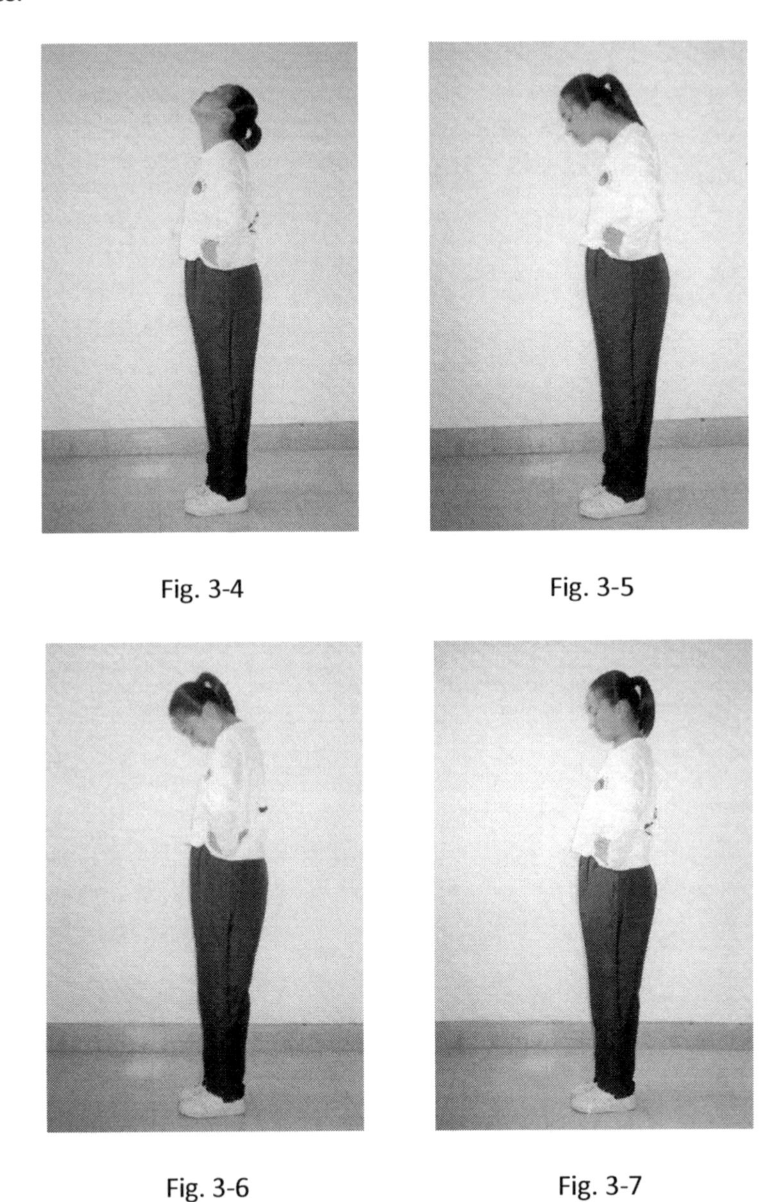

Fig. 3-4

Fig. 3-5

Fig. 3-6

Fig. 3-7

Opposite direction

Using the same principles, draw circle in the opposite direction. Repeat 9 times. Fig. 3-7 to Fig. 3-1 (in reverse sequence).

b. Dragon's Horns

The "bulges" (parietal eminence on each side of the skull) on the skull bone, which are approximately 2 inches above the ears, are called dragon's horns. The left dragon's horn moves downward diagonally to the left shoulder, then pushes up and to the right to draw a semicircle, returning to the beginning position, Fig. 3-8 to Fig. 3-9. Likewise, the right dragon's horn turns to the right to draw a semicircle, Fig. 3-10 to Fig. 3-11. Repeat the movements 18 times, 9 to each side.

Fig. 3-8

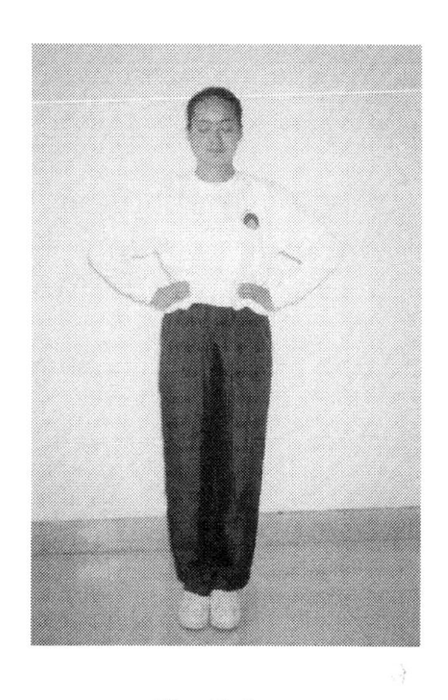

Fig. 3-9

Fig. 3-10

Fig. 3-11

Details

Preparation. From the praying position, slowly separate wrists until the tips of the middle fingers touch the sternum. Move fingers along the edge of the rib cage, lower hands to the waist, then turn hands until the palms are facing upward. Leading with the little fingers, the hands continue to turn backward and downward to rest on the waist. The thumbs slightly press Jīngmén (tip of the 12th rib) and the other fingers lightly press Zhāngmén章門 (slightly in front of and under the tip of the 11th rib) and Dàimài xué 帶脈穴 (about 1.8 inches underneath Zhāngmén). Jīngmén points are junction points for the vertical Meridian channels. If Jīngmén were pressed, Qì would flow into the vertical Meridian channels instead of the membranes.

a. **Crane's Neck**

Forward direction Crane's Neck

The forward direction focuses on the cervical vertebrae pushing backward (tucking in the chin) and pulling upward. By moving the head around Dàzhuī xué 大椎穴 (1st thoracic vertebra) as the pivot point through extending and bending the cervical vertebrae as the chin draws circles, we imitate the head movements of a walking crane. The purpose of this movement is to exercise the cervical vertebrae and the head.

1) **First tuck in the chin.** While tucking in the chin, Bǎihuì moves forward and downward as if looking at shirt buttons. The chin tucks in to the limit. Fig. 3-1.
2) **Pull the cervical vertebrae.** Hold the chin position as the cervical vertebrae push backward and upward. The head pushes upward and pulls up the spine. With Bǎihuì pulling and leading, pull up each cervical vertebra, one at a time, until it reaches Yùzhěn and no longer is able to move upward. Fig. 3-2.
3) **Lean the head backward.** With the chin still tucked in and Bǎihuì pulling, lean the head backward to the limit. Relax Yùzhěn. Fig. 3-3.
4) **Move the chin upward.** As the neck begins to relax, Bǎihuì pulls upward and backward. At the same time, the chin draws a circular arc and moves upward to the limit. Fig. 3-4.
5) **Forward and downward.** The chin continues to move forward and downward to draw a circle. Fig. 3-5.
6) **Inward.** Bǎihuì moves forward, downward and inward, as if to touch the chest, and to help the chin to move inward. This will create a downward and inward force from Bǎihuì, and a backward and upward force from the chin. Imagine the chin brushing the thoracic vertebrae and pulling the cervical vertebrae upward, from number seven to Yùzhěn, one vertebra at a time. Fig. 3-6 to Fig. 3-7.

Using the 1st thoracic vertebra as the pivotal point, and following steps **1)** to **6)**, draw a complete circle. Repeat 9 times.

Backward (reverse) direction

This movement imitates the crane eating and drinking. The principles are the same for the reverse movements as for the forward movements except the steps are in the opposite directions.

1) **Tuck in the chin.** Tuck in the chin until it touches the throat and hold the position.
2) **Move the chin downward.** Băihuì pulls upward and moves forward slightly. The chin, as if brushing the inner side of the cervical vertebrae, moves downward from 1st cervical vertebra to the maximum in a circular motion.
3) **Forward and upward.** The chin pushes forward and then upward. Following the upward movement of the chin, the body pulls upward at the same time.
4) **Pull the cervical vertebrae.** When the chin cannot move upward anymore, move Băihuì backward and upward to pull the cervical vertebrae upward (the body also will be pulled upward). At the same time tuck in the chin.
5) **Tuck in the chin.** Continue to push and pull up Băihuì, tucking in the chin until it touches the throat.

The movements from **1)** to **5)** form a circle. Repeat 9 times.

Common mistakes

The movements of the chin tucking in and the Băihuì pulling upward are not synchronized. They should be done at the same time. In the movements of the head leaning backward and the chin moving upward and forward, the chin's path is not round enough. The body center line is not maintained.

Keys to the Crane's Neck practice

The keys to this practice are in the chin's tucking-in/scooping-up movements and the cervical vertebrae's pushing-out/pulling-up movements. While the chin draws a circle, Băihuì also draws a circle simultaneously.

In the beginning stage of practice, use the chin to draw a maximum circle while the 1st thoracic vertebra serves as a stationary point. It is very important that the chin does not draw a straight line, it must be a circular movement. In the more advanced stage, the chin should synchronize with the shoulders' open-close movements and the chest's convex-concave movements. For example, in the forward direction Crane's Neck movements, when pulling up the cervical vertebrae, lean the body slightly backward, open the shoulders, and open up the chest so it expands in a slightly convex fashion, but do not protrude outward. As the chin moves forward and downward, the shoulders move slightly forward and inward as the chest moves in a slightly concave fashion. In the reverse direction, as the chin moves downward, the shoulders move forward and inward and the chest moves in a concave direction. In the upward motions, the shoulders open up, the chest opens and expands in a convex direction. The whole body relaxes.

With the movements of the body, shoulders, chest and chin, all of the vertebrae will behave like a string of pearls. Once the top one moves, the rest will follow it. A skilled practitioner will experience several frontal-backward curves in the spine. In advanced practice, instead of using the chin to draw circles, one draws circles inside the Yìntáng.

Another advanced practice method is to coordinate with acupuncture points. There are two groups of seven acupuncture points to work with. One is called the Small Seven Stars, another is called the Big Seven Stars. Normally, one begins with the Small Seven Stars. The Stars are Bǎihuì, Yìntáng, Dàzhuī, Rǔzhōng (2) and Fǔshě (2). In this method, the lower limbs remain stationary. Drawing circles inside Yìntáng combined with the chest's concave convex movements, the practitioner's head and body will have a certain amount of front and back snake-like movements. In addition, the Rǔzhōng and Fǔshě acupuncture points will have movement sensations.

The Big Seven Stars are Bǎihuì, Huágài (RN20), Mìngmén, Huántiào (2), Wàihuáijiān (2 外踝尖). In this method, the whole body needs to be relaxed. Use the head movement to drive the body and the lower limbs' movements. With the head's circular movement as the driving force, the body and lower limbs will have a snake-like movement.

Acupuncture point practice can strengthen the changes in Internal Qì, but one must practice in a totally relaxing state. Also, one cannot focus on the points, just be aware of them. If too much attention or focus is on the points, it will hinder Qì circulation.

b. Dragon's Horns

1) **Head leans to the left.** The left Dragon's Horn leans to the left, and the left shoulder and left ribs relax. The left ribs slightly move downward as the head leans to the left to the maximum, touching the left ear to the left shoulder. The left Dragon's Horn then pushes outward and upward, back to the beginning position. Fig. 3-8 to Fig. 3-9.

2) **Head leans to the right.** The right Dragon's Horn leans to the right, and the right shoulder and right ribs relax. The right ribs slightly move downward as the head leans to the right to the maximum, touching the right ear to the right shoulder. The right Dragon's Horn pushes outward and upward, back to the beginning position. Fig. 3-10 to Fig. 3-11.

Common mistakes

One common mistake is using too much force and not relaxing enough when pushing upward with the horn. The head just sways from side to side; it should have a pushing-upward motion. In addition, the chin moves too much and in a three-dimensional space; the chin should be as stationary as possible and the face should always face toward the front in a two-dimensional plane. The entire movement is practiced in a two-dimensional plane. Another mistake occurs when each shoulder is pushing downward from side to side—they should relax downward with minimal movement.

Keys to the Dragon's Horns practice

The degree of difficulty is much higher in practicing the Dragon's Horns than in the Crane's Neck movements. Proper postures are dependent upon the correct movements of the Dragon's Horns. Traditionally, the parietal eminence (about 2 inches directly above the edge of the ear) is called the Dragon's Horn. This movement uses the Dragon's Horns to draw a vertical sleeping "8" or an ∞ (an infinity sign).

When first learning the movements, use the hands to help pushing up each of the Dragon's Horns. Put both hands on the Dragon's Horns, and lean the head to the left. Relaxing the left side of the body (including the waist) will automatically lean the body to the left. With the chin pointing to the ground and stationary, the left hand pushes the left Dragon's Horn upward; as the horn is pushed up, the body is pulled up at the same time. As the left horn reaches the top of the movement, the right horn leans and drops to the right; and then the right hand pushes the right horn upward. Repeat the movements. If the entire body is relaxed, each vertebra in the spine will move.

In the beginning, we may draw a large sleeping figure "8." Once we become proficient, the movement should become smaller and less rigid. The smaller the head movement, the bigger the reaction in the spine. A skilled practitioner will experience side-to-side curves in the spine like that of a snake. The spinal motions occur only when the dragon's horns have an upward movement. Instead of using the horns to draw an infinity sign, ∞, an advanced practitioner uses the Bǎihuì to draw the ∞. Fig. 3-13.

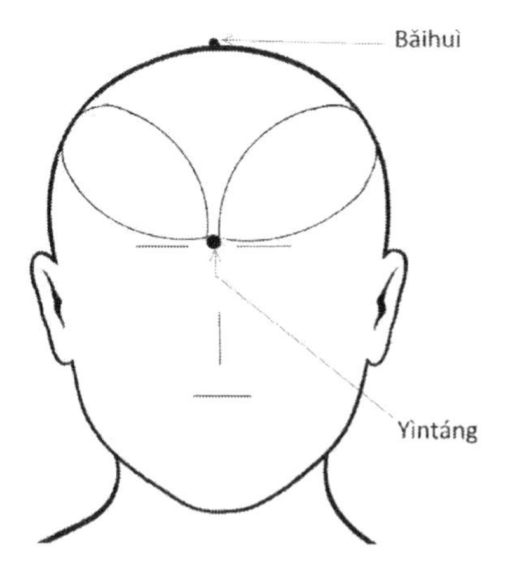

Fig. 3-13

The acupuncture points practice for Dragon's Horns is the Macro Seven Stars. Just be aware of the seven points and relax the whole body during the practice. Use the head movements to lead the head, the body and the lower limbs to move like a snake.

Purpose of Crane's Neck and Dragon's Horns

Preparation. Separating and lowering the hands along the rib cage can concentrate the inner organs Qì and open the Mùxué (募穴 acupuncture points in the chest and the abdominal area where the inner organs Qì concentrates.) Resting the hands on the waist with the thumbs lightly pressing Jīngmén 京門 can activate Jīngmén. Jīngmén regulates the body's vertical Meridians (Jīngmài 經脈). When the thumbs press Jīngmén, Qì will circulate in the vertical Meridians instead of in the lateral Meridians.

Jīngmén belongs to the Gallbladder Meridian and is the Kidney's Mùxué (Kidney Qì concentration point). Zhāngmén 章門 belongs to the Liver and is the Spleen's Mùxué. The thumb lightly pressing Jīngmén and the rest of the fingers lightly pressing Zhāngmén and Dàimài xué have four purposes.

- The thumbs lightly pressing Jīngmén and Zhāngmén can activate Spleen (postnatal) and Kidney (prenatal) Qì.
- Pressing the Liver Meridian (Zhāngmén) and the Gallbladder Meridian (Jīngmén) can merge Liver Qì and Gallbladder Qì (both belong to Shǎoyáng 少陽) and will strengthen Shǎoyáng Qì's circulation.
- Pressing Dàimài Xué can strengthen Dàimài Meridian's functions and will improve its regulatory functions.
- Pressing Zhāngmén can induce Gallbladder Qì into the Spleen to strengthen Spleen Qì functions.

In the forward Crane's Neck, by tucking in the chin and pulling up the cervical vertebrae, we activate the Governor Meridian, open up pressure points in the Governor Meridian, and activate Qì to move upward along the Governor Meridian. When the head leans backward, then moves upward, the Yùzhěn automatically will be relaxed and allows Qì to flow through the Conception Meridian more easily. Qì will move from the tailbone, to Dàzhuī, to Yùzhěn, and finally reach Bǎihuì. As the head moves forward and downward with the chin tucked in, Qì will be moved down to the Conception Meridian and the Dāntián. By doing the simple Crane's Neck movement, we activate the Governor and Conception Meridians.

Combining the hands pressing Jīngmén, Zhāngmén, and Dàimài, with the synchronization of the body's open and close movements, and with pulling the cervical vertebrae upward can activate the body's Meridians. Up to a certain point, one Crane's Neck cycle is roughly equivalent to one Microcosmic Orbit. Although the Body & Mind Method does not work on the Microcosmic Orbit, practicing Crane's Neck will reap the same benefits.

The Dragon's Horns movement first activates the Gallbladder Meridian and then stimulates the Liver Meridian. According to Traditional Chinese Medicine, the inner organs depend on the Gallbladder. The Shǎoyáng Gallbladder Meridian can activate the inner organs' Qīngyáng Qì 清陽氣. If we practice Dragon's Horns with the eyes closed, we will gradually feel the body getting lighter accompanied by a very comfortable upward feeling. This is the sensation of Qīngyáng Qì moving upward. When Qīngyáng Qì concentrates in the head, the brain will be nourished. The Dragon's Horns movement also can open Mǎo yǒu zhōu tiān (卯酉周天 one type of Orbital Qìgōng).

This movement works on the head and the central nervous system. The Crane's Neck activates the Governor and Conception, and the Dragon's Horns activates the Gallbladder Meridians. Exercising the head will increase and strengthen the circulation of Qì to the head to nourish the brain. The snake-like movements in the spine not only loosen up and stretch the vertebrae, but also massage the nerve tissues and the spinal cord, and will increase blood flow in the spine. In addition, this movement can clear the head and brighten the eyes.

Practicing this exercise can improve blood and lymphatic circulation in the neck and head areas. It is very effective in treating vertigo, headache, tinnitus, and nervous system abnormalities.

4. Open Arms and Rotate Wrists, Squeeze Shoulder Blades and Shrink Neck 寒肩縮項通臂肩

Movements

a. Open Arms and Rotate Wrists

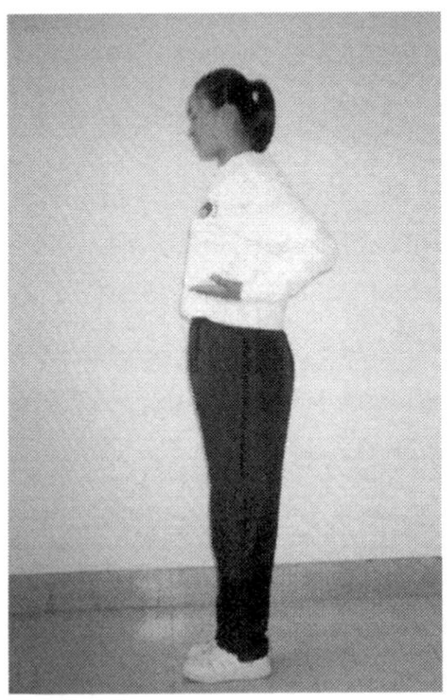

Fig. 4-1

Following the last movement (Fig. 3-11), relax the hands, and rotate palms upward to face the sky. Move forearms forward to form a right angle (90 degrees) with the upper arms. Lift upper arms to shoulder level with the fingers pointing to the sky while maintaining the 90-degree angle between the forearms and upper arms. Move only shoulders. Fig. 4-1 to Fig. 4-3.

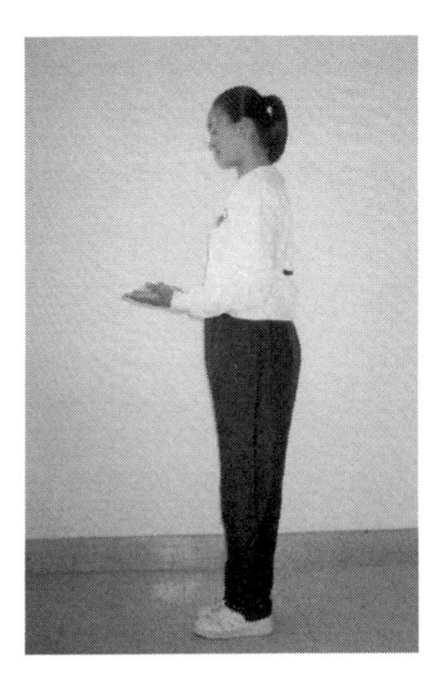

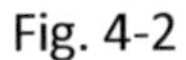

Fig. 4-2

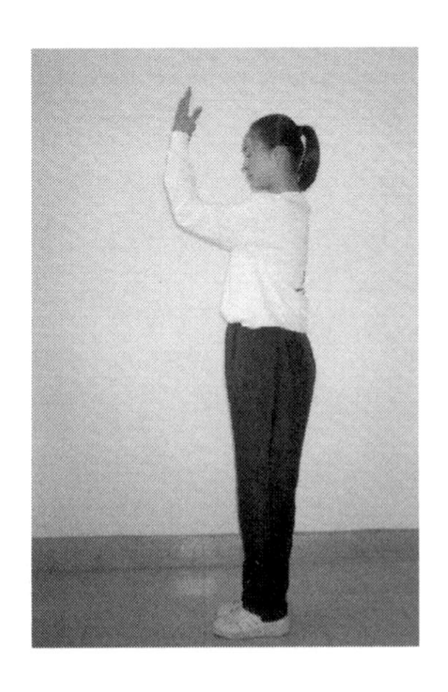

Fig. 4-3

Circle upper arms to the sides. Rotate palms outward, lower forearms to form a straight line. Then move the forearms up and down 3 times.
Fig. 4-4 to Fig. 4-6b.

Fig. 4-4

Fig, 4-5

Fig. 4-6

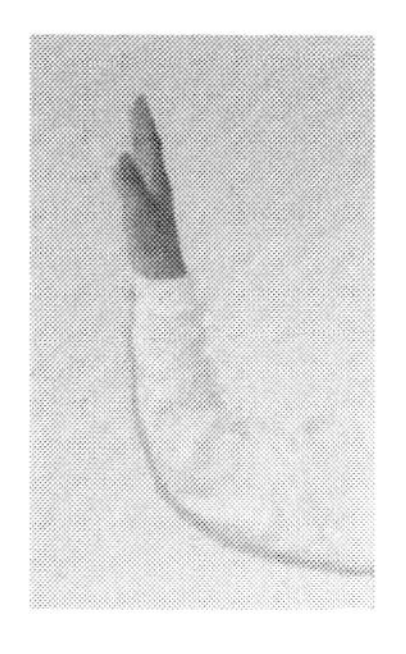

Fig. 4-6a

Fig. 4-6b

With the arms forming a straight line and the palms facing downward, rotate wrists forward and backward 3 times each using middle fingers to draw circles. Fig. 4-6, Fig. 4-7 to Fig. 4-8 [form starts in position Fig. 4-6].

Fig. 4-7

Fig. 4-8

b. Squeeze Shoulder Blades and Shrink Neck

With the head slightly leaning backward, tuck in the chin and shrink the neck while the shoulder blades are squeezed inward and the tailbone is raised upward. Relax the shoulders outward, the neck upward and the tailbone downward, and return back to the original position. Repeat 3 times. Fig. 4-9 to Fig. 4-12.

Fig. 4-9

Fig. 4-10

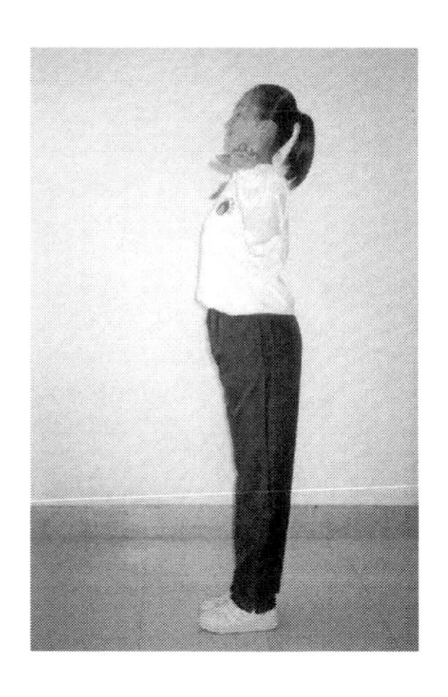

Fig. 4-11

Fig. 4-12

The left shoulder blade propels the right shoulder blade upward and pushes the right arm outward as the left arm contracts in a Waving Arms movement. The right shoulder then does the same movement to the left shoulder. Repeat 9 times and return to the beginning position. Fig. 4-13 to Fig. 4-16.

Fig. 4-13

Fig. 4-14

Fig. 4-15

Fig. 4—16

Details

a. Open Arms and Rotate Wrists

Following the last movement (Fig. 3-11, Dragon's Horns), relax and release the hands from the waist. Rotate the wrists until the palms face the sky as the elbows move toward the back. The hands form a straight line with the forearms, and the fingers point toward the front. Move the forearms forward until elbows touch the ribs. The forearms form a 90-degree angle with the upper arms. Using the shoulder joints as pivots and the elbows as moving points, move the elbows upward to shoulder level with the palms facing toward the back and the fingers pointing toward the sky. Maintain a 90-degree angle between the forearm and upper arm. Fig. 4-1 to Fig. 4-3.

Circle the arms to both sides. After the upper arms form a straight line, leading with the small fingers, rotate the forearms until the palms face outward. Then lower forearms to form a straight line. Using elbows as pivot points, leading with the middle fingers, move forearms up to form 90 degrees with the upper arms; then lower the forearms to form a straight line. Repeat this sequence 3 times. Fig. 4-4 to Fig. 4-6.

With the arms forming a straight line, the fingers naturally extended, and with the palms facing the ground, rotate the wrists. Using the wrists as pivot points, the shoulders and elbows are stationary, draw 3 circles with the hands—first to the front, down, back, and up. Lead with the middle fingers. The palms face the ground at all times. Next, draw 3 circles in the opposite direction. Return the hands and arms to one straight line. The rotations should be round and agile, slow and even. Fig. 4-6 to Fig. 4-8.

Common mistakes

After releasing the hands from the waist when first beginning this movement, the angle between the forearms and the upper arms is not 90 degrees. The elbows do not move upward to shoulder level with the upper arms parallel to the ground (the elbows are either too high or too low). The elbows are not circled completely to the side to form a straight line with the upper arms. The palms are facing toward the front instead of outward (away from the body) which occurs because the upper arms are not rotating sufficiently. The forearms are not perpendicular to the upper arms. The arms and the body are not in a two-dimensional plane. During the forearms up and down movements, the hands and forearms do not stay in a fixed position, and the upper arms are not stationary; instead, they also are moving up and down. In the final part of this section, the wrists should be rotating, and the fingers should not be moving and drawing circles, and the forearms should not be twisting.

Keys to the practice

While circling the arms to each side, the shoulders and the chest should be expanded. Maintain the right angle between the forearms and upper arms, and the upright forearm position throughout the movement. While rotating the palms outward, do not bend the wrists; the hands and forearms maintain straight lines. The forearms, upper arms and the body are in a two-dimensional plane. When drawing circles with the wrists, the tips of middle fingers lead the movement, the fingers should not bend, the palms face the ground, and the forearms remain stationary. If one can relax the fingers and palms in the movement to draw circles, Qì can reach the finger tips.

Attention should be given to the continuity of the movements. The movements may look rectangular outside, but the inner feeling should be circular. Once the techniques are mastered, do not wait until one movement stops before starting a new one. The transition from one movement to another should be seamless, e.g., in the sequence of moving the upper arms to shoulder level and circling to the sides. One should begin to circle the arms to the sides as the elbows reach approximately 3/4 the distance upward to the shoulder level. The path becomes an arch instead of a rectangle. When the forearms move up and down, one should maintain the elbow joints as pivots, and use the hands and fingers to draw arcs which allows Qì to reach the finger tips.

Purpose

These movements are designed to expand the chest, open up the shoulder joints, and relax the elbows and the fingers. The Shǒu Jīng Hé Xué 手经合穴 is located in the elbow area. The Hé Xué 合穴 is where Hand Meridian Qì enters the inner organs. The fingers' undulating movements (contracting and extending) will help in opening the Hand Meridians. Leading with the small fingers (belong to the Heart Meridian) to rotate the palms outward can activate the Heart Meridian. The expanding and circling arm movements increase lung capacity and improve circulation in the heart. This movement is effective in treating heart and lung problems such as emphysema, tracheitis, and cardiovascular diseases. Generally speaking, practitioners with heart and lung problems should practice more open arms and rotate wrists movements.

b. **Squeeze Shoulder Blades and Shrink Neck**

1) **Squeezing the shoulder blades.** Using the fingertips, slightly pull the arms outward to form a straight line. Contract the shoulder blades toward the 4th thoracic vertebra, and slightly bend and drop the elbows. The wrists are at shoulder height with the fingers are naturally extended and pointing slightly upward. Fig. 4-9 to Fig. 4-11.
2) **Shrink neck.** The body does not move. Lean the head slightly backward, tuck in the chin, and shrink the neck downward. Point the tailbone slightly backward and upward toward the fourth thoracic vertebra.
Fig. 4-9 to Fig. 4-11.

Common mistakes

The elbows squeeze instead of the shoulder blades (it should be the shoulder blades squeezing inward). The wrists drop below the shoulders (they should at or slightly above shoulder level). The Chin is not tucked inward. The cervical vertebrae press downward (they should relax downward) and the Mìngmén is pressed inward. The sacroiliac joint (not Mìngmén) should be pressed toward lower abdomen.

Keys to the practice

Head. Use the Bǎihuì to pull up the cervical vertebrae to loosen up the neck first—the head, with the chin tucking inward, and the neck (cervical vertebrae) lean backward approximately 15 degrees. Then the head and the neck as a whole relax downward toward the 4th thoracic vertebra. Do not force the vertebra downward.

Shoulders. Starting from the shoulder joints, press the shoulder blades toward the 4th thoracic vertebra at a 45-degree angle, and relax the elbows downward simultaneously. The chest will have a slightly convex movement.

Tailbone. With the sacroiliac joint as the pivot point, scoop the tailbone upward toward the 4th thoracic vertebra.

The body does not move. The four points—the head, the shoulder blades, and the tailbone—all contract toward the 4th thoracic vertebra at the same time. In releasing the contraction, the four points expand outward simultaneously.

Purpose

Normally, the area between the shoulder blades is seldom exercised. Squeezing the shoulders and contracting the neck will exercise and massage this area. This movement is similar to the body posture that occurs when one shivers. When stimulated by a sudden chill, the body needs to produce an extra amount of heat to counteract the cold sensations. There are many erector muscles in our body which produce a large amount of heat when they contract. Therefore, when there is a sudden chill, we shiver. In Traditional Chinese Medicine, this movement is called "strengthening the neck and back 項背强兀兀." Here, we intentionally use the movement to activate the Qì function.

This movement can activate Shàng jiāo 上焦, strengthen Yáng Qì and circulate Qì to the whole body. It is very beneficial to people with weak Yáng Qì, chronic debilitating disease, or chronic hypothermia.

> *Note: Shàng jiāo 上焦, Shàng means upper/above, jiāo means underneath the skin and muscle veins. Traditional Chinese Medicine divides the torso cavity into three sections and calls them Sān jiāo 三焦 (Sān means three, one common translation for the three sections is Triple Burner). Shàng jiāo is the torso cavity above the diaphragm where the heart and lungs are located. Shàng jiāo functions like mists, it circulates Qì, blood and air to nourish the whole body.*

There are many important pressure points in this area which regulate Qì flow to the heart and the lungs. Squeezing the shoulders inward will activate and strengthen these points. Consequently, the heart and the lungs are strengthened.

c. Waving Arms Movement

In the waving arms movements, Fig. 4-13 to Fig. 4-16, the left side is contracted while the right side is being extended and vice versa. The movements are snake like. When the right shoulder blade moves toward the spine, the left shoulder blade moves outward to the left. Simultaneously, the right upper arm squeezes inward through the shoulder joint, the right elbow sinks slightly, and the right wrist naturally bends. The fingers move naturally. Similar movements are repeated on the left side. Alternating movements of the shoulders result in an infinity sign when shoulders are viewed from the back.

Common mistakes

Both hands fall below the straight horizontal line. The shoulder blades are not contracting and extending outward. The body is not centered and is leaning toward the left and then toward the right. The arms are not in the same plane (two dimensions). Only the hands move when primarily the shoulder blades should be moving. One hand at a time should be moving.

Keys to the practice

The adjacent joints should move in the opposite direction in contracting and extending movements. For example, when the right scapula moves toward the spine, the left scapula will move to the left; at the same time, the right humerus moves inward from the shoulder joint, the elbow slightly drops, the wrist bends naturally, and the finger joints also move. With practice, the large joints will have snake-like movements and the small joints will have undulating movements.

Both arms should move at the same time, but focus is placed on the primary (contracting) side. It is the contracting side that pushes the extending side outward. The arms maintain a horizontal plane. With the contracting and extending motion, the arms have an upward and downward movement. The contracting side is slightly below the horizontal line and the extending side is slightly above the horizontal line. The contraction and extension should be performed simultaneously. During this practice, it is very important to maintain the body's center line.

Purpose

The waving Arms movements are designed to loosen up and maintain the agility of the upper limbs. Overall, this section is very effective in treating and preventing arthritis in the upper limbs as well as minimizing problems in the shoulder blades and the lungs.

d. Acupuncture point practice

The acupuncture points in this section are the Reverse Seven Stars. They are Yángchí (陽池 2), Jiānyú (肩髃 2), Dàzhuī (大椎), Táodào and Wěilű.

5. Erect Palms, Separate Fingers, and Open Meridians

直掌分指暢經脈

Movements

Fig. 5-1

The arms form a straight line at shoulder level. The body is centered. Leading with the middle fingers, erect the palms to form right angles with the forearms by thrusting the center of the palms outward and pulling the fingers backward toward the body. With the arms maintaining a straight line, contract the shoulder blades inward toward each other and then push out with the upper arms and wrists. Repeat 3 to 5 times. Fig. 5-1.

With the palms and forearms still forming right angles, separate the fingers. First separate the thumbs and the little fingers, and then the index and ring fingers. Push the centers of palms outward. Fig. 5-2, Fig. 5-3.

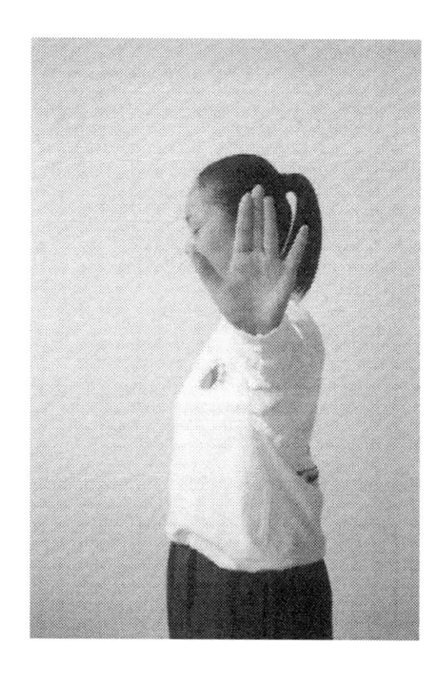

Fig. 5-2

Fig. 5-3

Close the fingers—index and ring fingers first, followed by the thumbs and the little fingers. Repeat Open and Close 5 to 7 times. Fig. 5-4, Fig. 5-5.

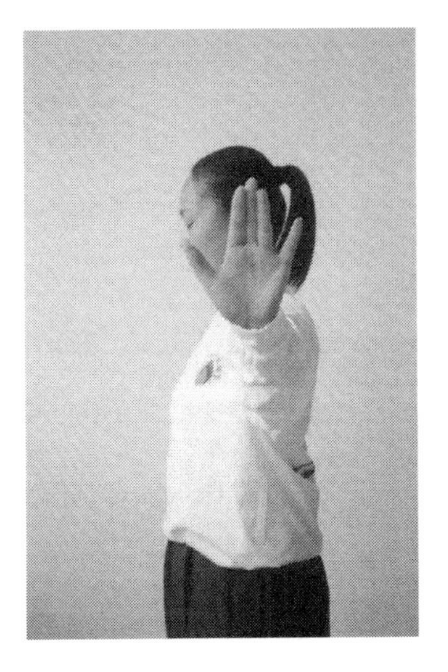

Fig. 5-4

Fig. 5-5

Relax the hands, curl the fingers downward like a claw, one joint at a time until the fingertips touch. Move the fingertips toward the centers of the palms. Fig.5-6, Fig. 5-6a, Fig. 5-7. Fig. 5-7a.

Fig. 5-6

Fig. 5-7

Erect the wrists, and straighten the fingers one joint at a time. Repeat claw hand movements 3 to 5 times. Fig. 5-6 to Fig. 5-9a.

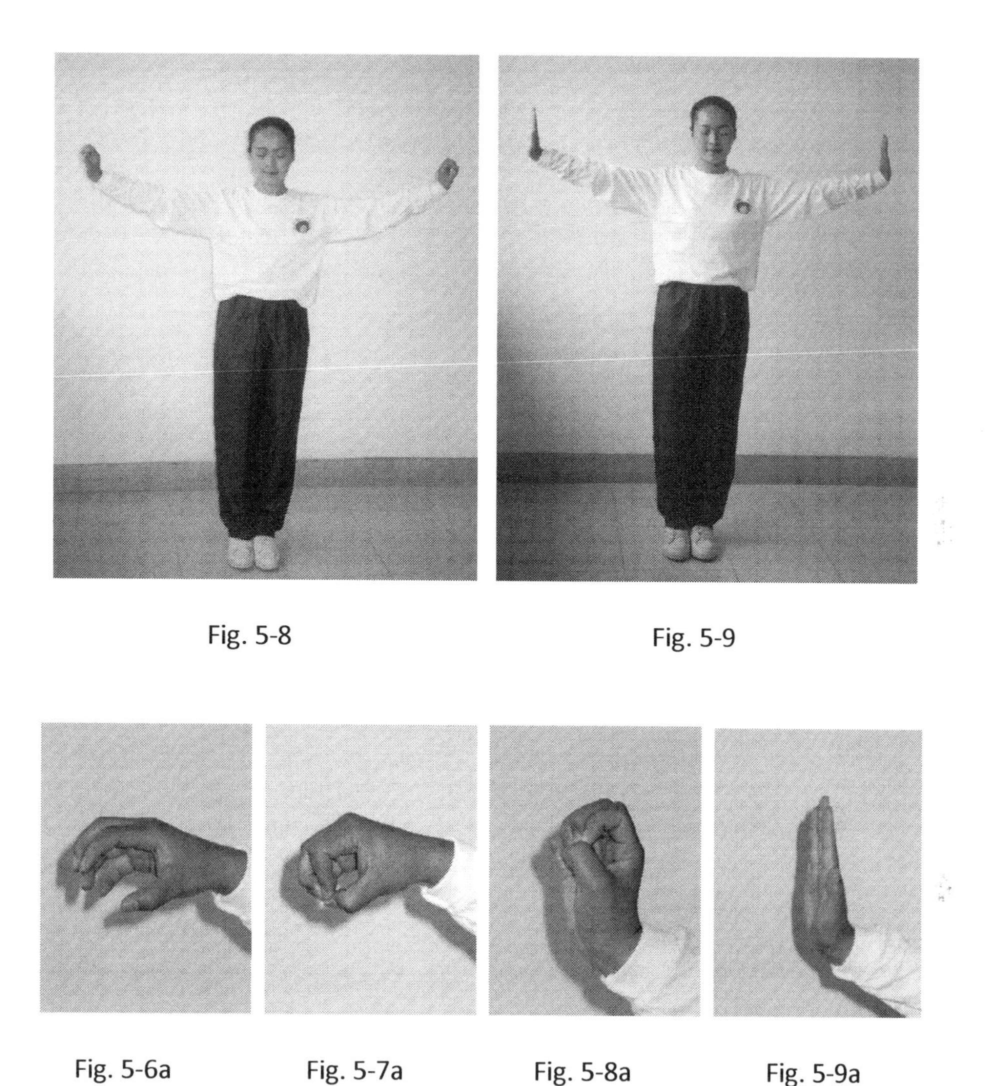

Fig. 5-8 Fig. 5-9

Fig. 5-6a Fig. 5-7a Fig. 5-8a Fig. 5-9a

Leading with the middle fingers, lower the hands to form a straight line with the arms. Repeat waving arms movements 3 times. Fig. 4-12 to Fig. 4-16.

Details

This section is divided into three parts: a. Erect palms & separate fingers; b. Curl the fingers and c. Waving arms movement.

a. **Erect Palms & Separate Fingers**

1) Erect the palms

The body is centered. The arms are level and form a straight line. Leading with the middle fingers, erect the palms to form a right angle with the forearms.

Leading with the wrists, the arms push outward, loosen up the shoulder and elbow joints. At the same time, the centers of the palms, wrists, and the front part of the fingers (inner side of the hand) thrust outward, and the back of the hands and the fingertips pull backward.

After the correct posture is obtained, with the arms maintaining a straight line, the shoulder blades contract toward each other to the maximum; the fingers are straight, and the palms are erect. While pushing outward, the shoulder blades push the wrists and the centers of the palms outward, and pull back the fingertips to the maximum distance. Repeat 3 to 5 times. Fig. 5-1.

Common mistakes

The center of each palm is not pushed outward in a thrusting outward motion. The elbows are bent in a contracting motion. The arms do not maintain a straight line throughout the movement. The movements are not from the shoulder blades. The body is not centered, the chest protrudes outward, the head leans backward, and the tailbone is not pointing toward the ground.

2) Separate the fingers

Following the last movement, [Fig. 5-1], push the palms outward and separate the fingers. First separate the thumbs and the little fingers simultaneously; then separate the index and ring fingers. The motion should be slow and even. Separate the fingers to the maximum distance, and push the palms outward from the base (the wrist) of the fingers. Close the index and ring fingers, followed by the thumbs and the little fingers. When closing, relax the hands slightly. Repeat 5 to 7 times. Fig. 5-2 to Fig. 5-5.

Common mistakes

The fingers are not erect pointing upward toward the sky. All the fingers open and close at the same time. The wrists are not pushed outward. The arms are not in a straight line.

Keys to *the Erect Palms & Separate Fingers* practice

The arms should be straight and level at all times. Because the eyes are closed during the movements, the way to determine whether the arms are level or not is by relaxing both arms; if the hands are heavy and the shoulders are light, then the hands are too low. If the hands are light and the shoulders are heavy, the hands are too high. While pushing outward, the wrists should remain stationary, the base of the palms and the hands protrude outward, and the fingertips/finger nails and the palms are pulled back toward the head. When practicing this way, Qì would go out from the fingertips and return back to the body, forming a loop. In separating the fingers, the movement starts from the base of the fingers; slightly relax the fingers when closing. In contracting the shoulder blades inward, the force remains horizontal. During the movements, the head, the body and the tailbone do not move.

b. **Curl the fingers.**

After separating the fingers, curl them downward. First relax the wrists; then the fingers and the palms curl downward. Beginning with the fingertips, use force to intentionally curl the fingers downward, one joint at a time, forming an eagle claw. Continue to move the fingers downward until the fingertips touch. At this time, the palms and the forearms should form a 45-degree angle; pull the fingertips toward the centers of the palms forming an empty fist. Erect the palms; then relax and extend the fingers one joint at a time from the palm to the finger tips. Repeat 3 to 5 times. Fig. 5-6 to 5-9a.

Common mistakes

The fingers are not curled downward one joint at a time. The thumb and little finger are not touching each other while the centers of each palm are pulling inward. The wrist is bent more than 45 degrees.

Keys to *the Curl the Fingers* practice

In curling the fingers, the hands act like eagle claws ready to catch a fish; the primary focus is on the fingertips. Relax the wrists first, leading with the fingertips, curl downward, one joint at a time, until all the fingertips touch each other. With the fingertips still touching each other, the fingertips gather toward the center of the palm; the wrists should not curl inward. This movement is designed to tense the outer arm tendons and to relax those of the inner arms. In uncurling the fingers, erect the palms while the wrist is the first pushing downward, then uncurl the bottom section, middle section and finally the top section of the fingers. Uncurling the fingers will relax the outer sides of the arms and will tense the inner sides.

c. **Waving Arms Movement**
(Same movement as described in **Section 4. *Open Arms and Rotate Wrists, Squeeze Shoulder Blades and Shrink Neck, Fig. 4-13 to Fig. 4-16.*)**

In order to loosen up the upper limbs' muscles and ligaments, one must use some physical force while practicing this section. Using physical force would create muscle tensions which will hinder the Qì flow. As the Qì pressure builds up, the relaxation between each movement (tension) will greatly improve the Qì circulation. Once one can be relaxed while using physical force, the volume of Qì circulating inside the Meridians will greatly increase. In order to relax and increase Qì flow, one must use physical force at the beginning.

This section does not focus on acupuncture points. It uses the 24 points in the hand and circulates from 1 to 24 and repeats. Fig. 5-10.

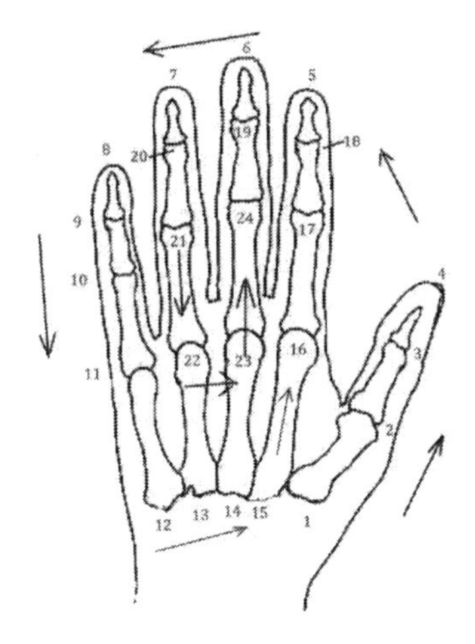

Fig. 5-10

Purpose

The main purpose for these movements is to activate the six Meridians in the hands. The three Hand Yīn Meridians (lung, heart and pericardium) originate in the chest and run through the inner arms to the fingers. The three Hand Yáng Meridians (large intestine, small intestine and Sānjiāo (三焦 Triple Burner)) originate in the fingers and run through the outer arms to the head. By tensing and relaxing the inner and outer arms through the finger movements, we activate both Yīn and Yáng Meridians. The separate finger movements stretch the inner arms and primarily exercise the three Hand Yīn Meridian; curling finger movements stretch the outer arms and exercise the three Hand Yáng Meridian. Yīn and Yáng Qì will balance and nourish each other.

In addition to activating the Meridians, this exercise focuses on strengthening Jǐng xué 井穴. Jǐng xués are the major points for Meridian Qì and External Qì to circulate in and out of the Meridians. With the exception of Zhōng chōng xué 中冲穴, which is located in the fingertips, the six Hand Meridians' Jǐng xués are located at the base of the fingernails. Because Jǐng xués are important areas where Hùn Yuán Qì enters the Meridians, by exercising the fingers, it will strengthen Jǐng xué's functions. As a result, the Qì in all six Hand Meridians will circulate more smoothly and with greater strength. The other benefits are about the same as in Section 4. It is very beneficial for pathological conditions above the diaphragm. Because the Yáng Meridians include the small intestine and large intestine Meridians, this exercise is very good for the gastrointestinal system.

6. Yi Qì Thrust 氣意鼓蕩臂肋堅

Movements

Lower the arms alongside the body and raise the hands to the chest to form a praying position. Lace the fingers together while raising the hands upward to the front of the forehead. Slowly rotate the palms upward and push the arms forward to form an ellipse. Fig. 6-1, Fig. 6-2.

Fig. 6-1

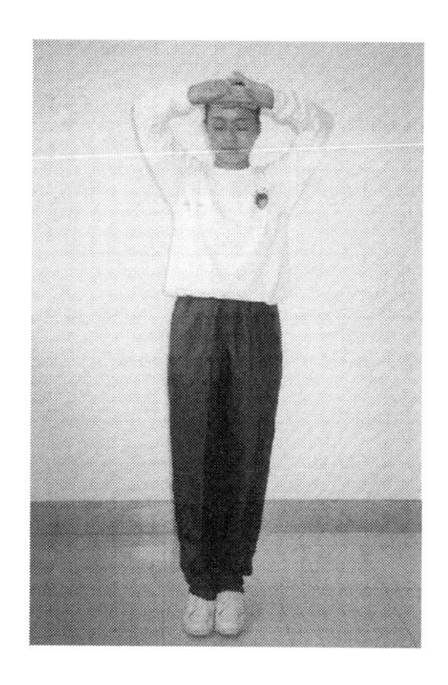

Fig. 6-2

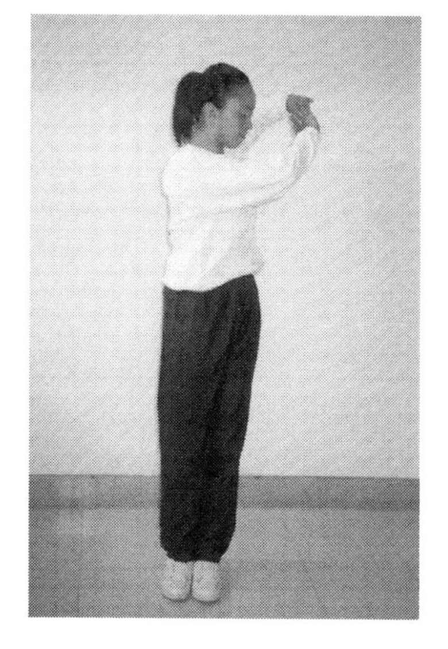

Fig. 6-3

Turn the upper body to the left. With the face facing left, and form a 90- degree angle with the feet. The hands are in front of the forehead and the arms form an ellipse with the left upper arm at shoulder level and the right forearm is at the same level as the right ear. The middle fingers are in front of the eyes. Fig. 6-3, Fig. 6-3a.

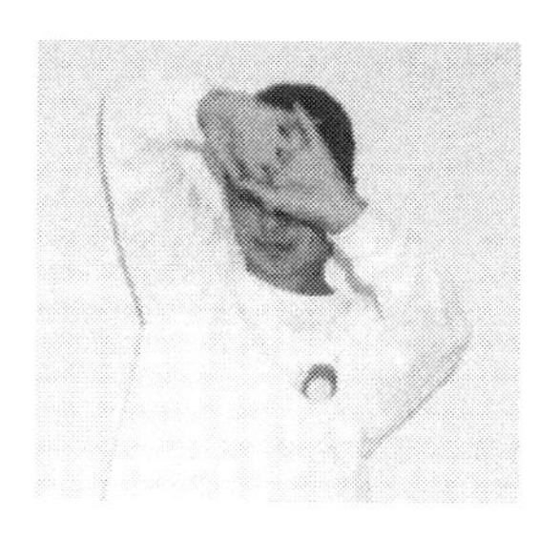

Fig.6-3a

Thrust the right rib upward from the Dāntián, then turn the upper body to the right by using the right ribs to pull the right shoulder, the right elbow and the hands to the front, forming an ellipse. The body is facing forward with the thumbs at eye level; the right forearm is at ear level, and the left upper arm at is at shoulder level. Fig. 6-4, Fig. 6-5.

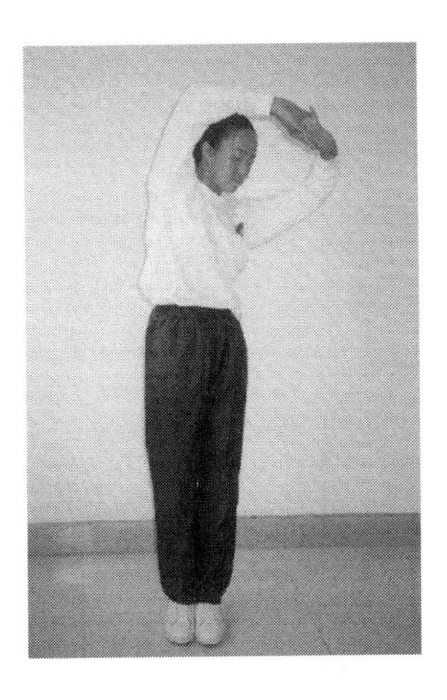

Fig. 6-4

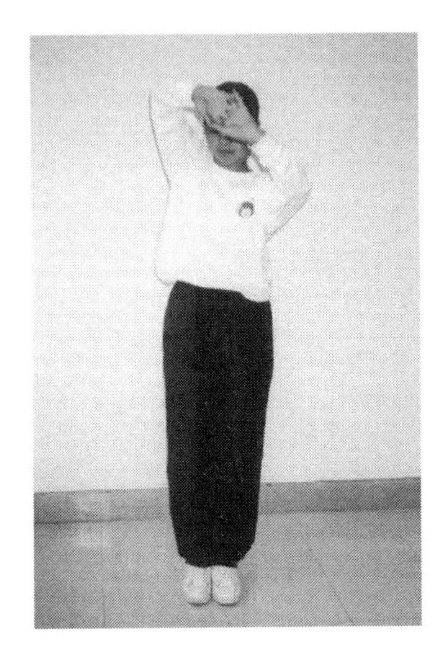

Fig. 6-5

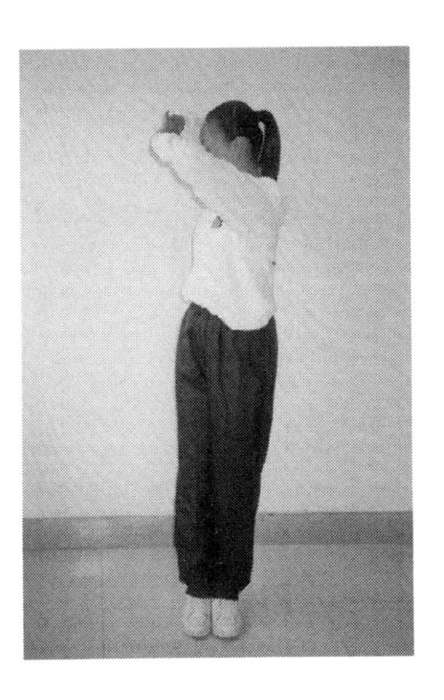

Fig. 6-6

Turn the upper body to the right, with the face facing to the right, and form a 90-degree angle between the upper body and the feet. The hands are in front of the forehead and the arms form an ellipse with the right upper arm at shoulder level, and the left forearm is at the same level as the left ear. The hands are approximately one fist's length from the forehead (distance from thumb to small finger). Fig. 6-6.

Thrust the left ribs upward, and turn the upper body to the left by using the left ribs to pull the left shoulder, the elbow, and the hands to the front of the body to form an ellipse. The body is then facing forward, with the thumbs at eye level, the left forearm at ear level and the right upper arm is at shoulder level. Repeat 18 times (9 times on each side). Fig. 6-7, Fig. 6-8.

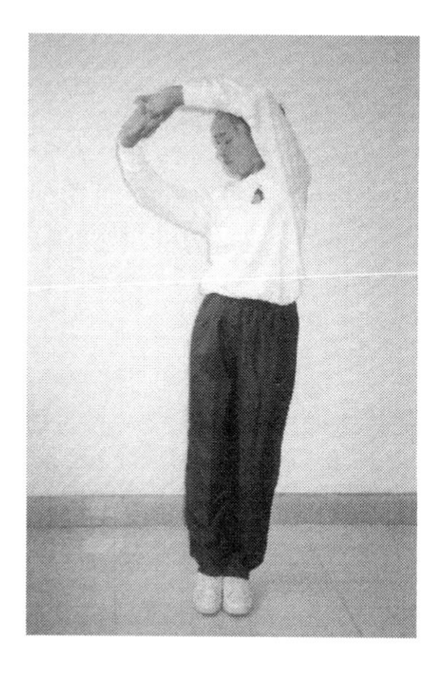

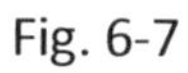

Fig. 6-7

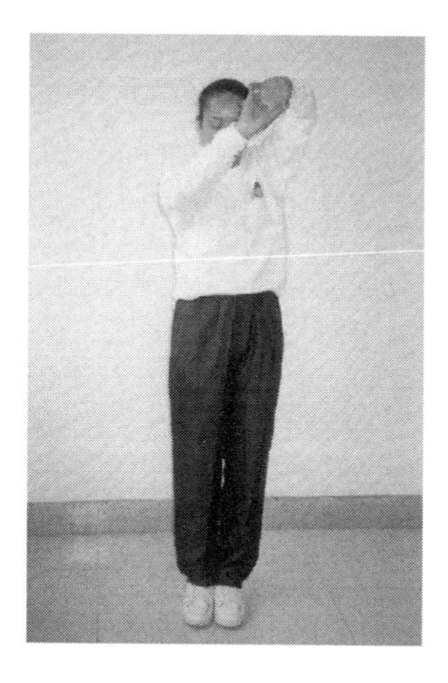

Fig. 6-8

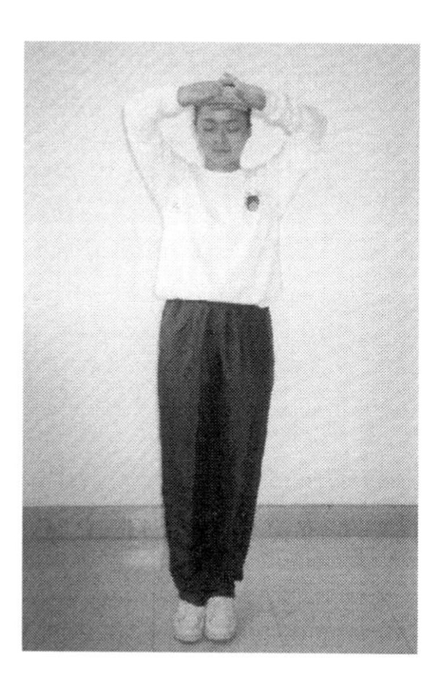

Fig. 6-9

After the last repetition, return the hands to the beginning position. Fig. 6-9.

Details

This section consists of three parts: the body turning to the left and then to the right; the arms forming a continually changing ellipse; and the Qì thrusting movements.

a. Beginning movements

At the end of the Waving Arm movements, slowly and evenly lower the arms to the sides, and then raise the hands upward to the chest level to form a praying position. Lace the fingers together while moving the hands upward to the front of the forehead; then slowly rotate the palms upward and push the arms outward to form a slanting ellipse. Both arms (shoulder, elbows, wrists, palms and fingers) must rotate from inward to outward and upward, exerting an outward and upward isotonic force. At this point, the backs of the hands should be facing the forehead. Fig. 6-1 to Fig. 6-2.

Common Mistakes

The arms are too straight. The elbows are locked. The arms do not rotate outward and upward.

2) Turning the body and forming ellipse movements

1) Turning the body

Relax the body and turn the waist to the left until the upper body is facing left and is forming a 90-degree angle with the front of the body. In the beginning, minimize the hip movement when turning the waist. In a more advanced practice, the lower limbs move naturally with the waist movements during the turning motion. Then repeat the same movements turning to the right.

2) The movements of the arms while turning

During the left turn, the left arm pulls the right arm to the left side: the left shoulder pulls left elbow; the left elbow pulls left hand; the left hand pulls right hand; the right hand pulls right elbow; and the right elbow pulls the right shoulder. This same sequence of movements also applies to the right turn. Fig. 6-3.

3) The positions of the arms

From the front to the left side, lower the left upper arm along the left ear to the shoulder level, with the right forearm at the right ear level. From the left back to the front, the arms form a "right up-left down" ellipse. From the front to the right, lower the right upper arm along the right ear to the shoulder level, with the left forearm at the left ear level. From the right back to the front, the arms form a "left up-right down" ellipse. During the whole movement, both arms maintain an outward and upward isotonic force. Fig. 6-4 to Fig. 6-9.

4) The relationship between the hands and the forehead
The hands are always in front of the forehead. When facing the sides, the hands are approximately one fist's length (10 cm) from the forehead; when facing the front, the hands are extended so that they are about an arm's length from the forehead.

The combination of **1), 2), 3)** and **4)** constitutes the "turning the body and forming the ellipse" movements.

Common mistakes

The hands move by themselves. The waist is not turning. The following hand pushes the leading hand. The body does not maintain its center line and leans sideways during the turn. The hands are not in front of the forehead. The hands drop below eye level. The back arm drops below the shoulder level. The hands are not kept at the proper distance from the eyes. The body does not turn at the waist with the Qì thrusting from the Dāntián.

Keys to the practice

The body should always be centered. Relax the arms, especially the shoulders. The crossed section of the middle fingers is always in front of the eyes and forms a straight line with Yìntáng. The shape of the ellipse changes with the body movement; the longest distance from the body is when the face is facing toward the front, the shortest distance is when the face is facing toward the side of the body. The ellipse plane is not parallel to the ground, it is about 45 degrees.

3) Qì thrusting

1) **Thrusting area.** Place the hands on the ribs with the tips of the thumbs slightly below the nipples. The areas under the centers of the palms are the targets for the Qì to thrust toward.
2) **Qì thrust.** Use Dāntián Qì to thrust as if pushing someone to the side. When the body is turned to the left side, thrust the right ribs—Qì thrusts from the Dāntián to the right target area. The right ribs push the right shoulder. The right shoulder pushes out the right arm. Turn the body to the right side, thrust the left ribs, Qì thrusts from Dāntián to the left target area. The left ribs push the left shoulder. The left shoulder pushes out the left arm.

Common mistakes

The shoulder thrusts instead of the Qì thrusting from the Dāntián. The back arm drops below the shoulder level. The body leans to one side when thrusting occurs—the body should remain upright. The body does not turn at the waist level when preparing to thrust the Qì from the Dāntián.

Keys to the practice

Do not use the lower arm to push the upper arm after the thrust. The thrusting movement is a slanting upward motion from the rib cage. Keep the upper body centered before and after the thrust; do not lean to one side.

The combination of **a, b,** and **c** constitutes the ***Yi Qì Thrust*** movements. The body turns 90 degrees to the left, the right ribs thrust (Dāntián Qì thrusts the right rib cage): the right ribs push the right shoulder; the right shoulder pulls the right elbow; the right elbow pulls the right wrist; and the right hand pulls the left limb. When Dāntián Qì reaches the arms and the elbows while thrusting the ribs, the upper limbs will be moved by the body's movements. It is the mind intent that moves Qì—Qì moves the body.

Purpose

The rib areas are important for Qì to be conveyed to the upper limbs. If the rib areas are obstructed or weak, Qì in the upper limbs will be stagnant. A weak rib area will hinder the Qì functions of the Liver and Gallbladder Meridians and cause a person to have weak vitality. The ability of Qì to move upward inside the Gallbladder Meridians is dependent upon the conditions and strength of Qì in the rib area.

Generally speaking, compared with rest of the body, Qì in the rib area is relatively weak. Using the Dāntián Qì to thrust this area will strengthen its functions. When this area is relaxed and strong, Qì will be able to circulate upward easily.

This exercise is good for the liver, the gallbladder, the diaphragm and the pleura (lining of the lungs), and the mucous linings of the intestine. In Traditional Chinese Medicine, Kidney Qì is Prenatal, Lung Qì is Postnatal, and this exercise will connect Pre- and Post-natal Qì to improve the life vitalities.

7. Bend Body, Arch Spine, and Loosen Governor Meridian 俯身拱腰鬆督脈

Movements

Fig. 7-1

Move hands upward to the top of the head with the fingers still laced together. Straighten the arms when the palms face the sky. Relax the shoulders and the arms. Push hands upward as if pushing an object. The wrists alternately draw a front-up and back-down circle. Repeat 3 to 5 times. Fig. 7-1 to Fig. 7-3.

Fig. 7-2

Fig. 7-3

Separate the hands with the palms facing forward and the upper arms touching the ears. Both the head and the arms move and extend forward, relax the waist and the back. The thoracic and lumbar vertebrae arch backward. The head and the hands move forward and downward as the waist pushes backward, and the vertebrae curl downward from the cervical to the thoracic to the lumbar spine until the hands touch the floor—the back forms an arch. With the palms touching the ground, press the hands downward three times. Fig. 7-4 to Fig. 7-7.

Fig. 7-4

Fig. 7-5

Fig. 7-6

Fig. 7-7

With the palms facing the floor, turn to the left and press downward three times; and turn to the right and press downward three times. Fig. 7-8, Fig. 7-9.

Fig. 7-8

Fig. 7-9

The body returns back to the center—the top of the head is downward toward the top of the feet. The hands scoop Qì backward until the thumbs, and the middle and index fingers touch the Achilles tendon. Retract the stomach and push out the back of the waist until the head touches the knees, while massaging the Achilles tendon with the middle and index fingers. Repeat 3 times.
Fig. 7-10, Fig. 7-11.

Fig. 7-10

Fig. 7-11

The hands scoop Qì forward and upward to the front of the body. With the upper arms touching the ears, move the back upward, one vertebra at a time from the lumbar to the thoracic to the cervical spine, and return to the beginning position. The body relaxes naturally. Fig. 7-12, Fig. 7-13.

Repeat all of these movements 5 to 7 times. Fig. 7-4 to Fig. 7-13.

Fig. 7-12

Fig. 7-13

Fig. 7-14

After the last repetition, turn the palms to face each other, lower the hands along the rib cage and rest them on the waist. Fig. 7-14.

Details

This section can be divided into four parts.

1) Rotate the wrists

Move the hands to above the head with the fingers interlaced and the palms facing upward. Straighten and pull the arms upward, relaxing the shoulders and the arms. Rotate one hand slightly as if the hand was pushing an object upward; then repeat with the other hand. The wrists alternately draw a front-up and back-down circle. Begin by moving and pushing the left wrist forward and upward, followed by pushing the left shoulder upward, and then pressing the left wrist upward. Straighten the left arm. The right arm, with the elbow slightly bent, is completely relaxed. Repeat the same movements with the right wrist. Stretch and move the wrists alternately to draw vertical circles. Fig. 7-1 to Fig. 7-3.

Common mistakes

The body leans to left and to the right. The chest is not relaxed. The abdomen protrudes outward. The tailbone is not pointing to the ground.

Keys to the practice

The following guidelines are for the upper body movements. While one side of the shoulder has a push-upward motion, the other side has a relaxed and downward motion. The shoulder pushes the upper arm, the upper arm pushes the elbow, the elbow pushes the wrist, and the wrist draws a vertical circle; the other shoulder is relaxed, and the elbow is slightly bent. During these movements, Bǎihuì pushes upward, the chin is tucked in, and the shoulders are used to push wrists upward to the maximum distance to pull up every vertebra and the rib cage. In addition to lifting the vertebrae and the rib cage, a proficient practitioner is able to pull up the heels and toes (lengthening the ligaments). A beginner should be able to pull up the waist. The vertebrae are pulled upward continually from the cervical to the thoracic to the lumbar spine. The chest should be hollow and relaxed. The stomach is tucked inward toward the spine. The waist is relaxed and is pushing backward.

2) Bend-body and arch-back movements

Relax and separate the intertwined fingers and turn the palms forward. Then the shoulders push the elbows upward to straighten the arms and pull up the body. The head remains centered; do not lean backward. With the vertebrae pulled up to the maximum distance, Qì is pulled upward, and the entire body might feel as if it is lifted. Next, relax the entire body beginning with the upper limbs, the neck, the chest, and the waist, and the lower limbs. The pulled-up Qì will move downward and permeate the whole body, some might have the sensation of feeling as if water is being poured down from the head to the toes. Fig. 7-4 to Fig. 7-7.

Spine curls downward movements. With the upper arms touching the ears and the chin pulling inward touching the chest, push the back upward, pull hands forward and then downward. Tuck the head inward, and curl the seven cervical vertebrae downward one at a time. Hollow the chest, push the back upward and backward, and curl the twelve thoracic vertebrae downward one at a time. Withdraw the stomach, push the lower back backward, and curl the five lumbar vertebrae downward one at a time. When the spine cannot go down any farther, the hands can use an up and down motion to help the downward curling motion. Finally, sucking in the stomach will help push the spine backward allowing the spine to go down further.

Common mistakes

The upper arms are not touching the ears. Cervical and thoracic vertebrae are not curling downward. Tailbone is not tucked in.

Purpose

This movement will loosen up each vertebra and the ligaments in the spine that help to adjust the nervous system. It activates and opens up the Governor Meridian.

3) Head touches the legs movements

a) **Press downward with the hands in front of the body.** With the palms touching the ground, the fingers pointing to the front, and the wrists next to the toes, the arms relax and press downward. When pressing, the forehead touches the knees, and the forehead and the knees pull upward, tuck in the abdomen and push the waist backward and upward. Press three times. Fig. 7-7.

b) **Press downward with the hands pointing to the left.** Turn to the left, with the palms touching the ground, fingers pointing to the left, and the wrist next to the left outer foot. Relax the arms and press downward. When pressing, the forehead touches the knees and the forehead pulls upward. Tuck in the abdomen and push the waist backward and upward. Press three times. Fig. 7-8.

c) **Press downward with the hands pointing to the right.** Turn to the right, with the palms touching the ground, the fingers pointing to the right, and the wrist next to the right outer foot. Relax the arms and press downward. When pressing, the forehead touches the knees and the forehead pulls upward. Tuck in the abdomen and push the waist backward and upward. Press three times. Fig. 7-9.

d) **Press downward with the fingers touching the Achilles tendon.** Return the body to the front. The hands scoop Qì toward the ankles. When the hands reach the ankles, the thumbs, the index fingers, and the middle fingers touch and massage the Achilles tendons. At the same time, the forehead touches the knees and the forehead pulls upward. Tuck in the abdomen and push the waist backward and upward. Press three times. If unable to touch the Achilles tendons, tap the calves slightly. The center of gravity should be in the balls of the feet. Fig. 7-10 to Fig. 7-11.

Common mistakes

The knees are bent. The waist does not push backward and upward. The head is lifted upward—the Băihuì should be toward the floor. The face should be toward the legs.

Purpose

The Bladder Meridian is located in the back of the legs. Massaging the Achilles tendons will adjust this meridian.

4) **Arching and lifting upward movements**

The hands scoop Qì toward the front until the upper arms touch the ears. With the tailbone tucked in and the hands as if holding a heavy object, curl the spine upward one vertebra at a time beginning with the lumbar vertebrae, followed by the thoracic and the cervical vertebrae. When the fingers are pointing to the sky, and the upper arms are still touching the ears, relax the body. Then use the arms to lead the whole body to move up and down, front and back in relaxing movements. Fig. 7-12 to Fig. 7-13.

Common mistakes

The upper arms are not [should be] touching the ears. The spine is in a straight line (it should be curved). The thoracic and cervical vertebrae are not (should be) curling upward one vertebra at a time. The waist or shoulders should not be used to move up the whole body—instead of using the spinal vertebrae. The knees are (should not) bent.

Keys to the practice

Although the purpose of this exercise is not to stretch the hamstrings, the legs should remain straight at all times. When bending down or coming up, the spine should curl up or down one vertebra at a time. The important intention is to move the spine and to loosen up the vertebrae.

Purpose

The arching-upward movement can close up the Governor Meridian and the Bladder Meridian. When moving upward, the back would automatically contract; this contraction will close all the acupuncture points in the Meridians and contains the Qì inside the Meridians. This particular movement is called "Qì into the bones" technique in Qìgōng.

5) **Acupuncture point practice**

There are two groups of Acupuncture points in this section.

- The first group is, Tiānzhù (天柱 BL 10), Dàzhù (大杼 BL 11), Nǚxī (女膝EX-LE 19). This group is used when the body is straight or standing when the wrists are rotating and the arms are gently moving up and down in a relaxing motion after finishing the upward movement of the spine. Fig. 7-13.
- The second group is Huìyīn, Yǒngquán, Láogōng, and the point between the navel and Mìngmén. This group is used when going down and coming up.

When arching upward, imagine the hands are holding a very heavy object that is being carried upward from Yǒngquán along the center of the leg bones to Huìyīn, and finally to the center of the body between the navel and Mìngmén. Once the arms are straightened (arms push upward), focus on the first group of Acupuncture points immediately, and at the same time, relax the whole body—relax from the top of the head down to the bottom of the feet. This is called "changing the bone" method in Qìgōng.

Overall Purpose

The main purpose of Section 7. is to loosen vertebrae, and to strengthen muscles and ligaments in the back. It also works on the Governor Meridian and Tàiyáng Bladder Meridians. The Governor Meridian governs the body Yáng Qì and the Tàiyáng Bladder Meridians primarily transport Qì to the inner organs. This movement is one of the most important methods for inducing Qì into the bones. It is very effective in treating spinal and back problems and in strengthening the nervous system.

8. Turn Waist, Move Kuà 轉腰涮胯氣歸田

Movements

Separate the feet to at least shoulder width and parallel to each other. Relax the hip joints and use them as pivot points to rotate the pelvic bone. Upper body slightly leans forward. Fold the Kuà (as if starting to sit down). Turn to the left (front, left, back and right) nine times, then to the right nine times. Fig. 8-1 to Fig. 8-6.

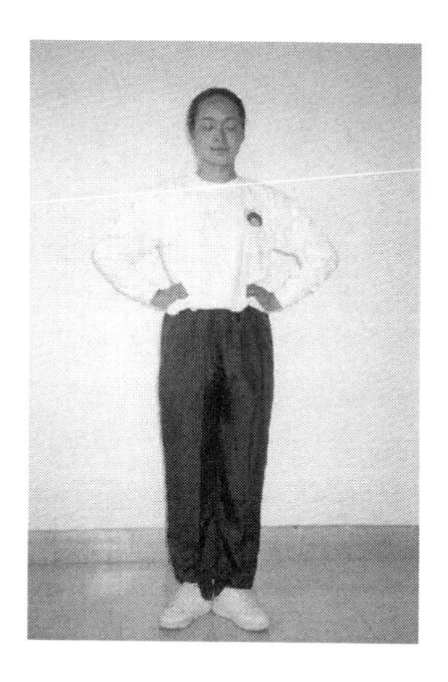

Fig. 8-1

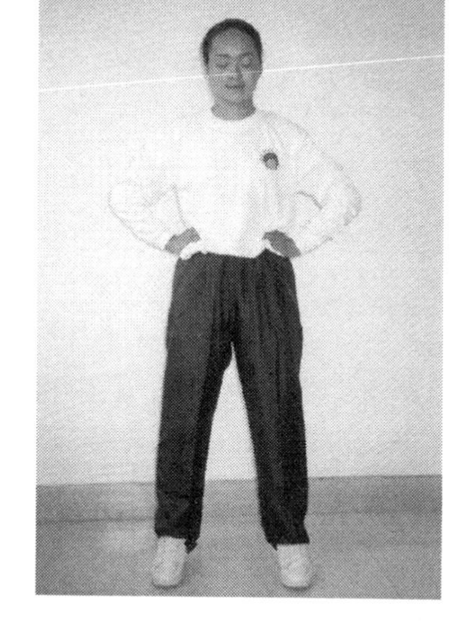

Fig. 8-2

Fig. 8-3

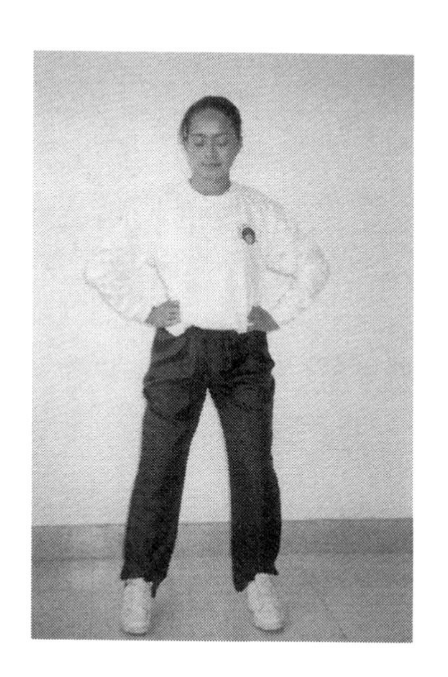

Fig. 8-4

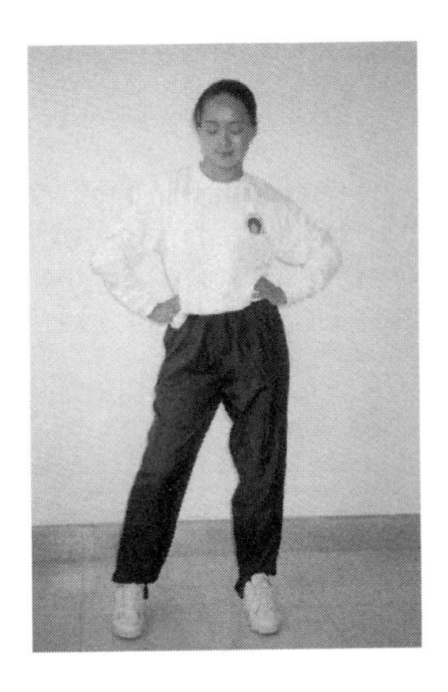

Fig. 8-5

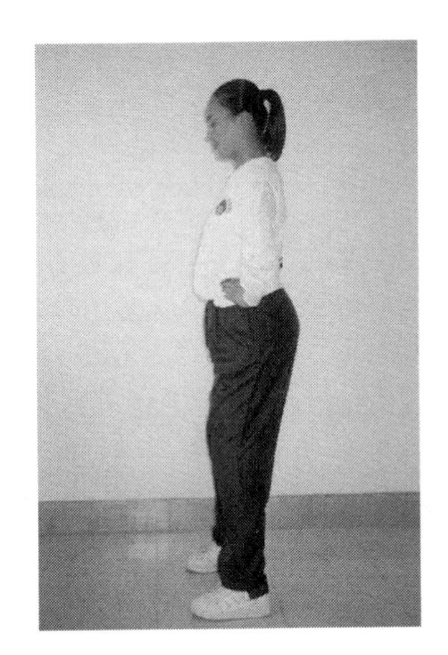

Fig. 8-6

Scoop the coccyx to the front and to the back in order to move the pelvic bone forward and backward nine times. The knees stay behind the toes.
Fig. 8-7, Fig. 8-8.

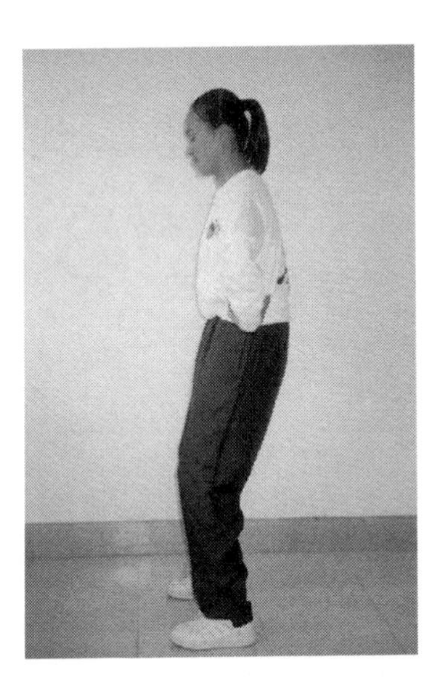

Fig. 8-7

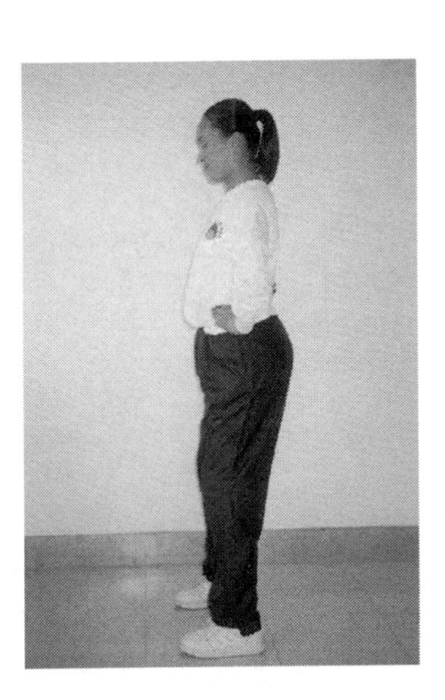

Fig. 8-8

Details

1) Hands rest on waist, and step on Qì movements

Turn the palms to face each other; then move the hands downward along the rib cage to rest on the waist. Step on Qì (with the feet touching the ground at all times), separate the feet to slightly wider than shoulder width apart. Lower the body slightly to create an angle between the body and the upper thighs; the knees cannot pass beyond the toes. Rotate the pelvic rim backward and downward while lowering the body to stabilize and root the lower body to the ground. At the same time, Bǎihuì is pulled upward. By sitting downward and pulling upward, the waist area will be emptied. With the coccyx pointing to the ground and Huìyīn raised, Dāntián Qì can be used to push Mìngmén out to loosen up the waist.
Fig. 8-1 to Fig. 8-2.

2) Turn the waist and move Kuà movements

Overall requirements: The areas from the top of the head to the tip of the sternum, and from the knees to the feet should remain immobile. The primary movement is below the rib cage and through the hips (the Kuà). Using the hip joints as supporting points and with the mind intent on the coccyx, use the coccyx to move the pelvis to draw circles between the inner arches of the feet. In order to fold the Kuà, the upper body is slightly forward and the lower body is sitting downward with the buttocks pushed toward the back.

a) **Circular movement requirement.** Imagine standing on a map with the front of the body facing north. The coccyx moves from the center to the front (N, north), to the left front (NW, northwest), to the left (W, west), to the left back (SW, southwest), to the back (S, south), to the right back (SE, southeast), to the right (E, east), to the right front (NE, northeast), and then back to the front. Repeat three times and then reverse the direction. Fig. 8-2 to Fig. 8-5.

b) **Detailed explanation of the circular movements**

(1) **To the front.** Scoop the coccyx to the front, pull up Huìyīn, and pull in the abdomen.
(2) **To the left front.** Move the coccyx and the abdomen to the northwest.
(3) **To the left.** The center of gravity for the pelvis shifts to the left hip joint. The left hip joint is higher than the right hip joint. The left side carries/supports the weight (solid) and the right hip is relaxed (empty). The coccyx points to the left.
(4) **The left back.** Move the coccyx to the southwest.
(5) **The back.** Move the coccyx backward to the maximum (use sacrum as pivot point, scoop the tailbone backward and upward) and relax Huìyīn.
(6) **The right back.** Move the coccyx to the southeast.
(7) **The right.** The center of gravity for the pelvis shifts to the right hip joint. The right hip joint is higher than the left hip joint; the right side is solid and the left side is empty. The coccyx points to the right.
(8) **The right front.** Move the coccyx and the abdomen to the northeast.
(9) **To the front.** Return to the beginning position to the north.

Common mistakes

The shoulders and upper body move and the body's center line is not maintained. The Kuà is not folded and the coccyx is not drawing a circle.

Keys to the practice

The body should remain centered (upright) and not leaning from side to side. The coccyx is pointing toward the ground throughout this movement. The body should have a "sitting-down feeling" as the Kuà is folded throughout these circular movements. If the knees are uncomfortable, push the buttocks out more toward the back and the weight on the feet is shifted more toward the back. The primary movement is below the sternum—the shoulders and upper body should not be moving.

3) Scoop the coccyx front and back movements

When scooping forward, contract the buttocks, and raise Huìyīn, the pelvic floor muscles, and the abdomen. Relax Huìyīn and the pelvic floor muscles while scooping backward. Fig. 8-7 to Fig. 8-8.

Common mistakes

The body moves up and down (do not straighten up the body—maintain the "sitting down feeling"). In the scooping to the front movement, the coccyx may be moved too far forward, tilting upward too far and lose the folding in the Kuà; instead of the coccyx scooping to the front and the back, the movement becomes a pelvis thrust.

Keys to the practice

The body should remain centered (upright) and not moving up and down. Maintain the folding in the Kuà area, and use sacrum as pivot point, tailbone (coccyx) scoops to the front (down-front) and back (down-back).

Keys to the Turn Waist, Move Kuà practice

At the beginning, the coccyx can draw a bigger circle, the feet can separate farther apart, and the body can lower downward a little bit farther. The Kuà remains folded throughout these movements—maintain the "sitting down feeling."

When one becomes proficient in the practice, the force should not come from the hip bones; one sinks the Dāntián Qì to the coccyx and turns the Dāntián Qì within the Dāntián. The movements should be slow and the waist should be relaxed. When combining the Dāntián Qì and coccyx to draw small circles, the circles may not be very obvious, but they are more effective than using the hip bones to draw bigger circles. In the beginning, the practice requires one to use the body-turning movements to lead the Qì to turn; in an advanced practice, it is the Dāntián Qì that is turning the body.

4) Acupuncture Point Practice

There are two points to pay attention to, one is Bǎihuì and the other is the center point between navel and Mìngmén.

Purpose

This exercise loosens up the waist, relaxes the coccyx and closes Huìyīn. It increases the storage of Qì in the Dāntián. Turning the coccyx activates the Yáng Qì to move up along the Governor Meridian. It is very effective in treating bladder, large and small intestines and reproductive problems.

According to Traditional Chinese Medicine, kidney Qì is prenatal Qì and lung Qì is postnatal Qì. When kidney Qì is insufficient, prenatal Qì will not be able to connect to postnatal Qì. Practicing this section can strengthen and replenish the kidney Qì and lead the lung Qì down to connect it with the kidney Qì to nourish the lungs; therefore, it is very effective in treating lung problems.

9. Open Front Kuà and Back Kuà 平足分胯分前後

Movements

a. Open Front Kuà

Fig. 9-1

Following the last movement, Fig. 8-8, the feet form a straight line by turning toes outward with the heels facing toward each other. The distance between the heels is approximately shoulder width apart. Straighten the legs and center the body. Separate the hands from the waist and turn the palms to face the sky. Move the forearms forward until the elbows touch the ribs and form a 90-degree angle with the upper arms. Lift the upper arms until the centers of the palms face Yìntáng. Fig. 9-1 to Fig. 9-3.

Fig. 9-2

Fig. 9-3

Turn the palms outward with the forearms and the fingers pointing to the sky. Circle the upper arms to the sides to form a straight line. Lower the forearms to form a straight line. Fig. 9-4 to Fig. 9-6.

Wave the arms by contracting the left shoulder blade and extending the right shoulder blade, and vice versa (same as Section 4. except that the legs remain separated.) Repeat three times. Fig. 4-11 to Fig. 4-14.

Fig. 9-4

Fig. 9-5

Fig. 9-6

Relax the knees and lower the body until the thighs are parallel to the ground (the body remains straight), and simultaneously lower the arms. When the hands are lowered to knee level, bend the forearms forward and clasp the palms in front of the body. Erect and move the palms to the chest level and form a praying hands position. Fig. 9-7 to Fig. 9-9.

Fig. 9-7

Fig. 9-8

Fig. 9-9

Use the fingertips and the wrists to draw three opposite-direction circles in each direction. Using the base knuckle of the third finger as a pivot point, the fingers circle in one direction while the wrists circle in the opposite direction. Fig. 9-10 to Fig. 9-13a.

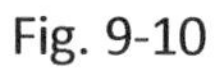

Fig. 9-10

Fig. 9-11

Fig. 9-12

Fig. 9-13

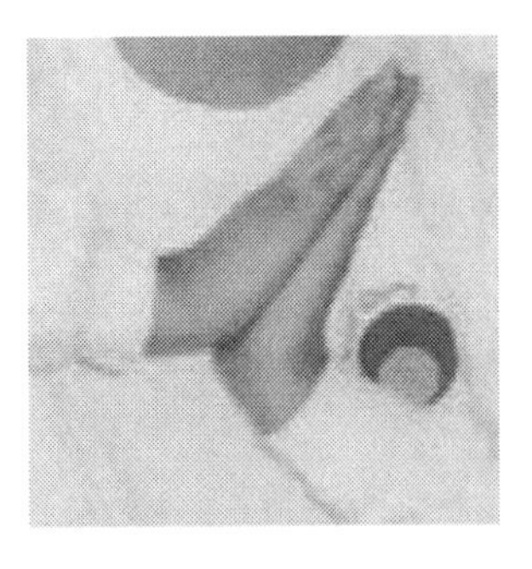

Fig. 9-10a

Fig. 9-11a

Fig. 9-12a

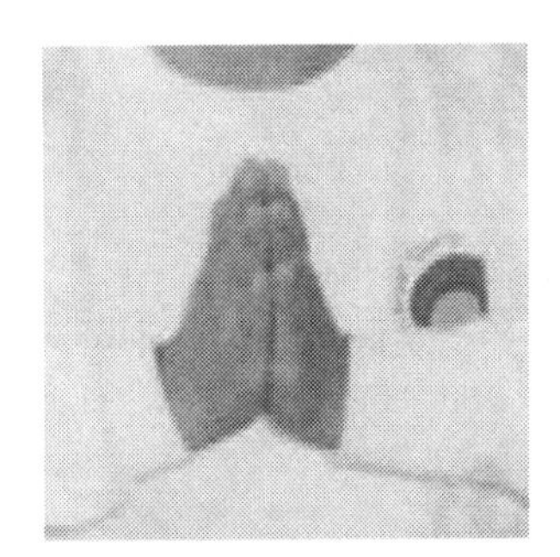

Fig. 9-13a

Leading with Bǎihuì, straighten the body. Raise the hands upward along the chest to in front of Yìntáng and turn the palms outward. Fig. 9-14, Fig. 9-15 Repeat movements five to seven times. Fig. 9-4 to Fig. 9-15.

Fig. 9-14

Fig. 9-15

At the end of the last repetition, the hands are resting in front of the chest in the praying hands position with the legs straightened.

b. Open Back Kua (Sacroiliac joints)

Following the last movement, turn the left toes inward and the right heel outward to form a straight line. The distance between the toes is approximately one foot's length. Lean the upper body forward about 35 degrees, straighten the legs, use sacrum as pivot point, scoop the tailbone backward and upward. Embrace the arms forward, relax the chest, and tuck in the chin. The middle fingers are pointing toward each other and the palms are cupped at Yìntáng level. Fig. 9-16, Fig. 9-17.

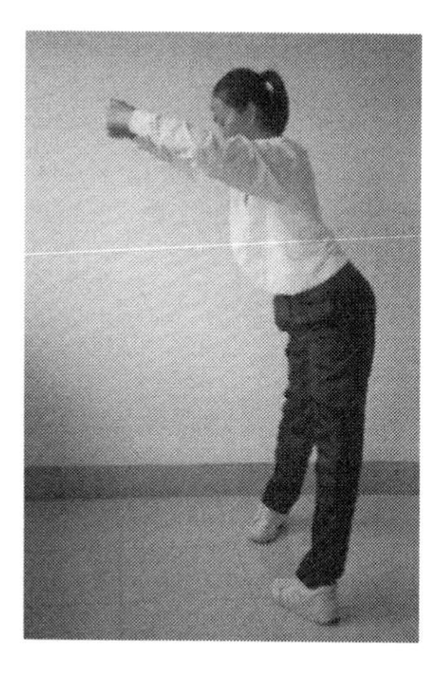

Fig. 9-16

Fig. 9-17

Rotate the knees inward and sit down slightly. Move the arms the upward and outward in a circular motion to shoulder level as if holding a huge balloon. Tuck in the abdomen and relax the waist. Relax the upper body and lean backward (from the fourth thoracic vertebra upward) as if observing the sky. Hold the posture. Fig. 9-18.

Push the head upward, straighten the legs, embrace the arms forward and return to Fig. 9-16 position. Repeat movement five to seven times. Fig. 9-16 to Fig. 9-18.

Fig. 9-18

At the end of the last repetition, push the head upward, straighten the body, move the hands upward to above the head and to shoulder width in a circular motion. When the hands face each other, cup the palms slightly; then lower the hands in front of the body and along the rib cage to rest on the waist. Step on Qì to close the feet. Fig. 9-19, Fig. 9-20.

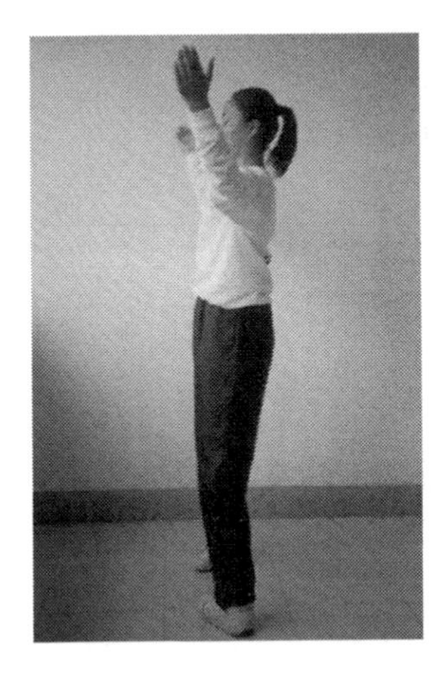

Fig. 9-19

Fig. 9-20

Details

a. Open Front Kuà (hip joints)

1) Turn the feet outward to form a straight line

Following the last movement, use the heels as pivot points, turn the toes outward to form a straight line with the heels pointing toward each other. The distance between the heels is approximately shoulder width apart. The legs are straight, and the body is centered and upright. Fig. 9-1.

Common mistakes

The hips turn with the toes. The heels are too close to each other. The body is leaning forward.

Keys to the practice

When turning the toes, the feet must be touching the floor at all times. Do not use the eyes to watch the turning movement. Do not turn the body with the toes. The body should be upright. Beginners can turn one foot at a time, and put the mind intent and the force on the big and little toes to stabilize the body.

2) Arm movements

Separate the hands from the waist, turn the palms upward with the fingers pointing to the front and the forearms parallel to the ground, move elbows backward and toward the ribcage. Move the forearms forward until the elbows touch the ribcage and form a right angle with the upper arms. Use the shoulder joints as pivot points and the elbows as moving points. Move the upper arms upward until the hands are in front of the forehead with the fingers pointing to the sky and the centers of the palms facing Yìntáng. At the same time, move the elbows inward to a distance that is slightly narrower than shoulder width. Fig. 9-2 to Fig. 9-3.

Leading with the little fingers, rotate the palms outward until the centers face the front and the thumbs are in front of Yìntáng. Use the shoulder joints as pivot points to circle the upper arms to the sides to form a straight line. While circling, the hands and the elbows move at the same time. Keep the thumbs at Yìntáng level and imagine that they are inside Yìntáng and pulling it open. After the upper arms form a straight line, lower the forearms. The arm movements should be continuous. Fig. 9-4 to Fig. 9-6.

The waving arm movements in the shoulders are slightly different from those in Section 4. and Section 5. ((Fig. 4-13 to Fig. 4-16)). In this section the upper arms' movements cause the upper body, the waist, the hips and then the lower limbs to naturally sway from side to side. Fig. 9-6.

Common mistakes

Both hands fall below the straight horizontal line. The shoulder blades are not contracting and extending outward. The body is not centered and is leaning toward the left and then toward the right. The arms are not in the same plane (two dimensions). Only the hands move when primarily the shoulder blades should be moving. One hand at a time should be moving.

Keys to the practice

The chest expands toward the sides. The elbows draw an arc along the horizon. Relax the body and remain centered/upright. Focus the mind intent and the force on the big and little toes to stabilize the body.

3) **Lower the body and raise the hands to form a praying position**

When lowering the body, relax the knees, sit on the pelvis, and point the knees in the same direction as the toes. At the same time, lower hands to the knee level. By the time the hands almost touch the knees, the thighs should be parallel to the ground. Move the forearms forward to scoop Qì; then put the hands together and move them to the front of the chest to form a praying hands position. Fig. 9-7 to Fig. 9-9.

Common mistakes

Lowering the hands and the body movements are not coordinated. The hips are not sitting down, the knees bend forward and pass beyond the toes. The body is not centered and is leaning forward.

Keys to the practice

Relax and open the knees toward the back. Relax the hips and the upper body; and focus on sitting the hips (the tailbone) downward. Allow the upper body to relax downward. The tailbone cannot be lower than the knees. Maintain the body center line. Fig. 9-9.

4) Turn the hands in front of the chest

The forearms form a straight line and the wrists are fixed, Fig. 9-9. Using the third joint of the middle finger as the fixed point, draw circles with the fingertips and the wrists. The forearms maintain a straight line, and the hands form right angles with the forearms. The shoulders, the elbows and the waist will follow the movements of the fingertips and the wrists. Fig. 9-10 to Fig. 9-13a.

Turn the palms

This movement consists of each hand drawing a half circle (turning left and turning right are the same except in opposite directions). With the bases of third metacarpal bone (the base knuckles of the middle finger) as a stationary point, rotate the hands 45 degrees with the fingertips pointing to the front and the wrists to the back (the axis of the hands and the body center line form a 45-degree angle).

Turning left

- **The left hand pushes the right hand.**
  From the beginning position, (the fingertips point to the left front, the wrists point to the right back) left hand (wrist) pushes the right hand to draw a counterclockwise half circle. As soon as the fingers point to the chest, relax the left hand.

- **The right hand pushes the left hand.**
  In the fingers pointing to the chest position, the right hand (wrist) pushes the left hand to draw a counterclockwise half circle.

Combining the above steps, the hands will form a complete left turn circle. Fig. 9-10a to Fig. 9-13a.

Turning right. Reverse the turning left direction.

Repeat turning each direction three times.

Common mistakes

The hips cannot maintain a sitting-down position. The body leans forward. The knees are not pointing toward the same direction as the toes. While drawing circles, the fingers are not pointing to the sky throughout this movement. Only the fingers are drawing circles without the movement of the wrists and without using the middle fingers as the fixed points.

Keys to the practice

Relax the upper body, lock the wrists to maintain the 90-degree angle between the hands and the forearms. The forearms maintain a straight line while the hands are drawing circles. Maintain the stability of the body. If one uses the base knuckles of the third fingers as stationary points and uses the fingertips and the wrists to draw circles, the shoulders, the elbows and the waist (and the tailbone for proficient practitioners) would follow these movements and also would draw circles. The body needs to be relaxed throughout these coordinated movements to occur in the upper and lower body.

5) **Straighten the body**
Leading with Bǎihuì, straighten the body by squeezing the hands as if the fingertips are touching the skull and pushing the body upward. At the same time, move the arms up. Relax the elbows and turn them slightly inward to a distance slightly shorter than shoulder width. When the body is straight, the palms should be in front of Yìntáng. Repeat **1)** to **5)** five to seven times. At the last repetition, maintain the praying hands position while straightening the body. Fig. 9-14.

Common mistakes

Using the legs to push the body upward instead of lifting upward with Bǎihuì. Do not bend the knees when in the upright position. The hands are too high or too low and are not in front of Yìntáng.

Keys to the practice

Tuck in the chin, the Bǎihuì pushes upward. Lift straight upward from Bǎihuì—do not lean forward. Squeeze the wrists to push the body upward. Maintain the center line of the body.

6) **Acupuncture Point Practice.** The acupuncture points in this section are the Big Seven Stars.

Purpose

The main purpose for opening the front Kuà is to loosen up the hip joints and to provide the foundation for sitting meditation. Squeezing the wrists and the hands as if the fingertips are pushing the skull upward leads the Central Meridian Qì (Central Meridian does not exist until one has enough Qì) upward to the Third Eye. Rotating the palms outward in front of Yìntáng opens up the Third Eye.

b. Open back Kua (Sacroiliac joint)

Following the last movement, turn both toes inward or the left toes inward and the right heel outward to form a straight line. If both toes turn inward, the distance between the toes is approximately one foot's length; use the big toes to stabilize the body. Fig. 9-16.

1) **Embrace forward**

Straighten the legs and stretch the legs toward the back; the pelvis rotates outward and backward. Move the tailbone outward, backward, and scoop upward; the sacrum presses in slightly. The upper body leans forward at a 35-degree angle. Hold the arms forward at shoulder level as if embracing a tree. The hands are approximately three inches apart, with the middle fingers and the thumbs at Yìntáng level. The palms face the body as if holding a ball; the chest is relaxed. Tuck the chin in and raise Bǎihuì. The mind focuses on the center point between the thumbs. Fig. 9-16 to Fig. 9-18.

Note: *It is normal to see white light after holding this position a long period of time (five to six minutes). When that happens, ignore it.*

Common mistakes

The body leans forward too much. The chest protrudes outward instead of expanding to the sides. Pressing the Mìngmén inward instead of the waist. The legs are not straightened. The big toes do not press downward. The tailbone does not scoop backward and upwards.

Keys to the practice

In order to stabilize the body with the toes turning inward, the big toes must use force to press the ground and there will be a reactive force from the ground. With the pelvis rotating outward and backward, the back of the legs should be stretched to the maximum, this force will be transferred upward along the inner legs to open up the Dāng (crotch). The tailbone scoops upward to press sacroiliac joint, the body leans forward 35 degrees and then relax downward. All the body weight should rest on the sacroiliac joint.

2) **Observe the sky**

Relax the knees. Then rotate the knees and the thighs inward. Move the hands upward and outward in a circular motion to ear level, forming an arch with the arms and the palms facing the sky as if holding a giant ball. Relax the waist, the hips and the coccyx. Pull the abdomen inward and lean backward from the fourth thoracic vertebra. Tuck the chin in and raise Bǎihuì. With the eyes closed, observe the sky at approximately a 45-degree angle. Repeat steps 1) and 2) two times. Fig. 9-18.

Note: *It is normal to see red light after holding the posture a period of time (five to six minutes).*

Common mistakes

The knees bend inward toward each other. The chin is not tucked in. The upper body leans backward from the Mìngmén instead of from the fourth thoracic vertebra. The stomach protrudes outward. The Coccyx is not pointing downward. The body is not relaxed.

Keys to the practice

The abdomen must be tucked in; the sacrum opens to the sides and wraps around as if drawing a circle or embracing a huge ball. The tailbone points to the ground; the pelvis maintains the upright position (cannot thrust forward). The chin must be tucked in.

3) Acupuncture Point Practice. The focus points are Shānzhōng (膻中穴 RN17) and Láogōng.

c. Closing

At the end of the repetition, push the head up, straighten the body, and move the hands upward in a circular motion to above the head. Turn the elbows inward slightly so that the palms face each other. Cup the palms with the wrists at shoulder width. Relax the shoulders and lower the elbows. Lower hands in front of the body, along the face to the chest. Then turn the palms inward and lower the hands along the rib cage until they rest on the waist. Step on Qì and close the feet. Fig. 9-19 to Fig. 9-20.

Purpose

The purpose of opening the back Kua is to loosen up the sacroiliac joint, so that the Dāntián area will be enlarged, allowing Qì to concentrate in the Dāntián area. The Gallbladder Meridian is located along the inner thighs, while the Bladder Meridian is located along the back of the thighs. By expanding the hip joints outward, rotating the thighs outward and pressing the sacrum inward, these two Meridians will join in the sacroiliac joint area.

When the knees are relaxed with the big toes turned inward and pressed toward the ground, the inner thighs relaxed and the outer thighs expanded with tension, Qì in the foot Shǎoyáng Gallbladder Meridian and the foot Tàiyáng Bladder Meridian will be pushed upward. When the Bǎihuì is raised, Qīngyáng Qì moves upward to nourish the head. When the chin tucks in, Qì will move downward to Dāntián to complete the circle. The back Kuà area is usually fixed and immobile. By loosening the back Kua, the tailbone will gradually be able to move and to turn. Opening the front and back Kuà can also strengthen Qì in the lower limbs. Embracing forward activates Lung Qì. Observing the sky activates Heart Qì. Lung Qì is associated with the color white, and Heart Qì is associated with the color red.

10. Bend Knees to Connect Three Joints 膝跪足面三節連

Movements

Following the last movement, squeeze the buttocks inward and move the hip joint (pubic area) forward. Expand the shoulder blades outward and then inward. Hollow the chest, withdraw the abdomen toward Mìngmén, and relax the waist. Embrace the elbows inward slightly, push the head up, tuck in the chin, and relax the knees and the ankles. Slowly squat down to the limit. The upper body and the thighs maintain a slanted straight line. Hold this position as long as possible. Push the Bǎihuì forward and upward to straighten the body slowly. Relax the whole body and return to the beginning position. Fig. 10-1, Fig. 10-2.

Fig. 10-1

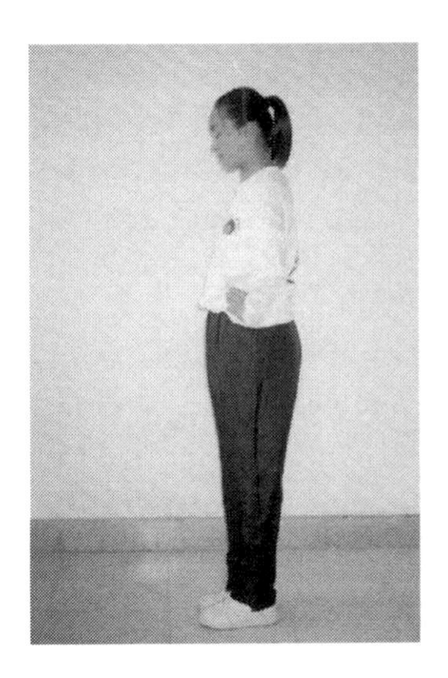

Fig. 10-2

Details

1) **Hip movements.** Squeeze the buttocks and wrap them around inward toward the front. Pull in Huìyīn and move the back Kuà (sacroiliac joint) forward.

2) **Relax the chest.** In order to be able to relax the chest, one must pull up the back, drop the shoulder blades, relax the shoulders, and create an empty space in the armpit area. Take a deep breath. Move the shoulders and the first thoracic vertebra upward to pull up the spine. Following the exhale, drop the shoulders and the shoulder blades down and toward the back. The shoulders scoop to the front slightly and the shoulder blades expand outward and downward to relax the chest. The edges of the shoulders pull

outward and upward to expand the chest. Then relax and drop the shoulders to relax the shoulder joints.

3) **Withdraw the abdomen.** The navel withdraws back to Mìngmén. Use the nose to pull up Huìyīn with an imaginary string.

4) **Squatting-down movement.** With the proper postures (Fig. 10-1), relax the waist and move the elbows to the front slightly. Pull up Bǎihuì, tuck in the chin, and relax the ankles (physically and mentally). Move the knees forward so that the thighs and the upper body form a slanted straight line. Then squat toward the ground. The knees must pass the toes and visualize them touching the ground. The shoulders lean back past the heels. The lower limbs are united as one unit; the heels must touch the ground at all times. The center of gravity is in the knees.

5) **Position of the head.**
   a) Yìntáng withdraws into the center of the head, then to Bǎihuì and is pulled upward by Bǎihuì.
   b) The tip of the nose looks for the chin, the chin tucks in to the Adam's Apple, the Adam's Apple to Yùzhěn, and then to Bǎihuì. In this way the Dāntián Qì will be pulled upward to nourish to body.
   c) The tip of the nose goes down toward Huìyīn. Huìyīn pulls up the centers of the feet and the knees. Mìngmén pulls up Huìyīn, and Bǎihuì pulls up Mìngmén.

6) **Straighten body up movement.** Bǎihuì moves forward and upward to pull up the body. If the knees push up the body instead, a loss of balance may occur. When the body is straightened, relax the whole body and let Qì permeate all the way to the feet. The center of gravity shifts back from the knees to the feet.

Common mistakes

The feet and/or the thighs are not touching each other. The thighs and the body do not form a straight line. The Kuà is not folded (should be folded). The abdomen and/or the chest protrude outward. Mìngmén is pressed inward. Body is not relaxed. The elbows are not embracing a ball in front of the chest. The legs push up the body instead of using Bǎihuì to pull up the body. Shifting the weight back and forth between the feet. The center of gravity (weight) is not in the knees.

Keys to the practice

Withdraw Yìntáng inward, tuck in the chin, Yùzhěn and Dàzhuī relax toward the back. The back pushes backward and outward, and the waist relaxes toward the back. It is essential to the movement to contract the buttocks and tip the pelvis forward. The thighs and the body create a straight line by moving the buttocks and coccyx forward. Do not bend the hip joints. Besides the upper limbs and the knees and the ankles, no other joint is allowed to bend. Shift the body's center of gravity to the knees. The lower limbs (inner sides of the legs) touch each other, and the feet are together. The heels must touch the ground. The ankles and both sides of the knees are relaxed.

When in the squat position, use the mind intent to pull up the pressure points Hèdǐng (鶴頂 EX-LE2), located in the upper edge of the knee, and pull up Huìyīn, Zhāngmén (章门), and Dàbāo (大包. The tip of the tongue touches the upper palate and Bǎihuì pushes upward. The whole body relaxes downward and all the weight moves toward the knees.

There are repetitions in every section of the Body & Mind Method except in Bend Knees to Connect Three Joints. It requires the practitioner to hold the position as long as possible (use audio as a guideline for staying in the position or your experience doing the practice). Squatting down creates a blockage in the knee area. The longer we hold the position, the more Qì will accumulate in the knees and the more uncomfortable we will feel. When the body straightens up slowly leading with Bǎihuì and relaxing the knees, accumulated Qì will rush to the feet like water rushing through a broken dam. The rushing Qì will gradually open the Meridians in the lower limbs. The longer and the lower we hold the posture, the stronger the rush will be. Some individuals may feel the Qì rushing all the way to the centers of the feet or to the toes.

7) **Acupuncture Point practice.** The focus points are Bǎihuì, Sùliáo (素髎穴 DU25), Huìyīn, Hèdǐng and Mìngmén.

Purpose

The main purpose of this exercise is to open and loosen up the knees. By opening up the knees, Qì will connect the three lower joints (hip joints, knee joints, and ankles) and the three sections of the lower limbs will connect as one. This movement also is very effective in treating lower limb joint problems and in increasing bone density because of its weight-bearing characteristics.

11. Spring leg, move foot to draw Taiji 彈腿翹足描太極

Movements

With the body centered, shift the weight to the right, lift the left leg until the thigh is parallel to the ground. The calf is naturally relaxed and perpendicular to the ground. Flex the toes up, then press down three to five times.
Fig. 11-1, Fig. 11-2.

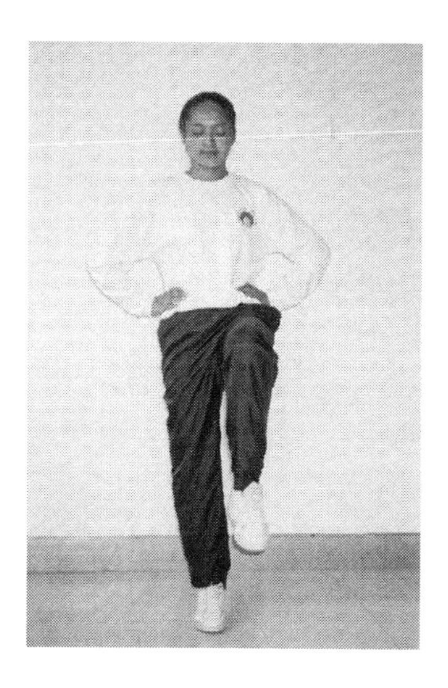

Fig. 11-1

Fig. 11-2

Draw circles with the back of the foot and the toes. First draw clockwise then counterclockwise circles three to five times each. Fig. 11-3a to Fig. 11-6a, and Fig. 11-3 to Fig. 11-6.

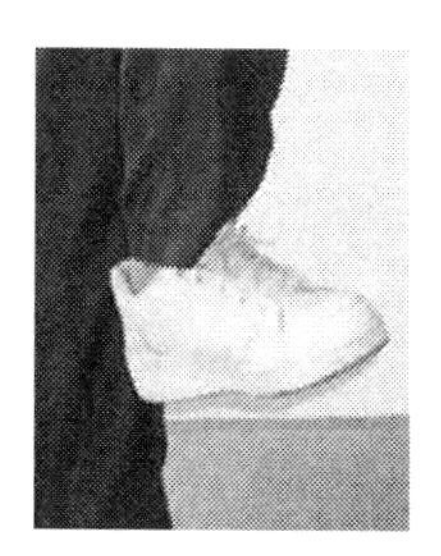

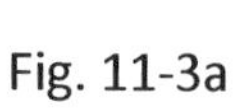

Fig. 11-3a

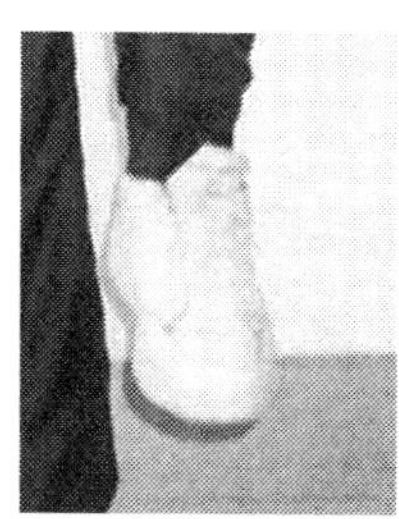

Fig. 11-4a

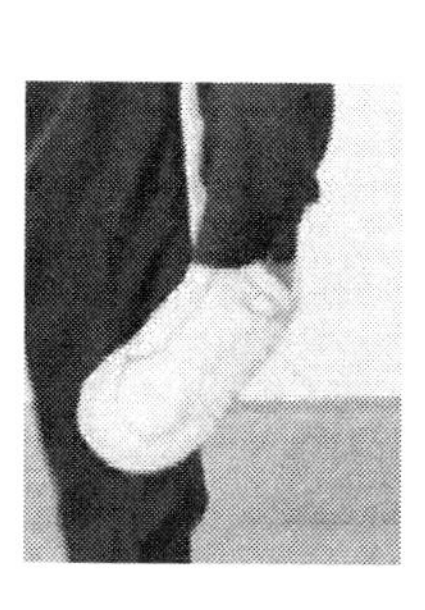

Fig. 11-5a

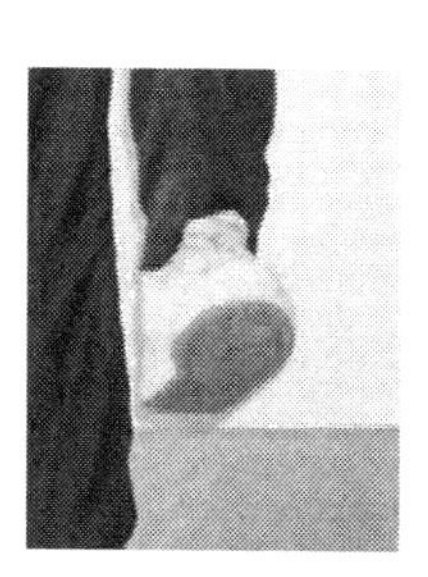

Fig. 11-6a

Fig. 11-3

Fig. 11-4

Fig. 11-5

Fig. 11-6

Straighten the back of the foot, then spring the foot outward at 45 degrees to the left front with the leg forming a straight line. Flex toes up and push heel out. Then point toes downward. Repeat three to five times.
Fig. 11-7, Fig. 11-8.

Straighten the back side of the foot; then turn the toes inward and draw circles, first clockwise and then counterclockwise. Repeat three to five times.
Fig. 11-3a to Fig. 11-6a.

Fig. 11-7

Fig. 11-8

Withdraw the big toe inward and move the leg back to the beginning position. Fig. 11-9.

Fig. 11-9

Repeat the same movements with the right leg. Fig. 11-1 to Fig. 11-9.

Details

1) **Move leg movement.** Shift the weight to the right. Lift the left leg with the heel moving up first, followed by the toes until the thigh is parallel to the ground. The calf is relaxed and naturally pointing (perpendicular) to the ground. The body will become substantial on the right side and insubstantial on the left. Keep the body centered with attention on the center of the left foot. Fig. 11-1, Fig. 11-2.

   Keys to the lift leg practice

   In order to maintain balance, the mind must be relaxed. When the mind becomes tense, the body will not be able to relax. The pelvis sits down slightly. Relax the body by taking a deep breath and exhale to sink Qì into the Dāntián. If the thigh cannot be held parallel to the ground, lower the foot or touch the heel to the ground. Do not lean the body to one side.

2) **Flex and press the foot and rotate the ankle movement**

   a) **Flex the foot.** The back of the foot pulls upward and back to the limit first. Then the toes pull upward and back to the limit.
   b) **Press the foot.** First the ankle and then the bottom of the foot press down to the limit. Then the toes point downward.
      Repeat **Flex** and **Press** three to five times.
   c) **Rotating the ankle.** Rotate the toes to the left, down, right, and up three to five times. Repeat the rotation in the opposite direction three to five times. Fig. 11-3a to Fig. 11-6a.

   Keys to the flex foot and rotate ankle practice

   The flexing and pressing movements must be slow and continuous. The toes rotate as if attached to a silk thread. The movements should be slow and rounded to avoid snapping the silk thread.

3) **Spring the leg out diagonally.** Straighten the back of the foot and spring out the leg diagonally at 45 degrees to the left front. The leg forms a straight line naturally. In the final position, the thigh should open 45 degrees to the side and should be lifted to a 45-degree angle off the ground.

   Keys to the spring leg practice

   Do not turn the foot and then spring out the leg. Both should spring out at 45 degrees. Do not turn the body after the foot springs outward. The body should remain centered. Do not thrust the pelvis forward; it should be withdrawn back slightly.

4) **Flex, stretch, and press the foot and rotate the ankle movements**

   a) **Flex the foot.** First pull the back of the foot upward to the limit first. Then pull the toes upward to the limit.
   b) **Stretch the foot.** Stretch the heel forward to the limit.

c) **Press the foot.** First Press down the ankle and the bottom of the foot to the limit. Then point the toes downward. Repeat **Flex**, **Stretch**, and **Press** three to five times.

d) **Rotating the ankle.** Rotate the toes to the left, down, right, and up three to five times. Repeat the rotation in the opposite direction three to five times. Fig. 11-7 to Fig. 11-8.

Keys to the practice

When the heel stretches, the leg remains straight. The remaining movement is the same as **1) *Move leg movement***.

Common mistakes

The body is not centered. It is either leaning toward the back and/or toward the side. The movements are not performed to the maximum limit of the stretches. The circles are not circular or even.

5) **Acupuncture Point Practice.** The acupuncture points in this section are the Big Seven Stars.

Purpose

In the previous ten sections, concentration was on the upper body. As a result, Qì becomes more concentrated in the upper body. This imbalance will sometimes create an uncomfortable feeling in the head. By moving the feet, the Qì sinks down and becomes more balanced. By focusing on the toe movements, one can effectively activate the Foot Meridians.

The combined movements of the toes and the legs activate the six foot Meridians (three Foot Yáng and three Foot Yin Meridians). Pulling the big toe inward while withdrawing the foot can activate the Liver Meridian and the Spleen Meridian. Cupping the center of the foot can activate the Kidney Meridian. If the mind intent extends the center of the foot all the way into the earth, one can absorb the Earth Qì into the body.

According to Meridian Theory, Yuán xué (原穴) is the area where the Inner Organ Qì stops and then passes through. The six Foot Meridians' Yuán xués are located in the ankle area: rotating the ankles can activate Qì in the six foot Meridians (Bladder, Stomach, Gallbladder, Spleen, Liver and Kidney Meridians). The spring leg and flex foot movement can activate the Yàngmìng Stomach Meridian located in the front of the thigh. The stretch and press movements can activate the foot Tàiyáng Bladder Meridians located in the back of the thigh. Once these Meridians are open, it will greatly improve the circulation of Qì and blood in the lower limbs.

This section's movements are very effective in treating problems in the joints, muscles, and ligaments of the lower limbs and in regulating blood pressure. It is also beneficial for people with liver or kidney problems.

12. Return Qì to One 回氣歸一轉混元

Movements

a. Hùn Yuán return to one.

Following the last movement, relax and separate the hands. Turn hands until the thumbs point to the front and the tiger mouth (opening formed by the thumb and the four fingers) points upward. The palms are slightly cupped and are facing each other at shoulder width and slightly below the waist. Fig. 12-1.

Fig. 12-1

Extend arms forward and downward diagonally, and then scoop Qì up with the hands as if holding a Qì ball to above and in front of the head. Turn the body to the left. Fig. 12-2, Fig. 12-3.

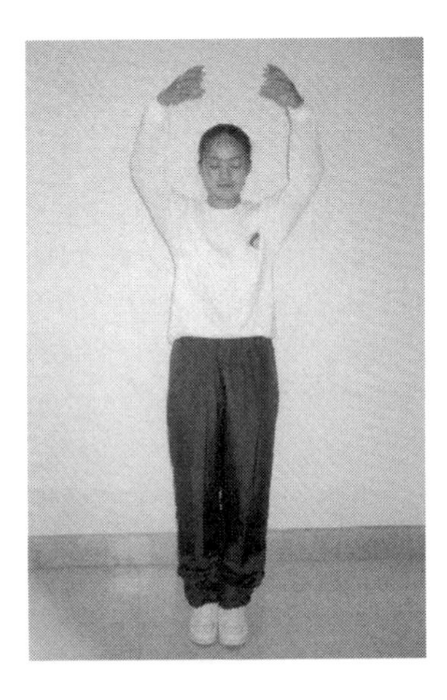

Fig. 12-2

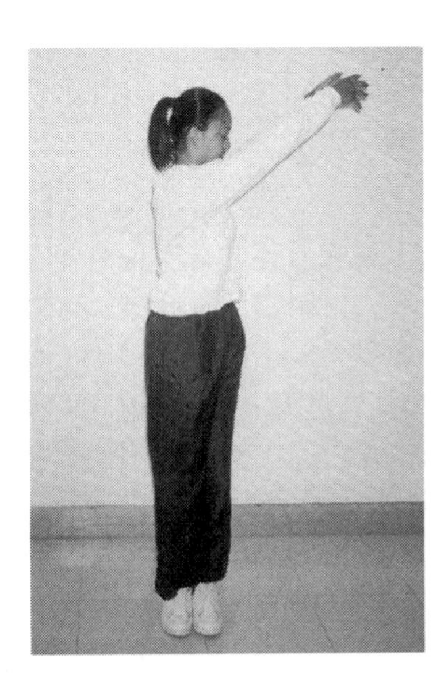

Fig. 12-3

Relax the whole body, drop the shoulders, sink the elbows, and the body squats down while turning to the left. During the squat, the arms draw a downward arch and follow the body turning from the left side to the front. Keep the body centered during the squat. Do not push the buttocks upward. As the body reaches the lowest point in the squat, the arms should arrive in front of the body with the hands in front of the knees. Relax the wrists and the fingers, allowing the fingers to point to the ground. Fig. 12-4, Fig. 12-5.

Fig. 12-4

Fig. 12-5

Fig. 12-6

Turn body to the right. The shoulders, elbows and wrists slightly lift up. The hands draw an upward arch toward the right side of the body until the hands arrive above and in front of the head as the body rises up from the squat. This would complete a full circle.
Fig. 12-6, Fig. 12-7.
Repeat Fig. 12-2 to Fig. 12-7 three times.

With the same principles, draw three circles in the reverse direction.

At the end of the last circle, move hands to above the head and keep the hands in that position. Perform three Crane's Neck movements in the forward direction (see Fig 2-1 to 2-8 for details). Fig. 12-7, Fig. 12-8, Fig. 12-9, Fig. 12-10, Fig. 12-7a.

Fig. 12-7

Fig. 12-8

Fig. 12-9

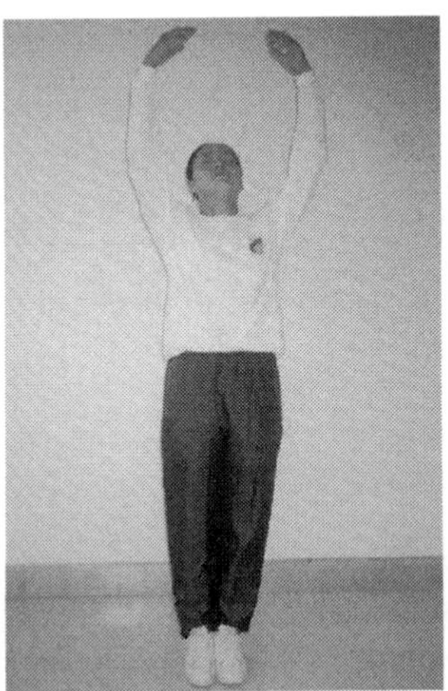

Fig. 12-10

Fig. 12-7a

b. Return (blend Internal and External) Qì to one

Lower the hands as if pulling the Qì ball to cover the head: move the wrists down and in toward each other followed by the palms and fingers (the hands do not touch each other). Relax the shoulders, lead with the elbows to lower and open the hands from both sides until the tips of the middle finger are next to the tip of the ears, the hands and forearms form a diagonal straight line.
Fig. 12-11 to Fig. 12-15.

Fig. 12-11

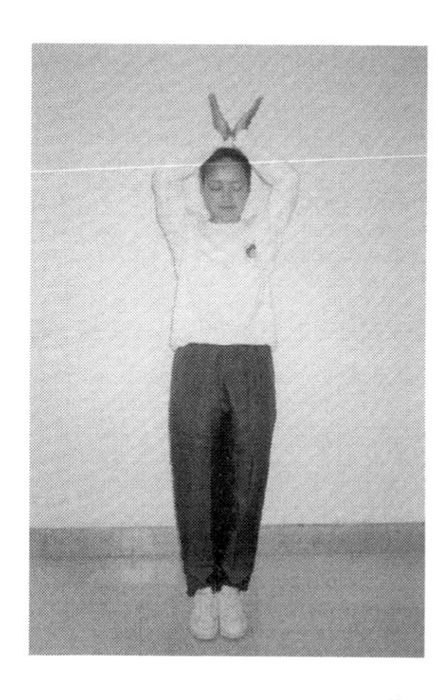

Fig. 12-12

Fig. 12-13

Fig. 12-14

Fig. 12-15

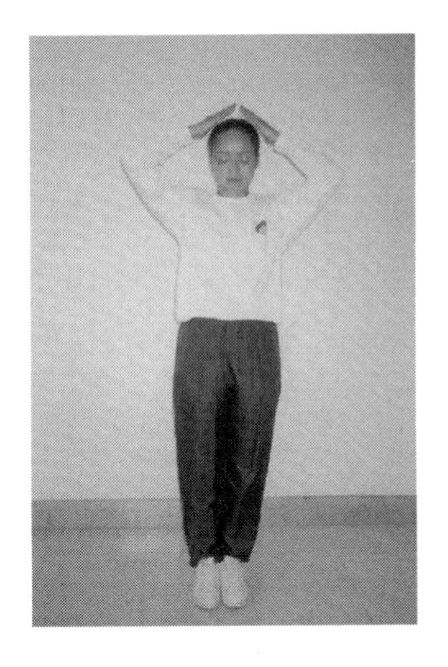

Fig. 12-16

Then move the hands upward along the same path, closing first, then opening, as in the letter "X". Fig. 12-16 to Fig. 12-19.

Repeat three times. Fig. 12-11 to Fig. 12-19.

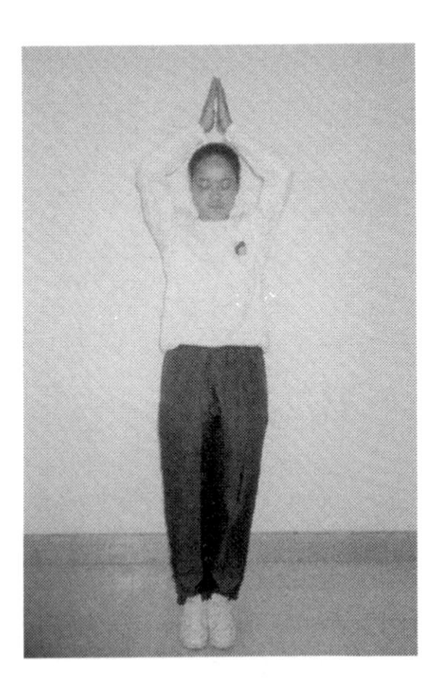

Fig. 12-17

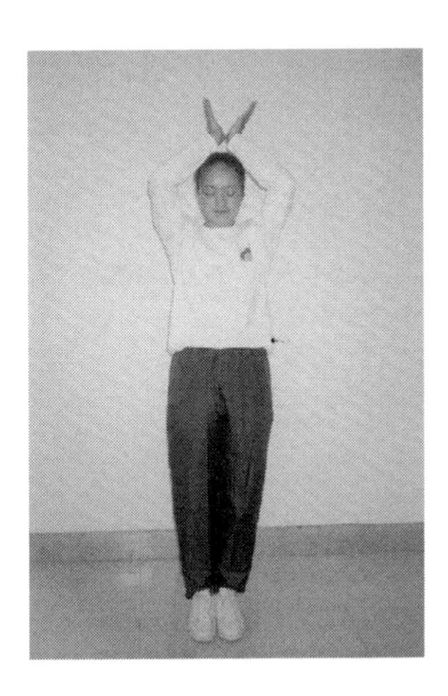

Fig. 12-18

Scoop the Qì up with the hands and pour Qì into the head. Relax shoulders and lower the hands in front of the face to the chest; rotate the palms inward until the fingers are pointing toward each other. Lower hands to the abdomen. Rotate palms until the fingers are pointing to the ground and continue moving downward in front of the legs to the feet.
Fig. 12-20, Fig. 12-21, Fig. 12-22.

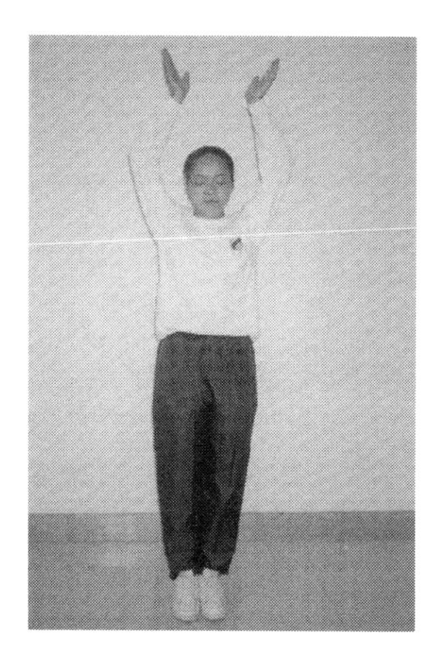

Fig. 12-19

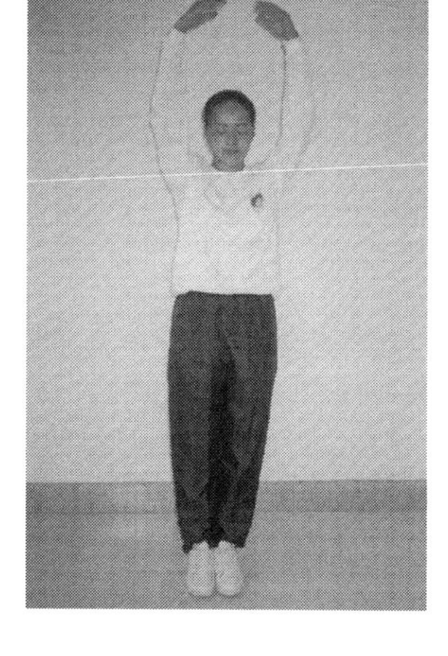

Fig. 12-20

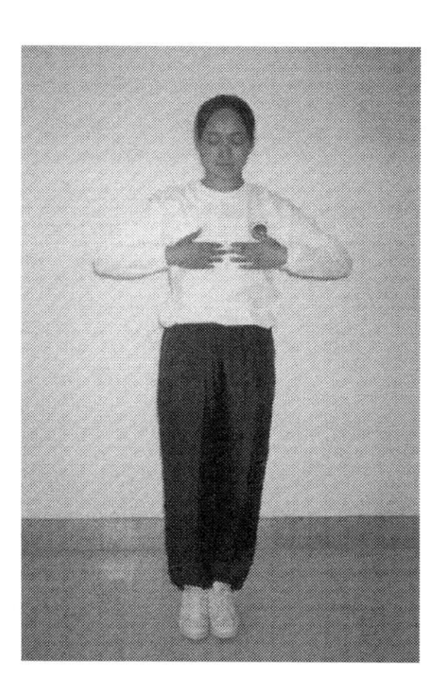

Fig. 12-21

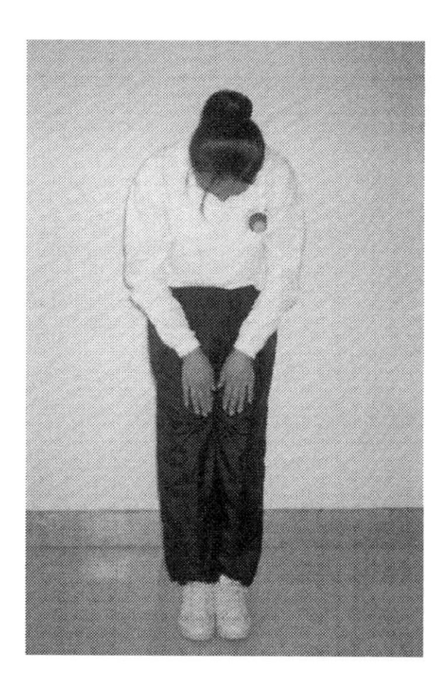

Fig. 12-22

Put hands on top of the feet with fingers on top of the toes. Press the hands downward and move the knees forward and down. Through mind intent, the hands go through the feet to connect with the earth. Then the hips move up and the knees shift back and up. The mind intent is to collect earth Qì into the body. Fig. 12-23, Fig. 12-24, Fig. 12-25, Fig. 12-26. Repeat 3 times.

Fig. 12-23

Fig. 12-24

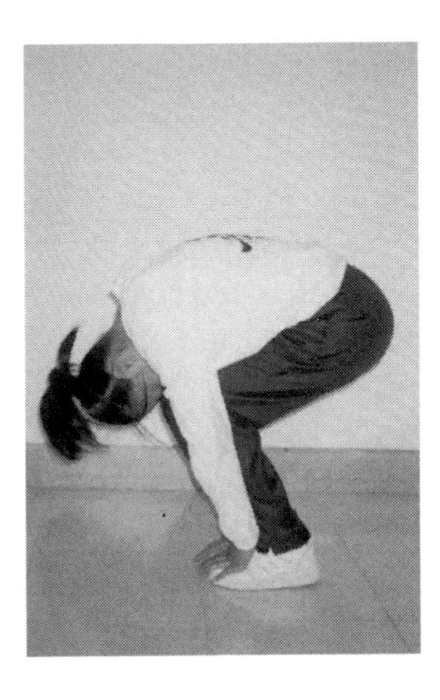

Fig. 12-25

Fig. 12-26

Separate the hands from the feet and move the hands slightly upward. Cup the palms, rotate and move the hands until the palms are facing the inner legs. Move the hands upward along the inner legs to the abdomen. Turn hands until the fingers are pointing toward each other at waist level and move up in front of the chest. Fig. 12-27, Fig. 12-28.

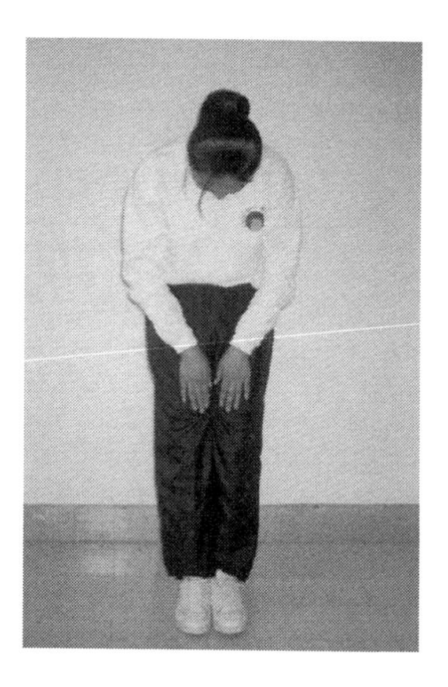

Fig. 12-27

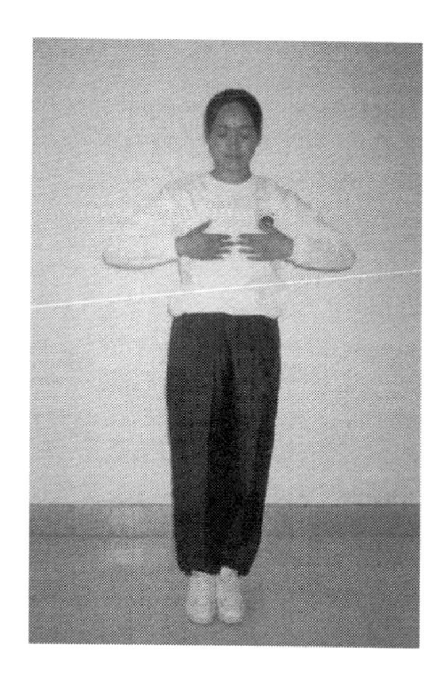

Fig. 12-28

Separate hands to the sides. Leading with the little fingers, rotate palms forward and place in front of the shoulders. Push the right hand forward until the arm is almost straight. Fig. 12-29, Fig. 12-30.

Fig. 12-29

Fig. 12-30

Relax wrist and turn palm to scoop Qì to the left, turning the body at the waist. At 90 degrees, the tip of the thumb touches Zhōngkuí (middle of the middle joint of middle finger). Bend the elbow and circle the hand around the shoulder to continue scooping Qì. At the same time, the body begins to return to the beginning position. Return arm to front of the left chest and press Qìhù (under the collar bone) with the tip of the third finger. Fig. 12-31, Fig. 12-32, Fig. 12-33.

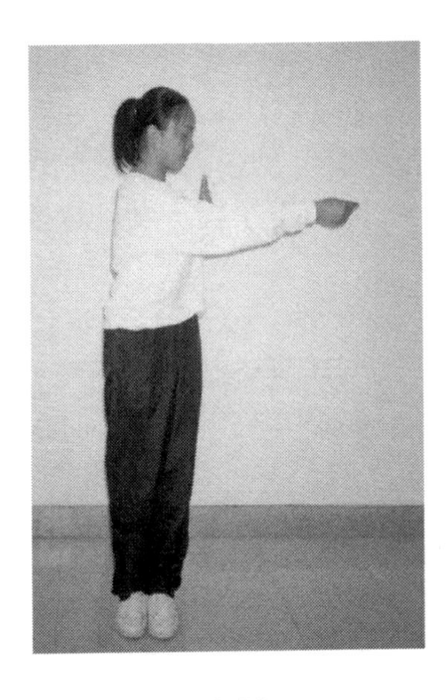

Fig. 12-31

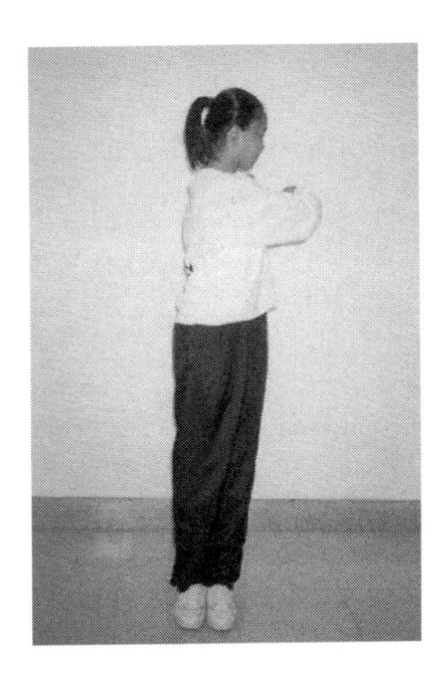

Fig. 12-32

Fig. 12-33

Fig. 12-34

Repeat the same movement with the left hand. At the end of the movement, the forearms should cross each other forming an "X" in front of the chest. The upper arms should form a 45-degree angle with the body with the elbows pointing downward diagonally. Breathe in and out three times naturally. When inhaling, the middle fingers press Qìhù slightly. When exhaling, release the pressure and pronounce the word "Tong" soundlessly. Fig. 12-34, Fig. 12-35, Fig. 12-36.

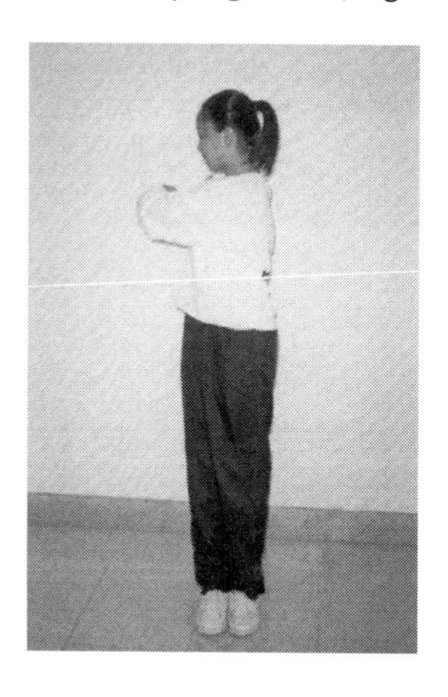

Fig. 12-35

Fig. 12-36

Release fingers and push forearms forward to form a 90-degree angle with the upper arms. With the wrists touching each other, turn palms to face the sky and rotate wrists to form a lotus palm. Close hands in praying position. Fig. 12-37, Fig. 12-38, Fig. 12-39.

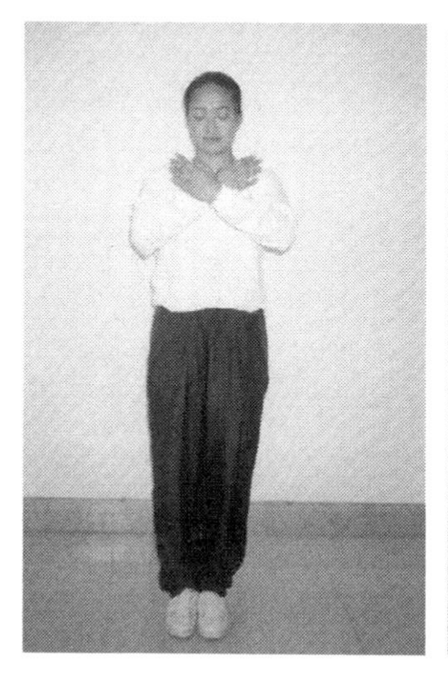

Fig. 12-37

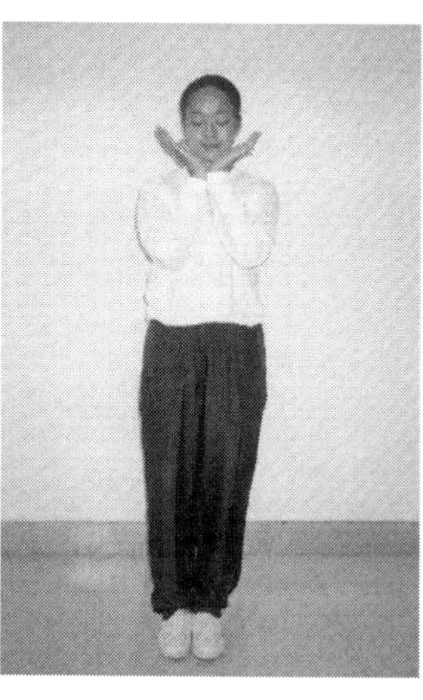

Fig. 12-38

Fig. 12-39

c. Closing

From the praying position, open hands to the nipple line. Then close hands until they are almost touching. Open and close the hands three times.
Fig. 12-40, Fig. 12-41.

Fig. 12-40

Fig. 12-41

Move the hands to the tip of the nose. Open and close three times.
Fig. 12-42, Fig. 12-43, Fig. 12-44.

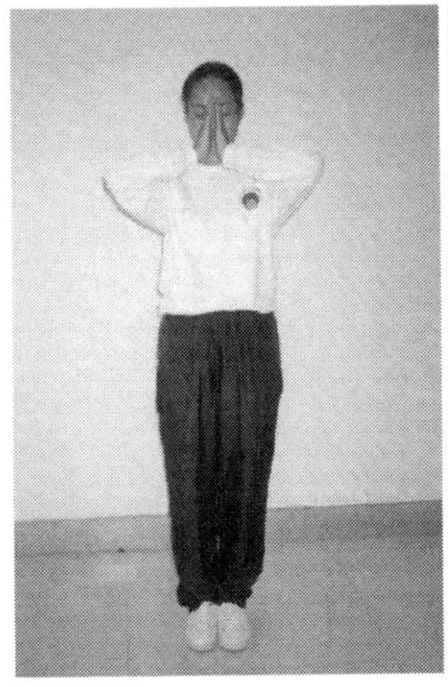

Fig. 12-42

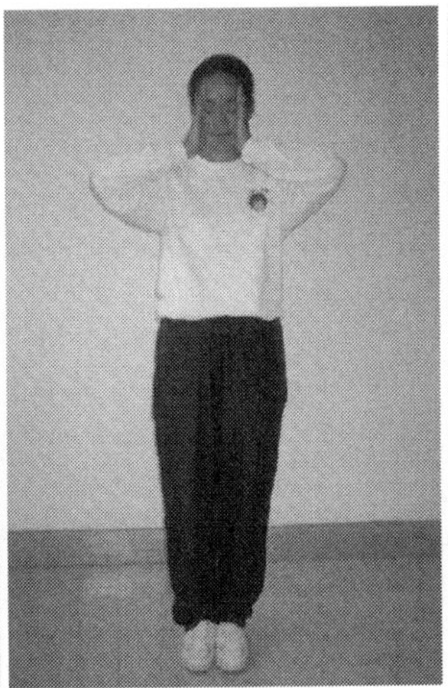

Fig. 12-43

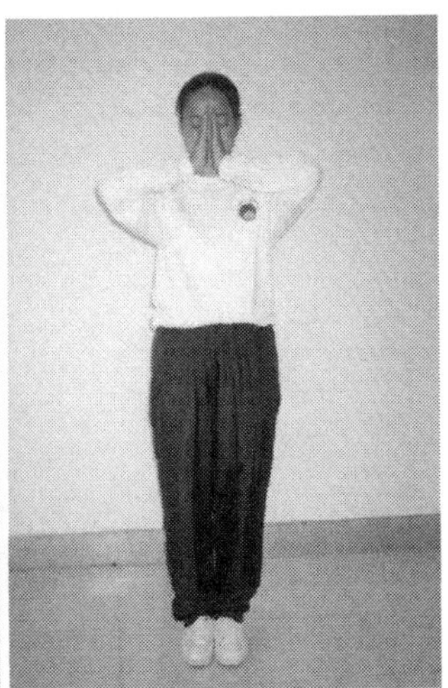

Fig. 12-44

Move the hands to Yìntáng. Open and close the hands three times.
Fig. 12-45, Fig. 12-46, Fig. 12-47.

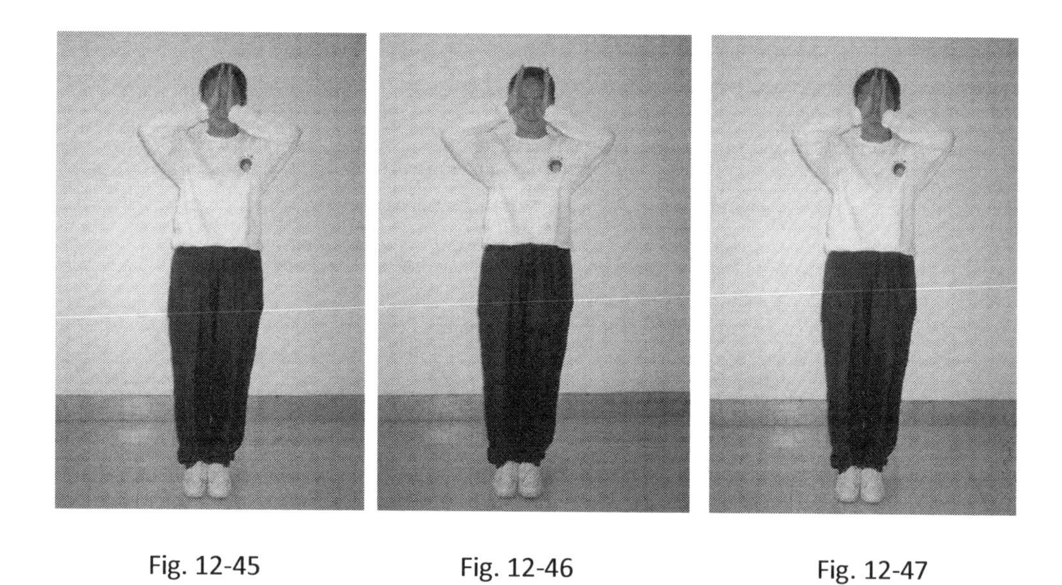

Fig. 12-45 Fig. 12-46 Fig. 12-47

Then move hands to Xìnmén (囟門 GV 22). Open and close three times.
Fig. 12-48, Fig. 12-49, Fig. 12-50.

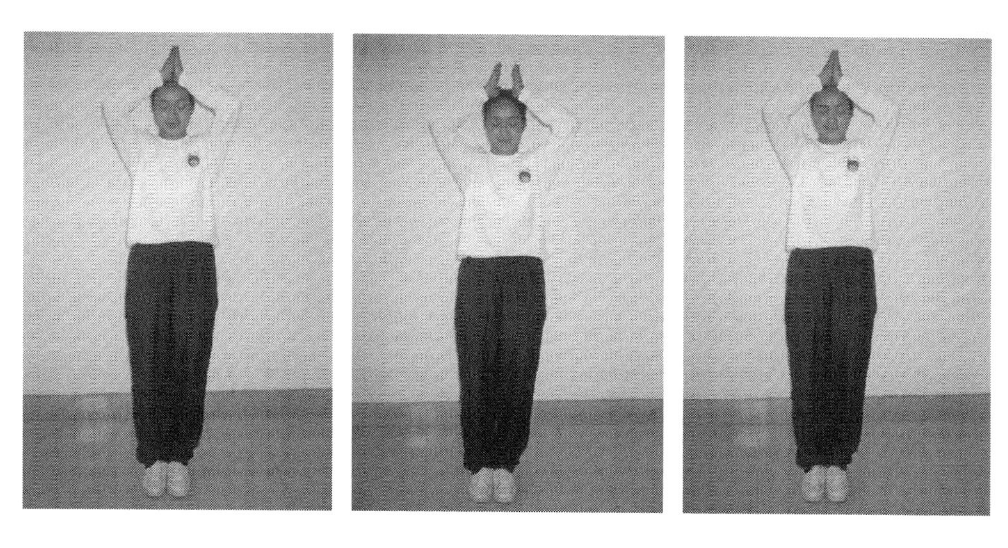

Fig. 12-48 Fig. 12-49 Fig. 12-50

Finally move hands to above Bǎihuì. Open and close three times.
Fig. 12-51, Fig. 12-52, Fig. 12-53.

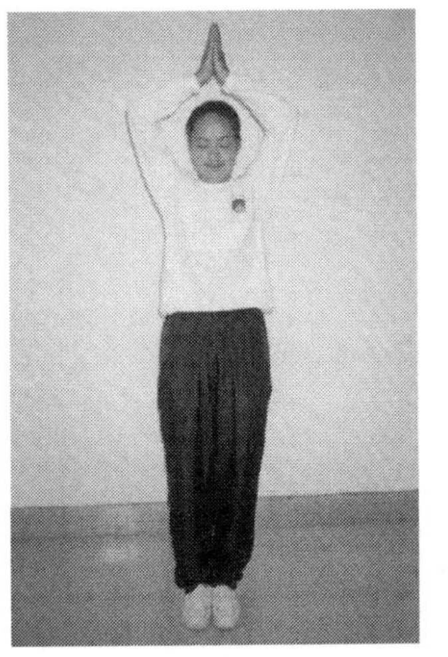
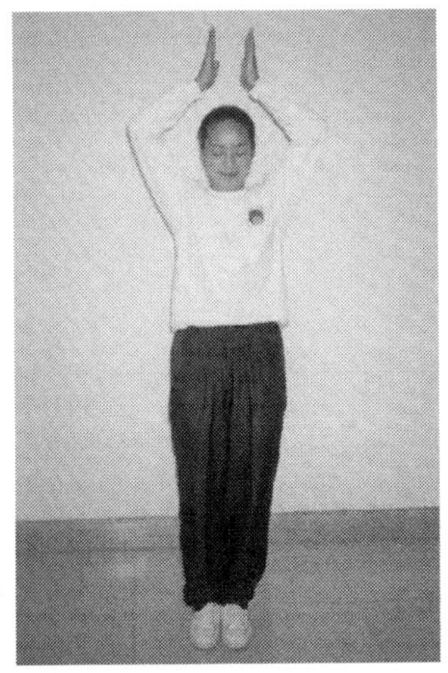
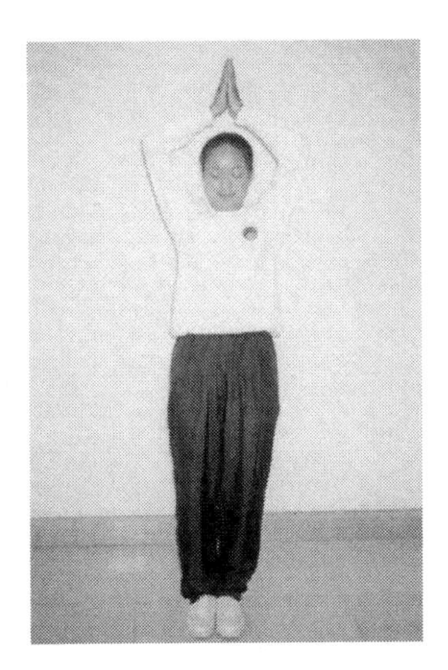

Fig. 12-51 Fig. 12-52 Fig. 12-53

Close hands and move them upward until the arms are straight, then stretch farther. Separate hands and turn palms forward. Fig. 12-54, Fig. 12-55.

Fig. 12-54 Fig. 12-55 Fig. 12-56

Lower the arms to form a straight line at shoulder level. Turn palms up to face the sky. Fig. 12-56.

Move arms forward to shoulder width. Withdraw the palms and arms slightly; middle fingers bend slightly to deliver Qì to Yìntáng. Withdraw the elbows backward and outward until middle fingers touch Dàbāo and deliver Qì inside the body. Move the hands to the back until the arms are almost straight, then circle the hands to the sides. Fig. 12-57, Fig. 12-58, Fig. 12-59, Fig. 12-60.

Fig. 12-57

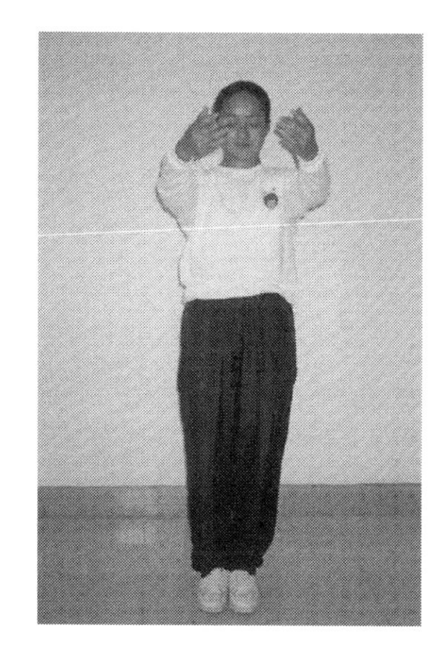

Fig. 12-58

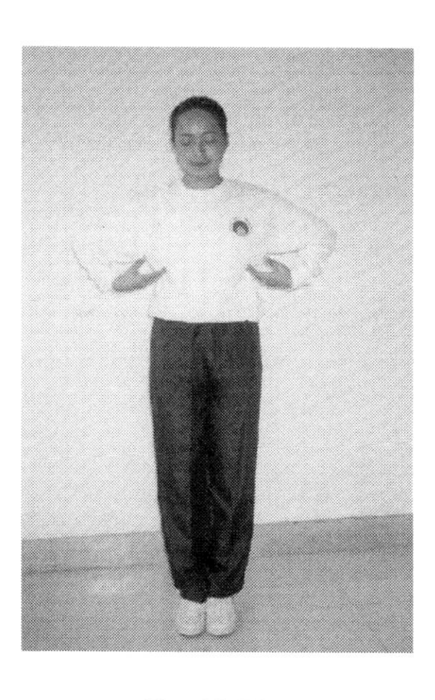

Fig. 12-59

Fig. 12-60

Turn the palms to scoop Qì forward and into the Dāntián. Close the hands in front of the navel (approximately one finger's thickness). The man places the left hand first in front of the navel and then places the right hand over the left hand. The woman places the right hand first and then the left hand over the right hand. Massage counterclockwise (left, up, right and down) nine times from small to large circles, then clockwise nine times from large to small circles. Place the hands upon the navel and relax for a few minutes. Slowly return the hands to the beginning position and open the eyes. Fig. 12-61, Fig. 12-62, Fig. 12-63, Fig. 12-64.

Fig. 12-61

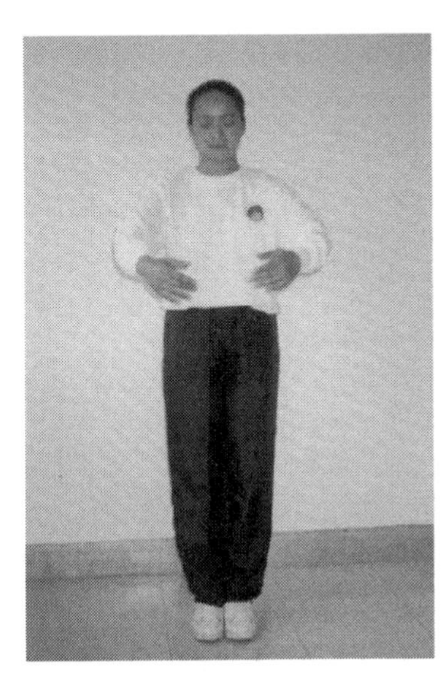

Fig. 12-62

Fig. 12-63

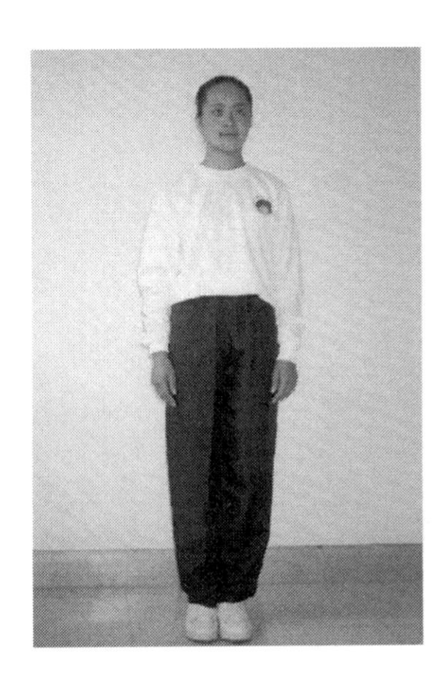

Fig. 12-64

Details

This section consists of three parts. Part one is Hùn Yuán return to one, part two is Return Qì to one, and part three is the Closing.

a. Hùn Yuán (blend Internal Qì) return to one

Hold the ball to draw circles

1) **Holding the ball.** Release hands to hold a ball in front of the abdomen. The arms are at shoulder width and the hands are holding an imaginary Qì ball. While rotating the body, the distance between the hands should remain constant. Maintain the feeling of holding a ball, not emptiness. When raising the ball up in front of the body, the shoulders move the elbows and the elbows move the hands. The Qì between the hands and the Qì inside the body should be connected. Fig. 12-1.

2) **Rotating the body to draw circles.** Relax the whole body, drop the shoulders, sink the elbows and sit the wrists. The arms draw a downward arch from the left side. At the same time, the body turns to the left using the waist and sits down. The hands move down while holding the ball. The body remains straight and centered. When the hands are in front of the knees, relax the wrists and the fingers. The fingers will automatically point to the ground. Turn the body to the right. When moving upward, slightly raise the shoulder blades, using the shoulders to lead the elbows and the wrists to move upward slowly. From the right side of the body, the hands draw an arch up to above the forehead. Repeat the movement three times. Reverse the direction. At the end of the last circle, the hands stop above the head. Fig. 12-2 to Fig. 12-7.

Common mistakes

The ball becomes big and then small, it should stay the same size. The ball is not in front of the body. The shoulders lean forward too much. The hips are not sitting down. The waist is not turning.

Keys to the practice

Holding the ball and turning the body are whole body movements. Both upper and lower limbs and the body are turning and drawing circles at the same time. The spine, shoulders and the joints must be relaxed, the body is centered. Shoulders must be flexible and cannot lean to the front or to the sides, tailbone points to the ground, and hips are sitting down. The body and arm movements should be synchronized and natural. In order to acquire a feel for the movement, we can practice either 1) or 2) independently. Once the movements become familiar, 1) and 2) should be performed simultaneously.

In the beginning, the body can lean slightly backward when turning to let the arms draw rounder circular circles. The mind intent should focus on connecting the ball to the body. While turning, imagine the ball is touching the body and connecting with the Qì inside the body.

Purpose of hold the ball to draw circles

The focal points of the Body and Mind method are different in each section. Consequently, the Qì and the Qì flow in the body become uneven. This sequence of movements balances and blends Internal body Qì into one integrated whole by moving every part of the body simultaneously.

Crane's Neck

After the last movement, move the hands to above the head and perform three Crane's Neck movements. The principles are the same as in Section 3 except that each movement is smaller in this section.

Purpose of Crane's Neck

The purpose of this movement is to induce Qì into the head for preparation to open the Tiānmén (Heaven's Gate). Fig. 12-8 to Fig. 12-10.

b. Return (blend Internal and External) Qì to one

1) Opening the top

The movements are down, close, open, up, close, open. The hands pull a Qì ball downward to cover the head to open the Tiānmén (Heaven's Gate).

Down: The palms close downward diagonally, starting with the wrists and followed by the palms and fingers. Fig. 12-11 to Fig. 12-12.

Close: The wrists close, then open. The palms close, then open. The fingertips close, then open. The hands almost touch, but do not touch during the closing movements. Fig. 12-13.

Open: Relax the shoulders. Leading with the elbows, move hands down diagonally from the sides until the tips of the middle fingers arrive next to the tips of the ears. The hands and forearms form a straight line.
Fig. 12-14.

Reverse the path when performing the up, close and open movements. When moving up, close first, then open, as if drawing an "X" over the top of the head. When the palms and the fingers open above the head, visualize the Tiānmén is opening. The distance between the wrists above the head should not be wider than the dragon's horns. The whole movement looks like a blossoming lotus flower. Repeat this movement three times. Fig. 12-15 to Fig. 12-18.

Common mistakes

When the hands open, they are too far apart—they go beyond the sides of the head. The hands and the upper arms do not form an "X" as they move above the head and toward the top of the head. The elbows do not open outward to the sides of the body.

Keys to the practice

The hands and the wrists must have open and close movements. The hands and the wrists should not move straight up and down above the head.

Purpose

The primary purpose is to combine the mind intent with the hand movements to open Tiānmén.

2) Inducing Qì

After the last movement, hands scoop Qì upward, as if holding a ball, and pour Qì into the head. Relax the shoulders and sink the elbows. Lower the hands along the face to the chest, then turn palms inward until the fingers point toward one other. When the hands reach the abdomen, slowly turn the fingers downward and lower the hands along the front of the legs until the centers of the palms rest on top of the feet with the fingers resting on top of the toes. Press hands down and move the knees slightly forward. Through mind intent, the centers of the palms pass through the centers of the feet to touch the ground. Then move hips upward, and shift the knees backward and upward slightly. Visualize pulling earth Qì into the body. Press down and up three times. Fig. 12-19 to Fig. 12-26.

Move the hands upward and above the feet slightly. Then cup the palms and turn the fingers outward 90 degrees in opposite directions. Lift the wrists slightly so that the palms are facing each other and the fingers are pointing toward the ground. The hands move next to the outside edges of the feet pulling up earth Qì and holding it between the hands. Circle the hands around the edges of the feet. Turn palms to face the inner legs and move up to induce Qì upward. When the hands pass the abdomen, turn the palms inward until the fingers point toward one other and move upward to the chest level. Separate hands by lowering the elbows and turn palms forward leading with the little fingers until the palms are in front of the shoulders. Fig. 12-27 to Fig. 12-29.

Common mistakes

In the press up and down movement, using the knees instead of the Mìngmén to press down and pull up. The chin is not tucked inward toward the neck. The head is not toward the earth—opening up the back of the neck. While straightening up the body, the tailbone is not pointing toward the ground.

3) Blending Qì to one

Lower the right wrist and push the right hand forward until the arm is almost straight. Relax the wrist and turn the hand to face the left leading with the little finger. Using the waist as pivot point, rotate the body to the left. At the same time, right hand scoops Qì to the left. At 90 degrees, the tip of the thumb presses the middle of the middle section of the middle finger Zhōngkuí (中魁穴 EX-UE 4) as the rest of the fingers curve naturally. Bend elbow and circle hand around the shoulder to continue to scoop Qì. At this time, the body begins to turn right, returning to the beginning position.

With continuous turning of the body, the hand should have moved around the shoulder to drop below the lower edge of the collar bone by the time the body is back to the beginning position. Then, the middle finger presses Qìhù (氣戶 ST 13 middle of the collar bone below its lower edge). Repeat this movement with left hand. Fig. 12-30 to Fig. 12-36.

Common mistakes

The waist is not turning, instead the hips also move twisting the lower body as well as the knees—the lower body should face forward. The body is not centered and is leaning over toward the side. The shoulders are not level. The head drops toward the side (toward the shoulder). Only the hand moves, and the tip of the thumb does not press Zhōngkuí.

Purpose

During the practice, a strong Qì field forms around the body. Scooping this condensed outside Qì into the body and blending it with the inner Qì is called "returning the Qì to one". There is a middle finger presses Zhōngkuí movement in the returning Qì sequence. The middle section of the middle finger is called Yùqīngjué (玉清訣) in the classic texts. There are twenty-four sections in the hands, Zhōngkuí is located at the middle joint of the middle finger. When the thumb presses Zhōngkuí, it will open up all the pressure points in the hand. When the thumb presses this central point, and the palm is cupped, Qì will enter the body.

According to Meridian theory, the thumb belongs to Lung Meridian, middle finger belongs to Pericardium Meridian, the lung regulates Qì, and the heart regulates blood. Pressing Zhōngkuí can merge Qì and blood. According to five Element Theory, the center of the thumb's first section belongs to the spleen, the center of middle finger's center section belongs to the pericardium. The spleen regulates mind intent, pericardium regulates the mind. Pressing Zhōngkuí will merge the mind and mind intent to stabilize the mental condition and enhances scooping Qì and activates Qì functions. Middle finger pressing Qìhù (Qì's door) induces Qì into the body.

4) Breathing and silently pronouncing "Tong"

At this time in the practice, the forearms are crossing each other forming an "X" in front of the chest. The upper arms point downward diagonally forming a 45-degree angle with the body. Inhale and exhale naturally three times. When inhaling, tips of the middle fingers press Qìhù. Release the pressure while exhaling, and at the same time, with the tongue touching the upper palate, pronounce the word "Tong" silently. Then, release the fingers and push the forearms forward to form a 90-degree angle with the upper arms (which remain stationary). Lower the fingers to turn palms to face the sky. Rotate the wrists outward in opposite directions until the hands and the forearms form an "X", a "lotus palm". Put the hands together and lower hands to form a praying position in front of the chest. Fig. 12-36 to Fig. 12-39.

Common mistakes

The breathing is not natural but forced. The tips of thumbs are not touching Zhōngkuí. The upper arms do not form a 45-degree angle with the body. Sounding the word "Tong" loudly, and the tongue is not touching the upper palate.

Purpose

The purpose for saying "Tong" is to use sound to activate Qì in the Central Meridian to induce it upward. When pronouncing "Tong" with the tongue touching the upper palate, Dāntián Qì will rush upward from the sacral area and the Tiānmén area will vibrate. Pronouncing "Tong" is to use sound to vibrate and open Tiānmén. Some practitioners may feel the vibration in the periosteum or inside the brain.

c. Closing

1) Five open-close movements

The open-close movement requires the elbows and the shoulders move simultaneously and that the hands and the forearms be fixed at a 90-degree angle throughout the movements. When the forearms maintain a straight line, the elbows lead the hands to do the open-close movement. These are not hand movements—the elbows and the shoulders are the primary movers. When closing, the hands are almost touching yet not touching. After practicing for a certain period of time, one may feel the opening and the closing of the inner organs and the head. This occurs because the open-close movement is not an isolated but a whole-body-Qì open-and-close movement. The sensation will not be there if one uses just the hands to open and close. Fig. 12-40 to Fig. 12-53.

a) **Shānzhōng (膻中 RN 17, the midpoint between the nipples) open-close.** The hands open to the nipples, with the second knuckles of the thumbs at Shānzhōng level.
b) **Tip of the nose open-close.** Hands open to the cheek bones with the tips of the thumbs at the tip of the nose level.
c) **Yìntáng open-close.** Hands open to the center of the pupils with the first knuckle of the thumbs at the Yìntáng level.
d) **Xìnmén (about two cm above the forehead) open-close.** Hands open to the center of the pupils with the thumbs inclined toward Xìnmén.
e) **Bǎihuì open-close.** Hands open to the Dragon's Horns with the fingers pointing to the sky and the wrists are about ten cm above Bǎihuì.

Common mistakes

The forearms do not form a straight line. The opening between the hands is too wide, extending beyond the perimeters of the body.

Purpose

The open-close movements blend the Internal and External Qì together. These movements create the foundation for practicing stillness Qìgōng.

2) The closing

Put the hands together and move them up along the body center line to above the head. When the arms are straight, hands stretch upward to the maximum to induce Shǎo Yáng Qì (少陽氣) and Qīng Yáng Qì (清陽氣) upward. Rotate the arms until palms are facing toward the front, then lower the arms to shoulder level to form a straight line. Rotate the arms until the palms face up toward the sky. Circle the arms inward and forward to shoulder width apart. Slightly bend the first knuckle of the middle fingers to reflect Qì into Yìntáng. Fig. 12-54 to Fig. 12-58.

Holding a Qì ball in the hands, lower and withdraw the elbows to the back until hands touch the rib cage. Then rotate elbows outward until the tips of the middle finger touch Dàbāo. Slightly press Dàbāo to deliver Qì inside. Continue rotating the elbows until the fingers are pointing backward. Extend arms to the back forming a straight line with the hands holding a Qì ball at Mìngmén level. Circle the arms to the sides of the body and naturally rotate arms to scoop Qì to the front and deliver it into the Lower Dāntián through the navel. Slowly close hands in front of the navel to approximately one finger's thickness away from the abdomen. Men place the left hand over the navel first with right hand overlapping the left hand. Women place the right hand over the navel first with the left hand overlapping the right hand. Draw nine circles from small to large. The maximum size of the circle uses the following guidelines: below the Zhōngwǎn (中脘穴 RN 12) on top, above the pubic bone on the bottom, and stay within the abdomen on both sides. Then reverse the direction and draw nine circles from large to small. Put the hands on the navel and nourish Qì for a few minutes. When the hands draw circles, mind intent is inside the abdomen and is turning with the hands. Fig. 12-59 to Fig. 12-63.

Purpose

The purpose of the closing is to collect nature Hùn Yuán Qì and the Qì in the surrounding Qì field which is formed by the body while practicing. Do not be careless just because it is the closing—it has re-adjustment effects on the whole body. This closing sequence is a "Pour Qì into the three Dāntiáns" (upper, middle, and lower Dāntiáns) movement. Drawing circles in front of abdomen balances and redistributes Qì inside the body.

Overall conclusion of Section 12.

- Hùn Yuán return to One rebalances and redistributes Qì inside the whole body.
- Return Qì to One and the Closing collect Nature Qì: Opening head movements collect Heaven Qì; Press Up & Down movements collect Earth Qì; Hands scooping movements collect the surrounding Qì.
- This section has "open" the Heaven's Gate information. For example, all of the following movements are inducing Qì upward to open the Heaven's Gate, Tiānmén: The Crane's Neck movements; open the top of the head movements; the five open-close movements; and the "Tong" sound.
- This section combines Posture Inducing Qì Method, Mind Inducing Qì Method and Sound Inducing Qì Method.
- This section combines the following concepts: posture Open-Close; breathe Open-Close; sound Open-Close; and mind intent Open-Close.

How to Practice the Body & Mind Method

The Body & Mind Method is Zhìnéng Qìgōng's second step Gong. It is a very important method in the Zhìnéng Qìgōng system. The first step Gong Lift Qì Up and Pour Qì Down Method is Shén and Qì Practice. By exchanging Internal and External Qì, Lift Qì Up and Pour Qì Down Method unites Shén and Qì; consequently, the passageways between the Body Qì and Nature Qì will be expanded and the exchanging functions will be strengthened. This is the foundation of Zhìnéng Qìgōng practice. The Body & Mind Method is Shén and Xíng Practice; it is intended to practice two things— Shén and Xíng. Practice Shén means to regulate the mind activities, practice Xíng means to regulate the body postures. The Body & Mind Method uses the movement of the body postures to activate the Meridian Qì and uses Shén to induce Qì into the body.

There was a saying in Qìgōng in the old days, "the best practitioner cultivates/practices Shén, and the average practitioner cultivates/practices Xíng (上士練神, 下士練形)." Therefore, many Qìgōng practitioners do not consider the best Qìgōng methods to be those which focus on the body or postures; consequently, they do not pay attention to or work on the body postures and as a result, many of them end up with the phenomenon called "have Qì, but no physical strength" (有氣無力) in Qìgōng. If we look at the historic background, we discover that not working on the physical body is a misconception. In the old days, most Qìgōng practitioners were highly educated or held high-status positions in the society. This privileged group of people considered mind to be the most important thing and looked down on any physical activities. Another major Qìgōng group was the religious practitioners, and they focused on using Qìgōng to obtain enlightenment. They cultivated the mind to achieve enlightenment; therefore, physical movements were not as important. Today, most people practice Qìgōng for both mental and physical wellness; therefore, we will have to reevaluate the ways of practicing.

Previously, we defined Qìgōng as the following:

> *Qìgōng is a training based on the theories of the Wholism of Life. It is a training that requires the participant to consciously use the mind intent to focus inward to transform, to improve, and to enhance life functions. Mental, posture, and breathing adjustments are the extensions of the inward training. It is a training which enables the participants to transform natural instinctive activities into conscious activities.*

Therefore, to practice Qìgōng, we must cultivate the mind, but at the same time, we cannot ignore the physical body. Shén cannot exist by itself; it must attach to the physical body. Corrected body posture can promote Qì circulation, and with better Qì circulation, Shén becomes healthier. If one does not pay attention to the body, Qì alone may not be able to maintain the body posture, especially when one is getting older. This is called "have Qì, but not strength, is an illness" in Qìgōng.

The Body & Mind Method emphasizes adjusting the physical body; the preparation states the detailed requirements and proper posture of every part of the body. The method requires precise execution and every movement has specific posture requirements. Focusing on the proper postures during the movements allows Qì and blood to circulate normally and eliminates side effects caused by improper posture. For example, if the waist area is concaved, it may hinder Qì's Up & Down functions resulting in Yáng Qì moving up too much and not being able to move down normally. This may cause high blood pressure and/or hinder the functions of the brain.

Since Xíng is appearance, Shén is mindfulness and Zhuāng is posture, in a broader sense, if one has the proper body postures and focuses on the body, then one is practicing the Body & Mind Method (Xíng Shén Zhuāng). Therefore, to practice the Body & Mind Method is to apply the posture requirements to daily routines. For example, while sitting, if one straightens up the spine, moves Mìngmén toward the navel slightly, relaxes the chest and moves up Bǎihuì, then one is practicing the Body & Mind Method. In narrower terms, the Body & Mind Method (Xíng Shén Zhuāng) is the second foundation method of Zhìnéng Qìgōng. The following are the guidelines for the practice.

1. A good foundation on External Hùn Yuán practice

Hùn Yuán means to transmute two or more things into one. The Body & Mind Method transmutes Shén and Internal Qì into one; it belongs to Internal Hùn Yuán. Previously, we had mentioned the Body & Mind Method is Shén and Xíng practice; some may wonder "how do Shén and Internal Qì transmute into one" in Shén and Xíng practice? The physical body is the physical form of concentrated Qì; within the body, there is un-concentrated Qì, which besides circulating within the body, also moves in and out of the body. Once we merge (transmute) Shén and Xíng, this un-concentrated Qì will automatically be part of the transmutation (Hùn Yuán). In order to do well in Internal Hùn Yuán, one must have a good foundation in External Hùn Yuán.

There are two ways to practice the Opening sequence, one is External Hùn Yuán practice and the other is Internal Hùn Yuán practice.

In ***the External Hùn Yuán practice***, at the very beginning, during the press downward to Lā Qì movement, the push-pull movement is performed as if drawing an arc along an elliptical route. Also, it should be performed with slightly up and down movements. This would cause the centers of the palms to protrude outward and to cup inward, creating one tension and one relaxation movement. When the hands push forward, the centers of the palms protrude outward and press downward. As the hands push to the maximum, cup and retrieve the centers of the palms. Protrude the centers of the palms outward when pulling back, cup and retrieve the centers as the hands move back to their original positions. This will create a "protrude-cup, protrude-cup" rhythm as the hands move back and forth.

When the centers of the palms protrude outward and press downward, the mind intent presses down into the xū kōng underneath the ground. The mind intent leads the Body Qì outward and into the xū kōng to merge with the Qì in the xū kōng. Relax the body. Cup the hands slightly when pulling back, absorbing the earth Qì as one draws this small ellipse. If one examines only the movement, it is a push and pull movement, but it actually uses the small protrude-cup motion to achieve the result of one open and one close movement. Following the open and close movement, the body expands outward and contracts inward; consequently, Internal Qì will move out and External Qì will be absorbed inside. When the practice becomes proficient, each Lā Qì will have two open-close movements, and there are one release and one absorb in each movement, and each movement contains Internal Qì release outward and External Qì absorb inward.

The Body & Mind Method requires our mind to stay within the body. In order to induce the surrounding Qì to enter the body, we use the Opening sequence to open up the pores in the skin and the acupuncture points (Navel, Mìngmén, Dàbāo, Yìntáng, Bǎihuì, etc.) in the body, so that during the practice, as soon as our mind focuses on an area, the External Qì will follow to enter that area; consequently, it will strengthen the results of the Body & Mind Method practice.

Internal Hùn Yuán practice requires merging the mind intent with the body and staying within the body at all times. From the very beginning (preparation), one must visualize that oneself is the Universe: the head is the sky, the feet are the earth, and the universe is within the body. Press earth to collect Qì (Lā Qì) is a whole-body movement (hands, arms, feet and the whole body), but no matter what is done, the hands never go outside of the body. By the same token, the pull back movements must stay within the body. The Lā Qì movement also releases the Internal Qì and absorbs External Qì. When the hands push forward, the body (mind intent) opens up and Internal Qì goes out; when the hands pull back to the beginning position, the body (mind intent) closes and absorbs External Qì inside. In the rotating palms and lifting Qì upward sequence, the hands move along the horizon, because one is the Heaven and the Earth, and the horizon is still within the body. This seems simple, but it is difficult to execute. One must let go of "oneself, the body" and does not have the feeling of the skin. This Internal Hùn Yuán practice depends on the proficiency of External Hùn Yuán.

For most practitioners, it is easier and more natural to practice the Opening using the External Hùn Yuán. In the External Hùn Yuán practice, once the hands are in praying position (Fig. 2-16), the attention should switch back to the body and it becomes Internal Hùn Yuán practice.

2. Shén (mind activities) and Xíng (movement/posture) merge as one

The Body & Mind Method requires the mind to merge with the body. During the practice, the mind must stay within the body throughout the whole routine (except External Hùn Yuán Opening); the mind concentrates on and stays with each movement. For example, in Crane's Neck, during the practice, the only thing in the mind is the Crane's Neck's movement; at the same time, the mind gives commands to the body to execute the movement, i.e., tuck in chin, move chin upward, pull up cervical vertebrae, etc. The brain gives the command, the body follows simultaneously.

Normally, when we learn a movement, we would have the image first, and then we conceptualize the movement. When we receive a command to perform the movement, we would retract the concept of the movement first, and then the concept becomes movement. For example, when we first learn the Crane's Neck, we follow the image (movement); after we learn it, the movement will become a concept. When we receive "tuck in chin" command, the brain would have the concept of the words; then the concept becomes the tuck in chin movement. As we focus on executing the movement, Shén and Xíng merge as one. We call this "conceptual approach." For most practitioners, using the conceptual approach, it is easy to maintain focus, but normally it is only for a short period of time. Any periods of time beyond thirty minutes become a challenge.

If we receive the command in an unfamiliar langrage or it is given nonverbally, then the concept of the words would not be registered by the brain, the image of the movement will become the command; then mental activities and body movements will be merged directly. We call this "Non-conceptual approach." Most practitioners can stay focused for a longer period of time using this approach.

As previously stated, one of the characteristics of Zhìnéng Qìgōng is verbal instruction. During the practice, the teacher uses verbal commands to synchronize the group movements to create a large Qì Field. This approach works very well in External Hùn Yuán practice, but not in Internal Hùn Yuán practice. Practicing Internal Hùn Yuán requires merging Shén and Xíng, and one cannot stay focused for a long period of time with verbal instructions. After one has learned the form, one may be able to focus and follow the teacher's command to practice at the beginning; but after a while, one still may be able to follow the command to execute the movement, but one's mind may have wandered or lost focus. Therefore, to practice the Body & Mind Method, one must combine both the conceptual and the non-conceptual approach.

Conceptual approach. Follow the teacher's verbal command to direct the movement. For example, in Crane's Neck, when one hears the "tuck in chin" command, without thinking, one concentrates on executing the correct tucking in the chin movement. This is conceptual thinking directing the body postures.

Non-conceptual approach. While receiving the verbal commands from the teacher, one gives oneself non-verbal commands *simultaneously.* But instead of following the teacher's command, one performs the movement following one's own command.

When combining the two approaches, one hears the teacher's instructions, the mind calls out (non-verbal) instructions, and then the body follows the instructions to do the movement. This way, the mind will be highly focused and stay within the movement. In turn, it will strengthen the mind's abilities to control the body postures, and Qì inside the body will be strengthened by automatically following the mind activities and body movements. Since the Body & Mind Method requires that Shén and Xíng merge together, all mind activities must stay focused and Shén must stay within the body, and Xíng must follow Shén's directions.

3. Correct Posture

In the Body & Mind Method, every movement is well defined and has specific requirements. The method is designed to work on the areas that we seldom move, such as small joints, small tendons, and the back. Therefore, the movements may be unfamiliar to some practitioners and may even feel awkward. For example, when it is done correctly, some may feel awkward doing the Open Arms movement and uncomfortable doing the Squeeze Shoulder Blades and Shrink Neck movement. It is because those areas are seldom exercised, but they are very important to our health.

Although the method is a routine with continuous movements, to be able to have correct posture, we should focus/practice on one section at a time. Only after we master a section do we move on to the next. Due to physical limitations, some practitioners may not be able to do the movements as correctly as required, but they should do it to the best of their abilities.

Most of us have acquired many unhealthy habits/postures in our daily life. To practice the Body & Mind Method is to correct those unhealthy postures; therefore, we may have unnatural feelings at the beginning. For example, when standing, a healthy person usually has a relatively straight spine to support the body weight, our spine is slightly concave in the waist area (Mìngmén presses toward the front). Due to bad habits or to not having enough Qì, some of us press the Mìngmén inward too much toward the navel to release the pressure (the body weight); this incorrect posture will block the Qì flow and create side effects such as lower back pain. The Body & Mind Method corrects the posture and builds up the Dāntián Qì to support the spine to the point that it largely eliminates the natural curve of the lumbar vertebra.

When discomfort occurs during the practice, we should pay attention to the form to make sure it is done correctly. If everything is done according to the requirements, then we should pay attention to the uncomfortable area to find out where and what hurts—the more details, the better. Paying attention to the details is part of concentration. If we stay with the practice despite the discomfort, it will increase our will power and self-control abilities; in turn, it will strengthen the mind's ability to direct the life functions.

Under normal circumstances, it is very difficult to be able to be aware of the activities inside the body. When we feel discomfort inside the body during the practice, if we focus our attention on the uncomfortable area, gradually, our consciousness will be able to be aware of the area, its depth, its size, etc. With practice, we can become aware of the muscle movements inside the body. It is the mental ability that is strengthened and is able to permeate inside the body; it is the first stage of Internal Vision.

Note: Internal Vision is not the eyes seeing things, it is a special internal feeling, a feeling that can sense the conditions inside the body. When the mind reconstructs the feeling as an image, it is called Internal Vision.

To be proficient in the Body & Mind Method, one needs to relax the body, be highly concentrated, and use Qì instead of muscles to do the movement. To achieve that, one needs to do "Endurance Training (耗功)" after learning the form. Endurance Training is to practice only one movement or one section of the form for the minimum of thirty minutes to an hour per practice for at least 100 consecutive days. Except for the Opening, every section or part of the section of the Body & Mind Method can be and should be the subject to Endurance Training. For example, one can practice the Preparation (Wújí zhuāng) for forty-five minutes, or Crane's Neck and Dragon's Horns fifteen minutes (not three or nine times) per direction (total forty-five minutes), or Separate Fingers alone for thirty minutes, etc.

Why do Endurance Training? It is to relax the body, to concentrate the mind and to let go of muscle tensions. Most practitioners can do Separate Fingers three repetitions with flying colors, yet at the same time, their body can be tensed, and the mind can be day dreaming. But after thirty minutes of separating the fingers, the arms are so tired that it is impossible for the muscles to tense up. When the arms are hurting so much, no one can think about anything else except the arms. As the acid builds up in the muscles, sooner or later, the muscles would give up and let Qì take over. Endurance Training trains the body to move from motor learning to procedural memory to Qì memory. With Qì memory, Qì follows the mind intent, Qì, not the muscles, moves the body. Moreover, in Endurance Training, the posture is either fixed or is repeated over and over. Qì will circulate in the same direction; consequently, passageways will be widened, and the volume of Qì will be increased inside the body.

4. Whole Body Movement

As a routine, the Body & Mind Method works on the body one section at a time; it begins with the cervical vertebrae and ends with the toes. To learn and do the movements correctly, at the beginning, one must focus on and practice one section or one area of the body at a time; but with progress, one should expand the attention to the whole body. Generally speaking, when one can perform the whole routine without losing balance with the eyes closed, it is time to expand the focus beyond the individual sections (beyond the area being worked on).

Our body relies on the sensory organs to maintain equilibrium. Normally, among all the sensory organs, the eyes have the most direct connections with the brain; therefore, the visual sensor (eyes) is the most important. When the eyes look at the environment (external subjects), Qì will follow and interact with the environment. As the environment is reflected to the brain, Qì returns back to the body; consequently, Shén, Qì and nature merge as an entity, and we obtain our equilibrium from this entity.

With the eyes closed, Qì would not be able to go in and out of the eyes; therefore, the internal and external environment will not be able to merge, and the body loses its reference for equilibrium. To maintain balance, the body relies on the habitual way; the habitual way of balance is to use both legs. When we lift one leg up, we deviate from the norm; before the Shén (brain) can establish the new norm (balancing on one leg), we would lose balance. To establish the new norm, we need to merge Shén and Xíng, Shén and Qì. With practice, the Body & Mind Method can strengthen our self-control abilities and we will remain balanced under any circumstance. When one can maintain/adjust the balance without using the eyes, it is the indication that Shén and Xíng, and Shén and Qì have merged as one; and one can proceed to practice the whole-body movements. Whole-body practice requires a relaxed mind and body; there cannot be tension in any part of the body. With a relaxed body, the mind can concentrate better; this concentration can be expanded from the sections to the whole body to merge as a whole. The whole-body practice has three steps.

Step one: Proficient in section practice. One must be able to do the section practice as required by the method. For example, in Crane's Neck, one can use the chin to draw a circle of maximum size while the first thoracic vertebra serves as a stationary point.

Step two: Connect the movement with the whole body. For example, in Crane's Neck, if one can relax the whole body (the first thoracic vertebra is no longer serving as a stationary point), when the head moves, it will create open-close movements in the shoulder, convex-concave movements in the chest, and the vertebrae will behave like a string of pearls, once the top vertebra moves, and the rest will follow. Gradually, as the head moves, the whole body would move and would have an undulating motion from the head all the way down to the toes.

Step three: Aware of the whole body. During the practice, it is extremely difficult for most practitioners to focus on more than one area of the body. When focusing on the head, one would forget about the hands and/or the feet. To be able to be aware of the whole body, special training is needed. Among all the methods, the most popular one is to expand the focus from the area we are working on to one or more selected acupuncture points. The most common points are the Small and the Big Seven Stars. These points are located in the strategic areas that cover the whole body. Traditional Chinese Medicine calls these areas "Shén and Qì visiting area" (神氣遊行之室). If we pay attention to these areas frequently, it will increase the Qì flow and strengthen the Qì functions.

Because the human mind is designed to discard inessential things, just knowing the locations of the acupuncture points would not work. In the old days, teachers mystified the points; they added religious elements into the practice to achieve concentration and reverence. For example, when the teacher showed/taught the students the locations of the Seven Stars, they called it "Setting the Seven Stars" (布七星) and they would go through a solemn ritual. According to the myth in Chinese Buddhism, the Big Seven Stars (the Big Dipper in the northern sky) are seven gods/stars that relieve hardship/disaster. From a religious point of view, setting the seven points in the body is to invite the Gods into the body; because Gods are in the body, the practitioner can achieve awareness and reverence; in turn, awareness and reverence can improve/balance one's mental conditions. From a Qìgōng point of view, the points are located in the strategic areas that connect the whole body, the stars are in Xū kōng (space), far away; when we go out to bring them in, our Internal Qì goes out, and when we are aware of the points, External Qì comes in. It is a Qìgōng technique that the practitioner uses to merge Internal and External Qì.

The traditional way to set the Seven Stars is that the teacher touches and emits Qì to the student's acupuncture points (this can be with or without religious intention). Normally, the student will have some sensations or special feeling in the point areas, thus the student will be able to be aware of them without focusing on them. If there is no teacher to set the points, one will set the stars for oneself. First locate the points, then use the finger to press and emit Qì to the point (one point at a time) until there is sensation, close the eyes, and memorize the point. For example, to set the Wàihuáijiān (外踝尖 EX-LE 9) of the Big Seven Star: find the Wàihuáijiān (on the highest prominence of the lateral malleolus on both ankles), use the fingers to touch and press them, and emit Qì to them; with the fingers still pressing, be quiet and serene, close the eyes, feel and visualize inside the ankles. Some will have a feeling of emptiness as if a Qì bubble is added inside; sit quietly to feel and to sense this Qì bubble and the emptiness inside. Although most practitioners would have an emptiness feeling, some may feel dimness (not too bright) inside, or some may feel brightness. Regardless of the sensation one may have, just memorize the locations and the feeling, and the points are set.

The Seven Star (acupuncture point) practice is not intended to keep focusing on or thinking about the Stars, but to be "aware of" but not "focusing on" (知而不守) the stars. Not focusing does not mean to forget but because it is during the practice, the points are there to be aware of; after finishing the practice, the points are gone. The purpose for the acupuncture point practice is to connect all parts of the body; if we focus on the points, Qì will become stagnate and will concentrate in the points, and the body is no longer connected as a whole.

5. Small Joints and extremities

One of the purposes of the Body & Mind Method is to expand the Qì cultivation to and in the extremities—hair (head), tips (tip of the fingers and toes, tailbone), small joints (fingers and toes) and skin. The volume of Qì exchanging between the extremities and nature is very large; therefore, one must pay attention to the extremities. In addition to the regular practice, one must incorporate the practice into daily life. Move the extremities as often as possible, curl the fingers and toes, move the tailbone, do some Crane's Neck, etc. When the extremities Qì is sufficient, the body Qì is sufficient, and the body is healthy.

6. Practice must be guided by the mind intent

Every section of the Body & Mind Method has special functions and serves many special purposes. Before practicing each or any section, one's mind should have the idea of in what way (functions) that particular section would affect the body; in other words, one should have an idea of the purposes of the sections, and allow this idea (the purposes or results of special functions) to guide the practice. For example, one of the special functions of Crane's Neck is to move Qīngyáng Qì upward to nourish the brain; so, when we hear the command/instruction "Crane's Neck, Dragon's Horn," immediately, the mind should have a concept or intent of moving Qīngyáng Qì upward to nourish the brain. During the practice, we are not just doing the movements; we are doing the movements with the concept/intent in our mind to move Qì up to nourish the brain. But we cannot keep thinking "move Qì up to nourish the brain" during practice; the idea is to have the concept/intent, and then to let go of it.

There is a contradiction in the statements "doing the movements with the concept/intent to move Qì up to nourish the brain" and "cannot keep thinking move Qì up to nourish the brain" during practice. How can both be correct? We will use the following example to illustrate how this contradiction works.

There is a meeting at 2 p.m. that you need to attend. It is 11 a.m. and there is still work needed to be done and you still need to have lunch. So you work faster to finish the work and have a fast lunch; all these are done under normal mental conditions, but they are under the intention of attending the meeting. Because 2 p.m. is approaching, time is getting short, it is urgent, so you concentrate and work faster to finish the work and have some lunch, then go the meeting. This urgency is inside the whole sequence of events—work, lunch, etc. To finish the work early is not done by focusing on "I have a 2 p.m. meeting, I need to hurry up" while working; it is done by being aware of the 2 p.m. meeting and changing the intent (go to the meeting) into action. You hurry up because of the meeting, you are aware of the meeting but are not focusing on it. The actions are united by one common goal—the meeting. All movements are performed under the requirement/direction of attending the meeting; the concept/intent of attending the meeting becomes the action.

Every section of the Body & Mind Method has a well-defined purpose. Depending on the purpose/intention, there are many different levels of practice within the routine or the same movements. For example, in routine/form practice, there is the basic level which includes eliminating illness and strengthening the body, the intermediate level includes opening the Meridians and strengthening Qì flow, and the advanced level includes moving Qì into the muscles, opening Tiānmén and developing Internal Vision, etc. Regardless of the level of practice, one must have a clear idea of the purpose, especially if one has some deficiency in a certain area. Ideally, we use the whole-body practice, from top to bottom, to strengthen every part of the body. When we have enough Qì, Qì will permeate into and strengthen every part of the body and achieve the intended results; this is a slower process. When there is deficiency in a certain area, the mind should have a clear idea of which movements' intents/purposes are designed to strengthen that particular area and change the intentions into actions. Concentrate the efforts on correcting the deficiency by practicing only one or a few sections until the body is balanced, and then work on the whole body; this is a faster process.

In conclusion, to be proficient in the Body & Mind Method, one must have the following:

- A good foundation in External Hùn Yuán practice (i.e., Lift Qì Up and Pour Qì Down Method).
- Merge Shén and Xíng, use both *conceptual* and *non-conceptual approach.*
- Practice with correct postures.
- Pay attention to whole-body movements.
- Work on the small joints and extremities.

Tap Along the Meridians

循經導引法

1. Introduction

Tap along the meridians is a very important part of Body & Mind Method. Its main function is to strengthen the Meridian's lateral abilities. One tap consists of one pressing and one pulling action/movement . As indicated in the name, this method uses the taping technique to tap along the Meridians to achieve lateral opening results. It does not tap along one Meridian at a time. The fingers tap along either the three Yin or the three Yáng meridians.

The routes for the twelve meridians are as follows:

The hand Yin Meridians run from the chest to the hands along the inner arms; and
the hand Yáng Meridians run from the hands to the head along the outer arm.
The foot Yáng Meridians run from the head to the feet along the back of the body; and
the foot Yin Meridians run from the feet to the stomach along the inner legs.

Note: Yàngmìng (Stomach) Meridian runs in the front and is not tapped.

The following directions are for tapping:

Hand Meridians:

Downward: Tap along the inner arm.
Upward: Tap along the outer arm.

Foot Meridians:

Downward: Tap along the back of the body.
Upward: Tap along the inner legs and front of the body.

2. Opening

Movements

Rotate the hands backward and then downward, press the earth to collect Qì. Then push forward fifteen degrees and pull back to the beginning position. Repeat three times. Fig. 13- 1 to Fig. 13-4.

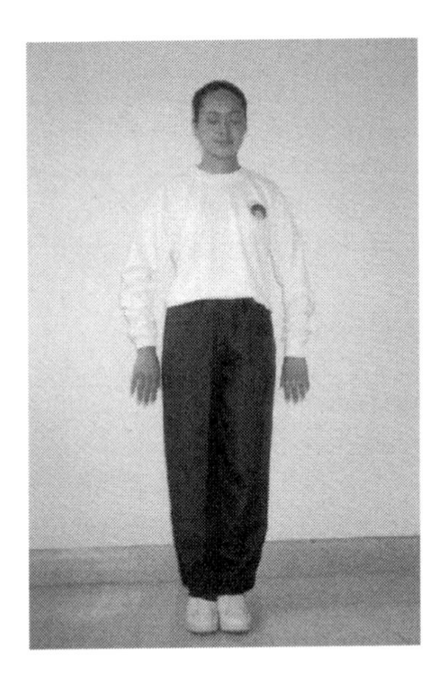

Fig. 13-1

Fig. 13-2

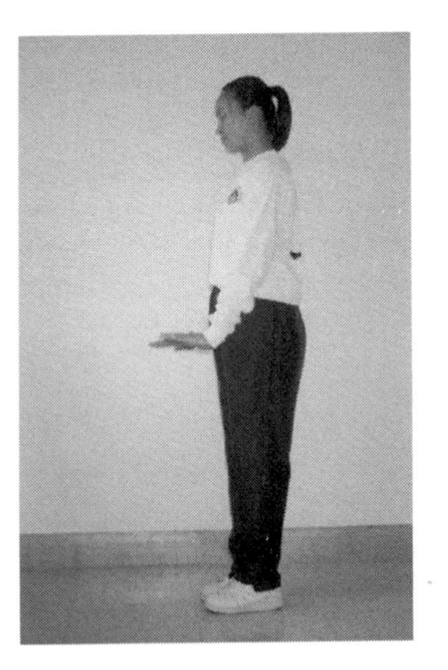

Fig. 13-3

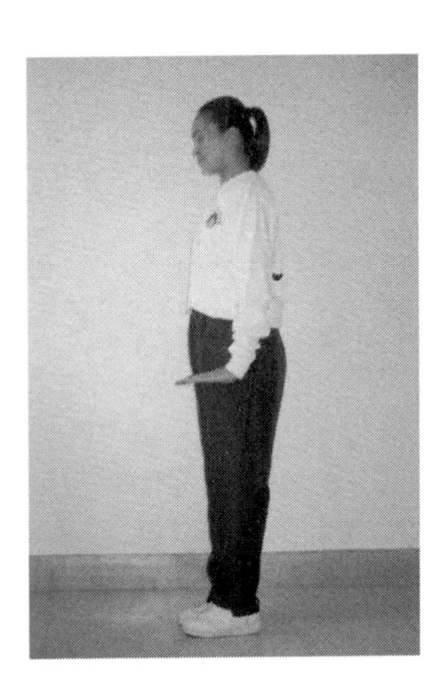

Fig. 13-4

Relax the wrists and turn the palms to face each other. The hands lift Qì upward to the navel level and deliver it to the Dāntián through the navel.
Fig. 13-5, Fig. 13-6.

Fig. 13-5

Fig. 13-6

Turn the palms downward and circle them around to the sides of the body.
Fig. 13-7, Fig. 13-8.

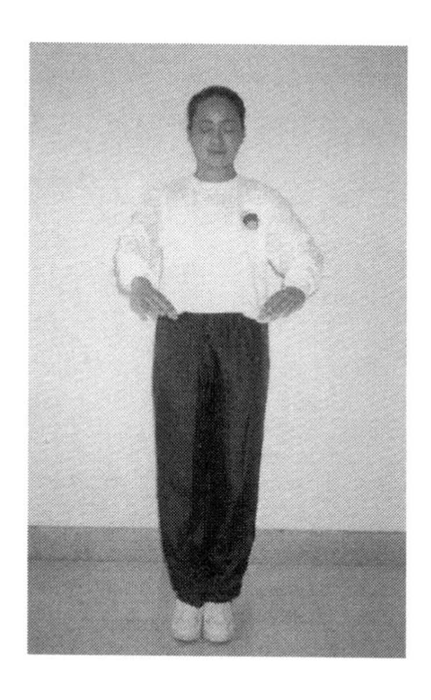

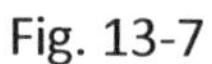

Fig. 13-7

Fig.13-8

Continue to turn and scoop Qì to the back. Point to Mìngmén and deliver Qì to the Dāntián through Mìngmén. Fig. 13-9, Fig. 13-10.

Fig. 13-9

Fig. 13-10

Move the hands upward and forward to the underarms; with the tips of the middle fingers lightly press Dàbāo and deliver Qì inside the body. Rotate elbows backward until fingers point to the front. Fig. 13-11, Fig. 13-12.

Fig. 13-11

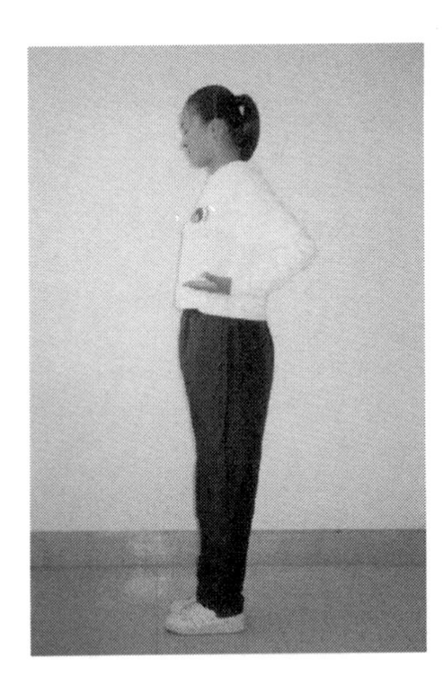

Fig. 13-12

Extend the hands forward with the palms up to shoulder level and width. Slightly bend the middle fingers to reflect Qì into the head through Yìntáng (between the eyebrows). Rotate the arms forty-five degrees until the palms are facing each other diagonally; then circle the arms around to the sides forming a straight line. Fig. 13-13, Fig. 13-14.

Fig. 13-13

Fig. 13-14

Rotate the arms to turn the hands down, then up to scoop Qì upward. Lift the hands upward in a circular motion until the hands are above the head. Put the hands together and lift upward farther. Then lower the hands to chest level forming a praying position. Fig. 13-15, Fig. 13-16.

Fig. 13-15

Fig. 13-16

3. Tap along the Hand Meridians

From the praying hand position, separate and lower the hands along the rib cage. Then rest the hands on the waist with the thumbs slightly pressing Jīngmén (京門 GB 25) at the tip of the 12th ribs. Separate the feet to shoulder width. Separate the hands from the waist, turn the left palm to face the sky and extend the left hand forward at a forty-five degree angle. At the same time, the right hand moves up along the rib cage, passes Qīmén (期門 LR 14), Shānzhōng (膻中 RN 17) and to the left Yúnmén (雲門 LU 2) Note: Both hands should move at the same time, when the left hand reaches the front, the right hand should touch Yúnmén. Fig. 13-17, Fig. 13-18.

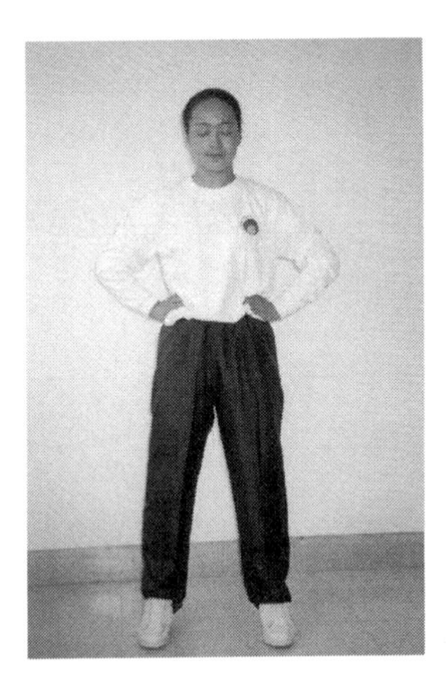

Fig. 13-17

Fig. 13-18

The left arm remains relaxed and maintains the same position, the right hand taps down along the inner left arm, along Qūchí (曲池 LI 11), Dàlíng (大陵 PC 7), Láogōng (勞宮 PC 8) to the fingertips. Fig. 13-19 to Fig. 13-21.

Fig. 13-19

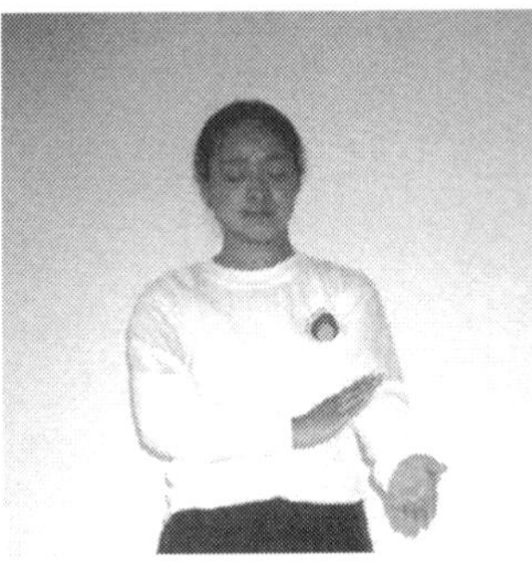

Fig. 13-20

Fig. 13-21

Turn the left palm down and move to the right fingertips. The right arm remains relaxed and maintains the same straight line position with the palm facing the ground. The left palm taps up along the fingertips, the back of the palm and the outer right arm, and passes Wàiguàn (外關 SJ 5), Qūchí, Bìnào (臂臑 LI 14), and Jiānyú (肩髃 LI 15) moving to the base of the right side of the neck. The mind intent moves upward to the head. Fig. 13-22 to Fig. 13-24.

Fig. 13-22

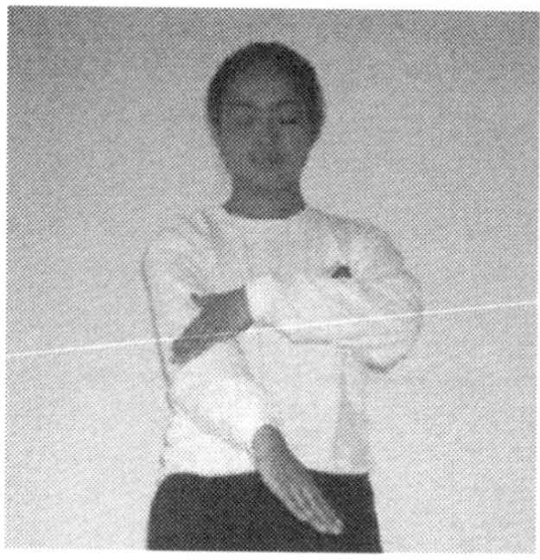

Fig. 13-23

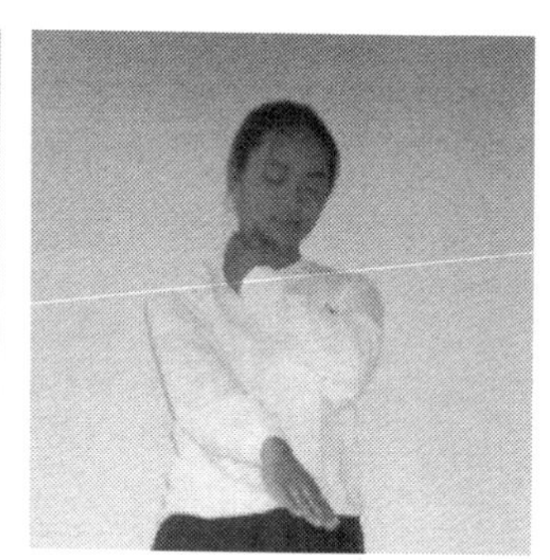

Fig. 13-24

Once the mind intent reaches the top of the head, the mind intent returns downward. The left palm follows the mind intent to move down to the collar bone, and then to the right Yúnmén. At the same time, turn the right palm to face the sky. This is the exact posture as in the beginning except with the right arm. The left palm taps down along inner right arm, passes Qūchí, Dàlíng, Láogōng to the fingertips.
Fig. 13-25 to Fig. 13-27.

Fig. 13-25

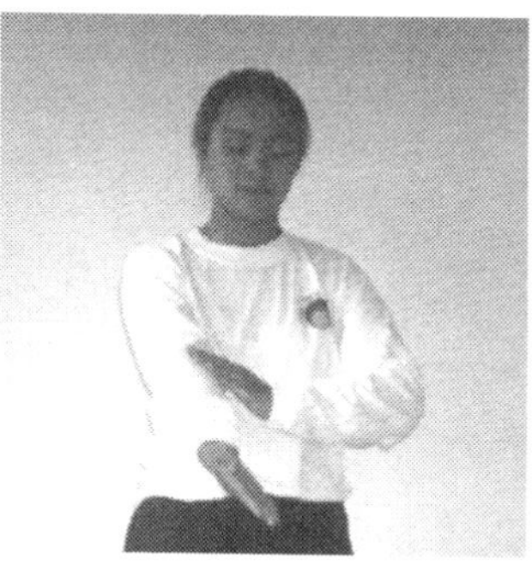

Fig. 13-26

Fig. 13-27

Turn the right palm over and place palm on left fingertips. The right palm taps up along the outer left arm, passes Wàiguàn, Qūchí, Bìnào, and Jiānyú to the base of the left side of the neck. The mind intent moves upward to the head.
Fig. 13-28 to Fig. 13-30.

Fig. 13-28

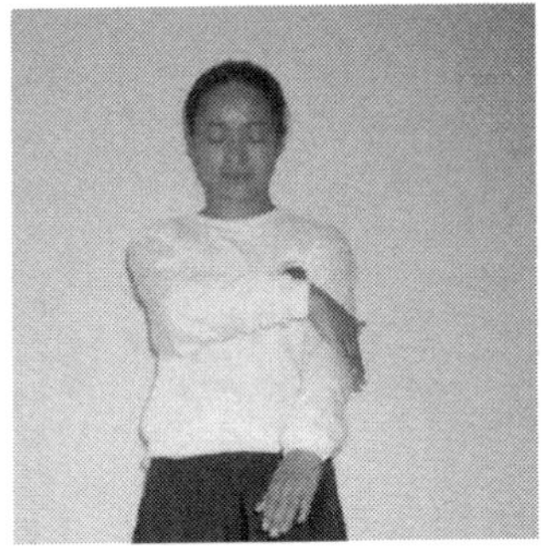

Fig. 13-29

Fig. 13-30

The right hand moves down, passing the collar bone, Yúnmén, Shānzhōng, Qīmén to rest on waist. At the same time, withdraw the left hand to the right side, across the abdomen, and rest the hand on the waist. Fig. 13-31, Fig. 13-32.

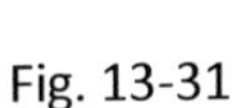

Fig. 13-31

Fig. 13-32

The above sequence of movements has worked on both the hands' three Yin Meridians and the three Yáng Meridians. The next sequence of movements is the same except starting with a different hand.

Separate the hands from the waist, turn the right palm up to face the sky and extend the right hand forward at 45-degree angle. At the same time, the left hand moves up along the rib cage, passing Qīmén, Shānzhōng, and to the right Yúnmén. Fig. 13-33 The left hand taps down along the inner right arm, along Qūchí, Dàlíng, and Láogōng to the fingertips. Fig. 13-33 to Fig. 13-35.

Fig. 13-33

Fig. 13-34

Fig. 13-35

Turn the right palm down and move to the left fingertips. The right palm taps up along the outer left arm, passes Wàiguàn, Qūchí, Bìnào, and Jiānyú to the base of the left side of the neck. The mind intent moves upward to the head. Fig. 13-36 to Fig. 13-38.

Fig. 13-36

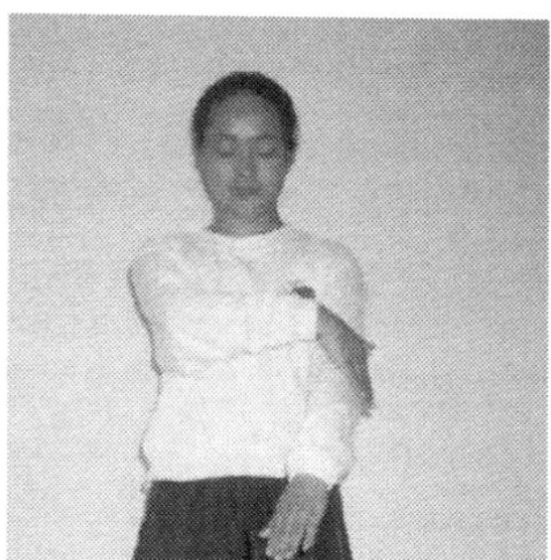

Fig. 13-37

Fig. 13-38

The right palm moves down to the left Yúnmén. At the same time, turn the left palm up to face the sky. The right palm taps down along the inner left arm, passes Qūchí, Dàlíng, and Láogōng to the fingertips. Fig. 13-39 to Fig. 13-41.

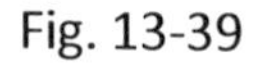

Fig. 13-39

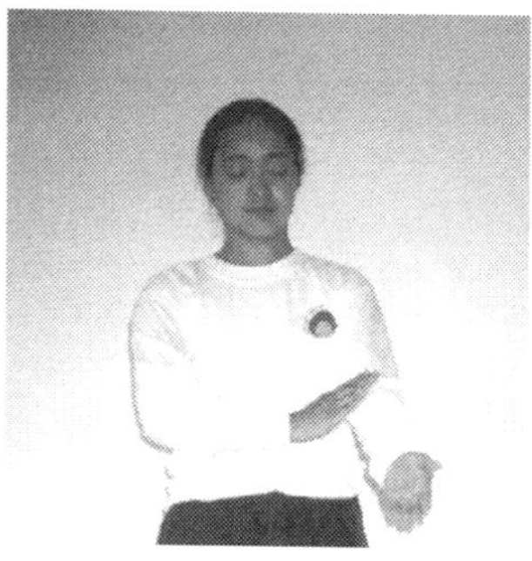

Fig. 13-40

Fig.13-41

Turn the left palm down and move to the right fingertips. The left palm taps up along the outer right arm, passes Wàiguàn, Qūchí, Bìnào, and Jiānyú to the base of the right side of the neck. The mind intent moves upward to the head. Fig. 13-42 to Fig. 13-44.

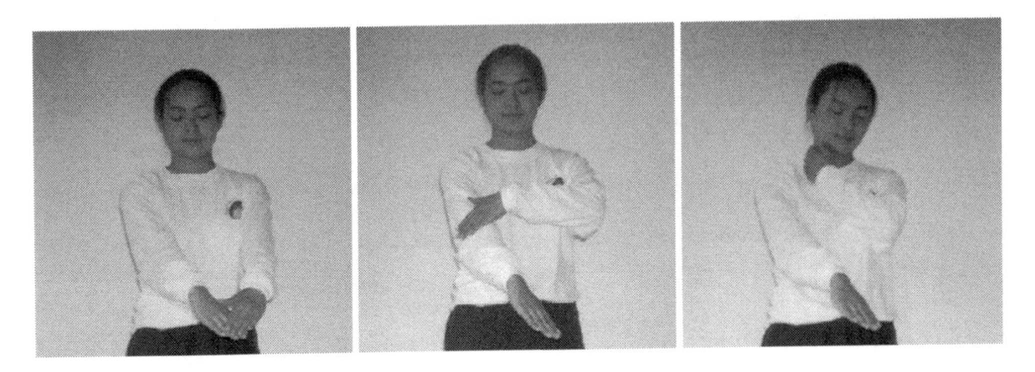

Fig. 13-42 Fig. 13-43 Fig. 13-44

The left hand moves down, passing the collarbone, Yúnmén, Shānzhōng, and Qīmén to rest on the waist. At the same time, withdraw the right hand to the left side, across the stomach, and rest on the waist. Fig. 13-45, Fig. 13-46.

Fig. 13-45

Fig. 13-46

4. Tap along the Foot Meridians

Turn the palms inward and upward along the ribcage to the celiac plexus—the middle fingers touch each other. The elbows move outward and upward until the forearms are parallel to form a straight line. Use both palms to tap up along the chest, to the neck. Then change to use the tips of the middle fingers to tap the throat. When reaching the chin, gradually turn the fingers upward and tap the face with the whole palm, relax the elbows. Fig. 13-47 to Fig. 13-49.

Fig. 13-47

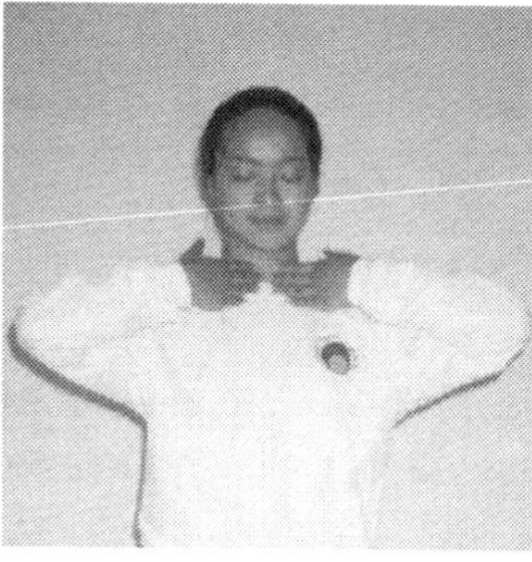

Fig. 13-48

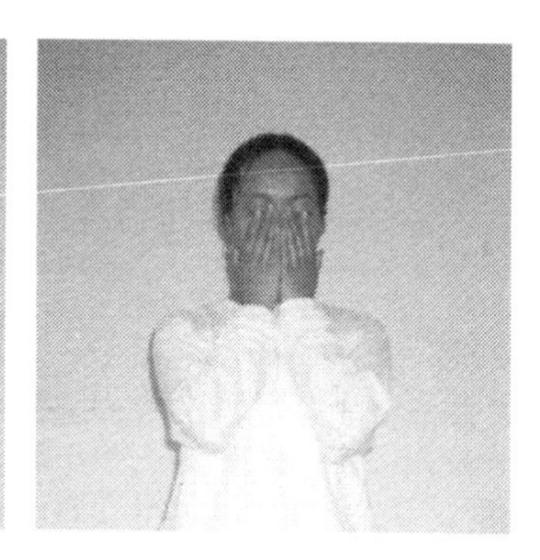

Fig. 13-49

Gradually tap upward, to the forehead, Xìnmén (囟會DU22), Bǎihuì (百會DU20) and Yùzhěn (玉枕BL9). Fig. 13-50 to Fig. 13-52.

Fig. 13-50

Fig. 13-51

Fig. 13-52

The palms cover the ears. The fingers hit Yùzhěn to vibrate the lower brain in the following order: both index fingers hit once; both ring fingers hit once; and both middle fingers hit once. Then all three fingers hit together three times. This is called "Sound the Heaven's Drum". Fig. 13-53 to Fig. 13-55.

Fig. 13-53

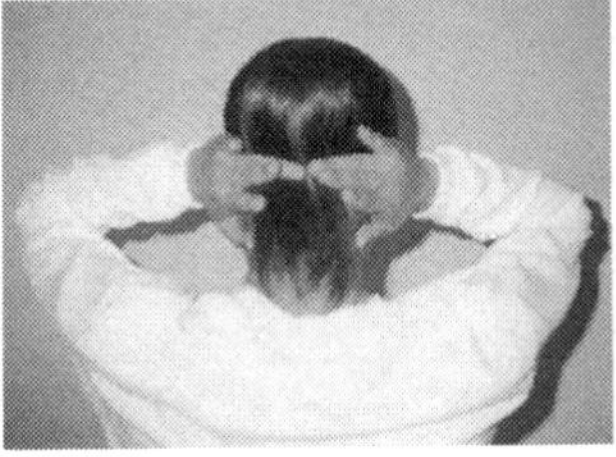

Fig. 13-54

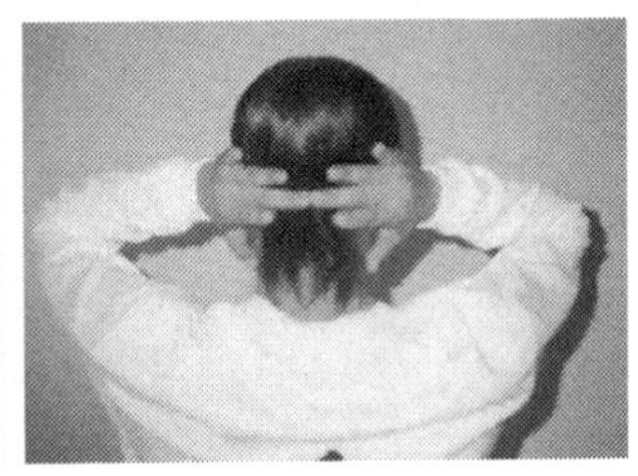

Fig. 13-55

Continue to tap down along the neck until the arms cannot go any farther down the back. Stop the physical tapping, and circle the hands over the shoulders and the under the shoulders to the back. Then, move the hands up along the back and with the mind intent connecting the path, resume physical tapping downward along the spine.
Fig. 13-56 to Fig. 13-58.

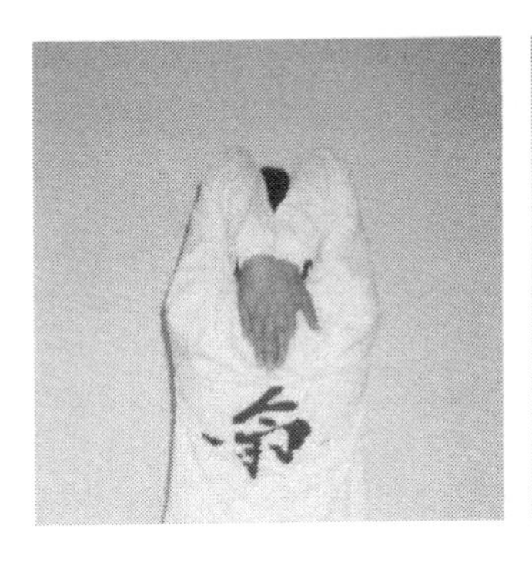

Fig. 13-56

Fig. 13-57

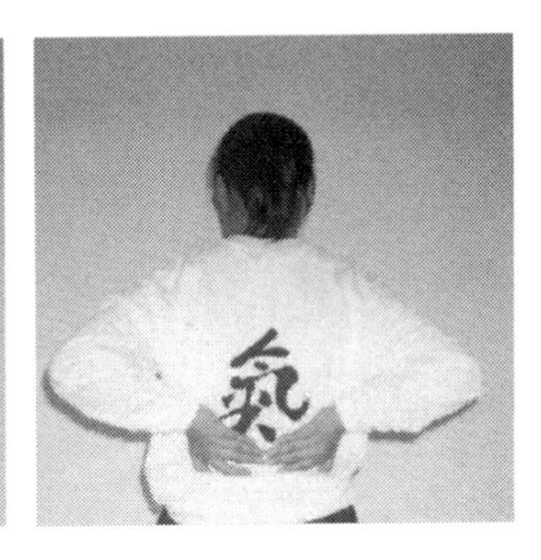

Fig. 13-58

The body curls downward, gradually bending the knees. After the hands pass Huántiào (環跳 GB30), the thumbs stay on the outer sides of the legs with the tips pointing toward the front while the fingers move to the back sides of the legs. Use the hands to tap along the outside of the legs; when the fingers reach the feet, use the fingertips to tap along the outside edges of the feet until the fingers reach the toes. The finger tips tap the toes. Fig. 13-59 to Fig. 13-61.

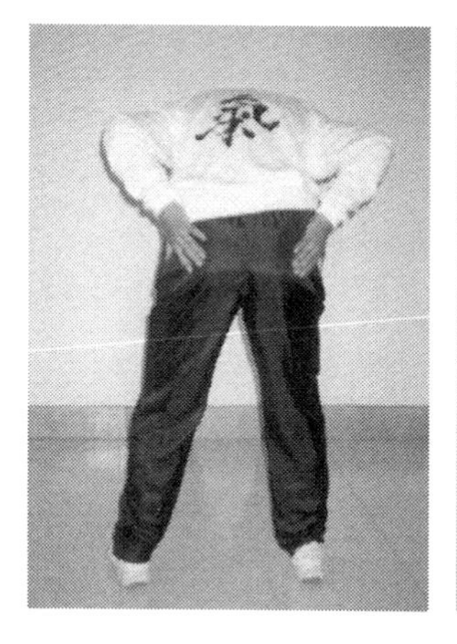

Fig. 13-59

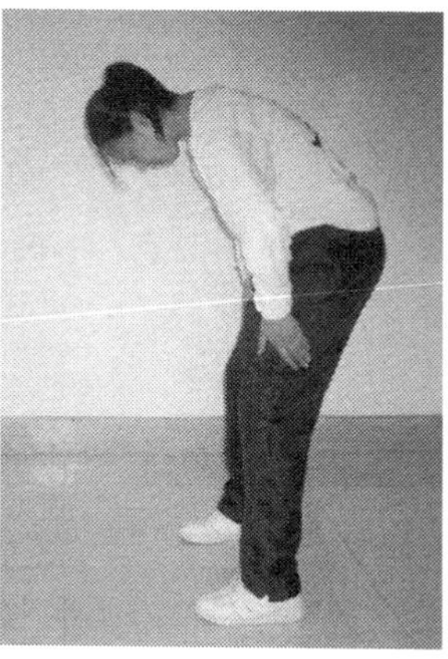

Fig. 13-60

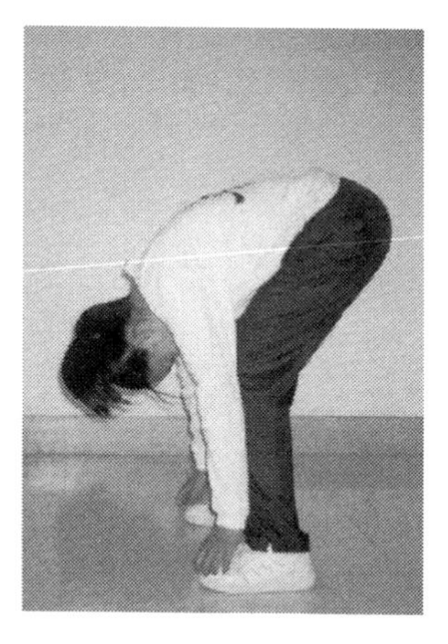

Fig. 13-61

Continue to tap along the inner feet, the inner legs, the stomach, and the chest. At the same time, gradually straighten up the body. Repeat the same movement twice. This completes the tapping of the six foot Meridians. Fig. 13-62 to Fig. 13-64.

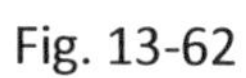

Fig. 13-62

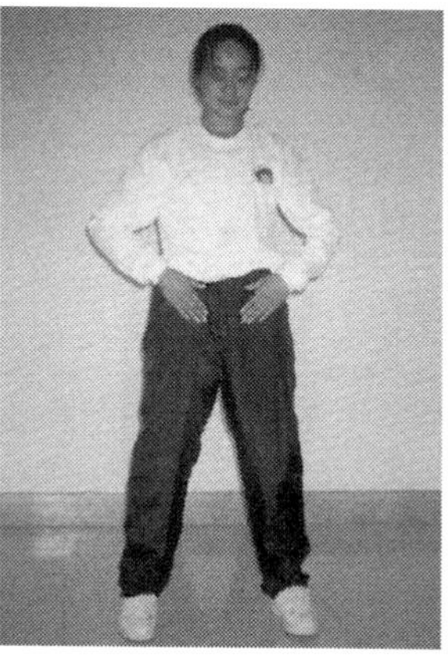

Fig. 13-63

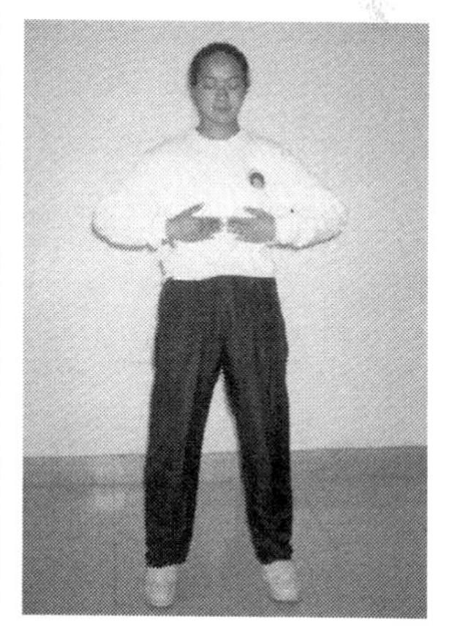

Fig, 13-64

Note: Three repetitions of tapping along the hands and feet constitute one cycle.

5. Closing

After the last repetition of Tapping along the Foot Meridians, close the hands in a praying position. Move and close the feet. Move the hands up until the arms are straight, then stretch farther upward. Separate the hands and turn the palms forward. Lower the arms to form a straight line at shoulder level. Turn the palms up to face the sky. Fig. 13-65 to Fig. 13-67.

Fig. 13-65

Fig. 13-66

Fig. 13-67

Move the arms forward to shoulder width apart. Withdraw the palms and the arms slightly; the middle fingers reflect Qì to Yìntáng. Move the elbows backward and outward until the middle fingers touch Dàbāo and deliver Qì inside the body. Move the hands back to the limit behind the body and circle the hands to the sides. Fig. 13-68 to Fig. 13-71.

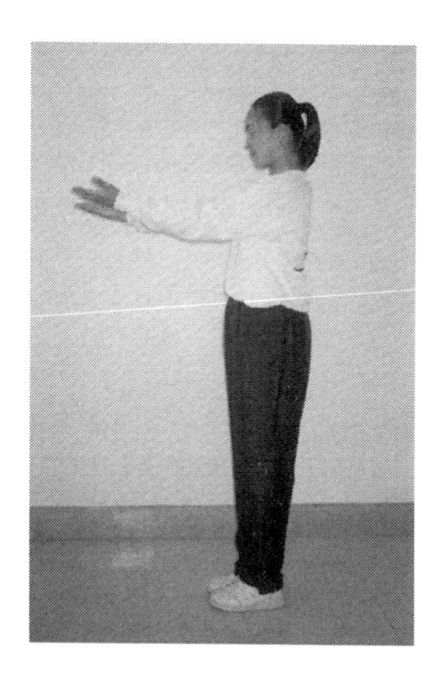

Fig. 13-68

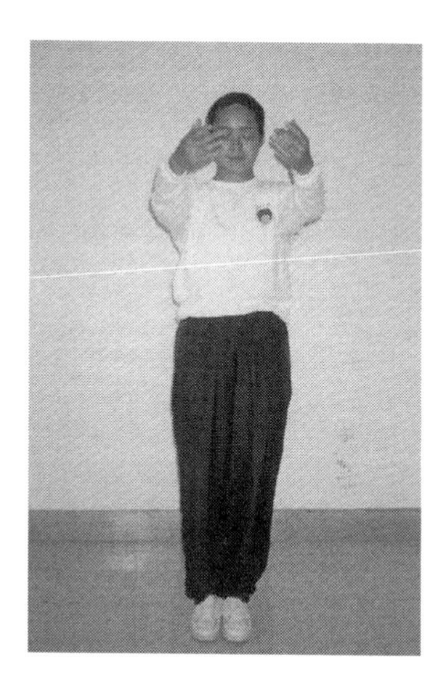

Fig. 13-69

Fig. 13-70

Fig. 13-71

Turn the palms to scoop Qì forward and into the Dāntián. Put the hands upon the navel. The man first puts the left hand against the navel and then places the right hand over the left hand. The woman first puts the right hand against the navel, and then places the left hand over the right hand. Relax for a few minutes. Slowly return the hands to the beginning position and open the eyes.
Fig. 13-72 to Fig. 13-75.

Fig. 13-72

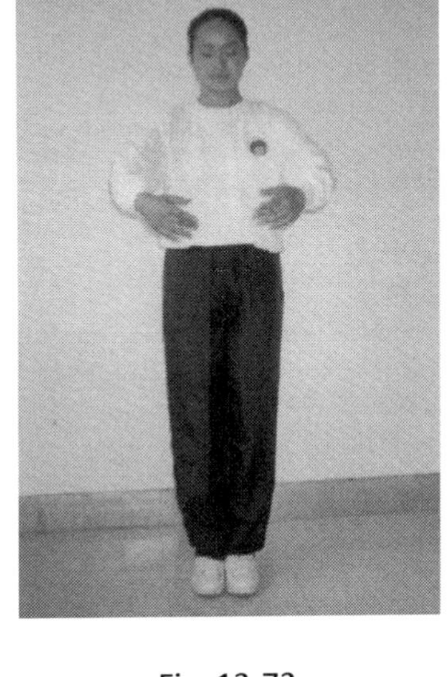

Fig. 13-73

Fig. 13-74

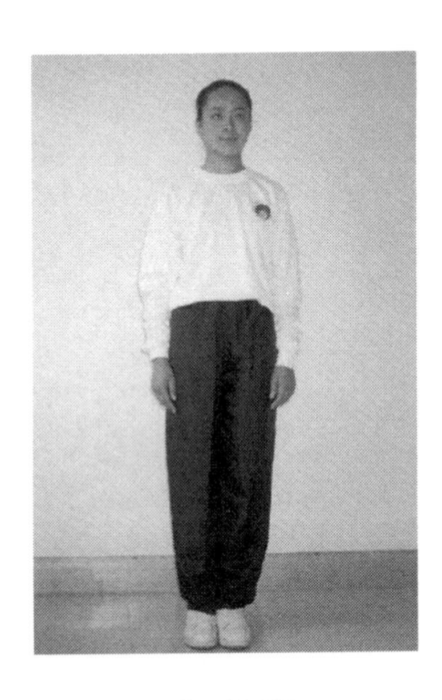

Fig. 13-75

Keys to the practice

a. **Tapping.** The most important and also the most difficult part of this method is the tapping

    1) ***Movement***. It should be soft, even and continuous. In the beginning, the hands should touch the skin at all times. Once the technique is mastered, separate the hands from skin about 1 to 3 cm.
    2) ***The hand area used for tapping.*** With the exception of the thumbs, the area to use to tap the Hand Meridians is between the middle joint of the fingers and Láogōng. The foot Meridians tapping uses either the fingertips or the whole palm.
    3) ***Speed***. There should be a minimum of two taps per second; the faster the tapping, the better.
    4) ***Timing***. From the shoulder to the fingertips and back to the shoulder takes about ten cycles of natural breaths. From the head to the toes takes about twenty-four cycles of natural breaths.
    5) ***Mind intent***. One of the main purposes of this method is to strengthen the function of permeability of the internal structures of the body to exchange Qì with Nature. The mind intent should focus on the in-out permeability. When the hand touches the skin, the mind intent permeates into the center of the bone. When the hand leaves the skin, mind intent pulls out from the center of the bone, permeates the muscle, and the skin to reach outside the body. The movements combine with the mind intent to strengthen Qì's lateral in-out functions. This method does not work on any particular Meridian; therefore, do not focus on any particular Meridian during each movement.

b. **Switching the hands.** When switching the hands, the movement should be smooth and rounded. For example, when the right palm taps to the tip of left hand, the left hand extends out to the right slightly in a circular motion; at the same time, the right hand moves backward to the left in a circular motion. Then turn the left hand naturally on top of right hand. Fig. 13-21 to Fig. 13-22.

c. **Sound the Heaven's Drum.** With the bases of the fingers pressing the head, the palms cover the ears. The tips of the fingers hit Yùzhěn to vibrate the lower brain in the following order: the index fingers hit once; the ring fingers hit once; and the middle fingers hit once. Repeat the movements three times, then all three fingers hit Yuzhen simultaneously three times. The vibration will create a drum-like sound inside the brain. Fig. 13-51 to Fig. 13-55.

d. **The Tapping Routes.** This method does not follow any particular Meridian route, it follows the general directions of the three Yīn Meridians and the three Yáng Meridians of both the feet and the hands.

    1) The three hand Yin Meridians are located from the chest to the hands, and Qì circulates along the inner arms. The three hand Yáng Meridians are located from the hands to the head, and Qì circulates along the outer arms. Therefore, the upper limb tapping moves along the inner arm when tapping toward the

hand; and the tapping moves along the outer arm when tapping toward the head.

2) The three foot Yáng Meridians are located from the head to the foot, and Qì circulates along the sides of the body and the back. The Yàngmìng jīng (陽明經 Stomach Meridian) travels downward from the face to the neck, the chest, the abdomen and reaches the top of the foot, and Qì circulates along the front of the body; it would not be part of the downward tapping sequence. The three foot Yīn Meridians are located from the feet to the stomach, and Qì circulates along the inner legs. Therefore, the tapping of the foot Meridians is from the back of the legs moving downward, and moving upward is along the inner legs.

Purpose

The main purpose of the Body and Mind Method is to cultivate the exchange of External Hùn Yuán Qì with Internal Qì at the cellular level. Even though Meridian Qì is strengthened by this method, Qì tends to pool in localized areas. The tapping technique is used to pull Qì in and out of the tissues in a direction perpendicular to the Meridians to further refine the body's ability to exchange Internal and External Qì as well as to distribute localized Qì more evenly throughout the body to enhance health.

APPENDIX: ACUPUNCTURE POINTS

Bǎihuì (DU 20) 百會 On the midline of the head, 17 cm directly above the midpoint of the anterior hairline, approximately on the midpoint of the line connecting apex of the ears.

Chéngjiāng (RN 24) 承漿穴 In the depression in the centre of the mentolabial groove.

Dàbāo (SP 21) 大包 On the lateral side of the chest on the middle axillary line in the 6th intercostal space.

Dàimài (GB 26) 帶脈穴 Directly below LR-13 (Zhāngmén) at the crossing point of vertical line through free end of 11th rib and horizontal line through umbilicus.

Dàlíng (PC 7) 大陵 In the middle of the wrist crease between the tendons of palmaris longus and flexor carpi radialis.

Dàzhù (BL 11) 大杼 5 cm lateral to Táodào (Du 13), at the level of the lower boder of the spinous process of the first thoracic vertebra.

Dàzhuí (DU-14) 大椎穴 Below spinous process of 7th cervical vertebra approximately at level of shoulders.

Dū Mài 督脈 Governor (Governing) Meridian.

Fǔshě (SP 13) 府舍 In the middle of the crease where leg joins the body, one finger-width up from the top of the pubic bone, four finger-width out of the midline.

Gāohuāng (BL 43) 膏肓穴 10 cm lateral to the Du Meridian, at the level of the lower border of the spinous process of the fourth thoracic vertebra, on the spinal border of the scapula.

Huágài (RN 20) 华盖 On the midline of the sternum, level with the junction of the first intercostal space and the sternum.

Huántiào (GB 30) 環跳 At junction of lateral ⅓ and medial ⅔ of distance between prominence of greater trochanter and hiatus of sacrum.

Huìyīn (RN 1) 會陰 In the center of the perineum, Males: between the anus and the scrotum, Females: between the anus and the posterior labial commissure.

Jīanjǐng (GB 21) 肩井 On the shoulder directly above the nipple at the midpoint of a line connecting GV 14 and the acromion at the highest point of the shoulder.

Jiānliáo (SJ 14) 肩髎 Posterior and inferior to the acromion, in the depression about 1 cun posterior to Jianyu (LI 15) when the arm is abducted.

Jiānyú (LI 15) 肩髃 Antero-inferior to acromion on upper portion of deltoid muscle; when arm is in full abduction point is in depression appearing at anterior border of acromioclavicular joint.

Jīngmén (GB 25) 京門 On lateral side of abdomen on lower border of free end of 12th rib.

Jíquán xué (HT 1) 極泉穴 At the apex of the axillary fossa, where the axillary artery pulsates.

Láogōng (PC 8) 劳宫 At center of palm between 2nd and 3rd metacarpal bones but closer to latter and in part touching tip of middle finger when fist is made.

Mìngmén (DU 4) 命門 Below spinous process of 2nd lumbar vertebra.

Nǚxī (EX-LE 19) 女膝 Back of the ankles.

Qìhù (ST 13) 氣戶 Middle of the collar bone below its lower edge.

Qīmén (LR 14) 期門 Between the 6th and 7th ribs, on the mid-clavicular line.

Qìūxū (GB 40) 丘墟 Anterior and inferior to external malleolus in depression on lateral side of tendon of extensor digitorum longus.

Qūchí (LI 11) 曲池 When elbow is flexed, point is in depression at lateral end of transverse cubital crease.

Qūzé (PC 3) 曲澤 On the transverse cubital crease on the ulnar side of the biceps brachii tendon.

Rèn mài 任脈 Conception Meridian.

Rénzhōng xué 人中穴 A little above the midpoint of the philtrum, near the nostrils.

Rŭzhōng (ST 17) 乳中 In 4th intercostal space, in center of nipple, 13 cm lateral to anterior midline.

Shānzhōng (RN 17) 膻中 On anterior midline at level with 4th intercostal space, midway between nipples.

Shénmén xué (HT 7) 神門 At the ulnar end of the transverse crease of the wrist, in the depression on the radial side of the tendon of muscle flexor carpi ulnaris.

Shénquè (RN 8) 神阙 Navel.

Táodào (DU 13) 陶道 Below the spinous process of the first thoracic vertebra.

Tiānjǐng (SJ 10) 天井 When the elbow is flexed, the point is in the depression about 3 cm superior to the olecranon.

Tiānzhù (BL 10) 天柱 4.5 cm lateral to Yǎmén (Du 15), in the depression on the lateral aspect of trapezius muscle.

Wàiguān (SJ 5) 外關 On the dorsal aspect of the forearm, on the line connecting SJ 4 and the tip of the elbow, 7 cm above the transverse crease of the wrist between the ulna and radius.

Wàihuáijiān (EX-LE 9) 外踝尖 On the highest prominence of the lateral malleolus.

Xiǎohǎi (SI 8) 小海 When the elbow is flexed, the point is located in the depression between the olecranon of the ulna and the medial epicondyle of the humerus.

Xìnmén (DU 22) 囟門 On the head, 7 cm cun directly above the midpoint of the anterior hairline, 10 cm anterior to DU 20.

Yángchí (SJ 4) 陽池 On the radial side of the wrist. When the thumb is tilted upward, it is in the depression between the tendons of muscle extensor pollicis longus and brevis.

Yìntáng (EX-HN3) 印堂 Midway between medial ends of two eyebrows.

Yǒngquán (KI 1) 涌泉 On the sole, in the depression when the foot is in plantar flexion, approximately at the junction of the anterior third and posterior two thirds of the sole.

Yúnmén (LU 2) 雲門 20 cm lateral to the anterior midline, below the clavicle in a depression medial to the coracoid process.

Yùzhěn (BL 9) 玉枕 Located in the depression superior to the external occipital protuberance.

Zhāngmén (LR 13) 章門 Slightly in front of and under the tip of the 11th rib.

ZhǎngQìáng (DU 1) 尾閭/長強 Midway between the tip of the coccyx and the anus.

Zhōngchōng (EX-UE 11) 中冲穴 Located in the fingertips.

Zhōngkuí (EX-UE4) 中魁 The middle of the middle joint of the middle finger.

Zhōngwǎn (RN 12) 中脘 On the anterior median line of the upper abdomen, 15 cm above the umbilicus.

Zhǒuliáo (LI 12) 肘髎 When the elbows is flexed, the point is superior to the lateral epicondyle of the humerus, about 3.5 cm superolateral to Quchi (LI 11), on the medial border of the humerus.

Meridian abbreviations

BL: Bladder Meridian.

DU (GV): Dū Mài, Governor (Governing) Meridian (Vessel).

EX-HN: Head and Neck Acupuncture Points.

EX-LE: Lower Extremities Acupuncture Points.

EX-UE: Upper Extremities Acupuncture Points.

GB: Gallbladder Meridian.

HT: Heart Meridian.

KI: Kidney Meridian.

LI: Large Intestine Meridian.

LR: Liver Meridian.

LU: Lung Meridian.

PC: Pericardium Meridian.

RN (CV): Rèn mài, Conception Meridian.

SJ: Sān jiāo Meridian.

SP: Spleen Meridian.

ST: Stomach Meridian.

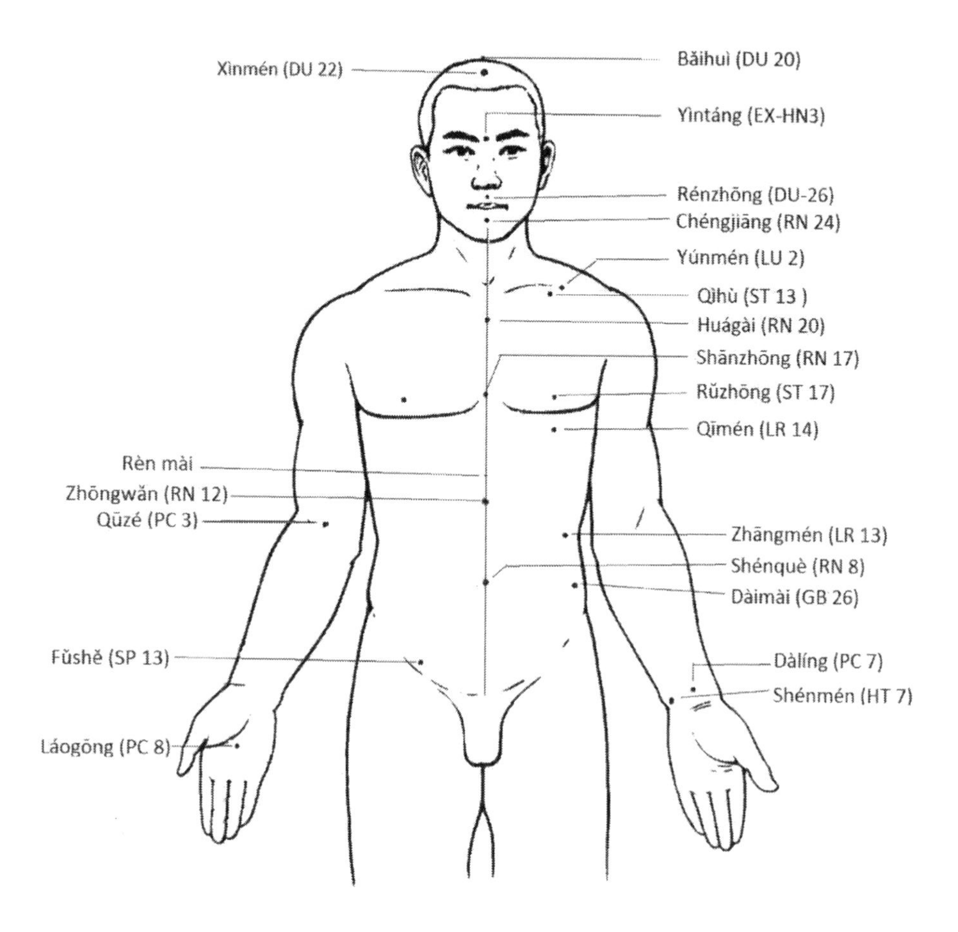

Acupuncture Points

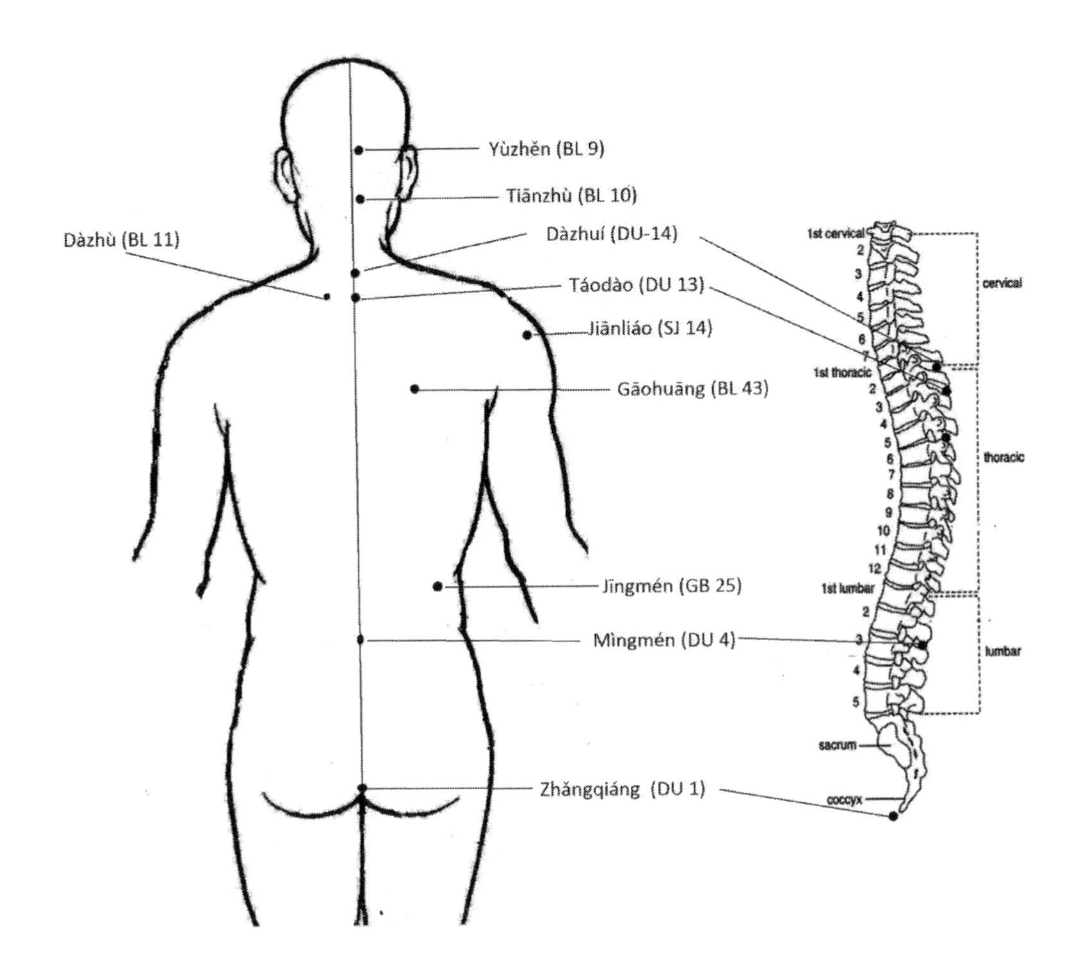

Acupuncture Points

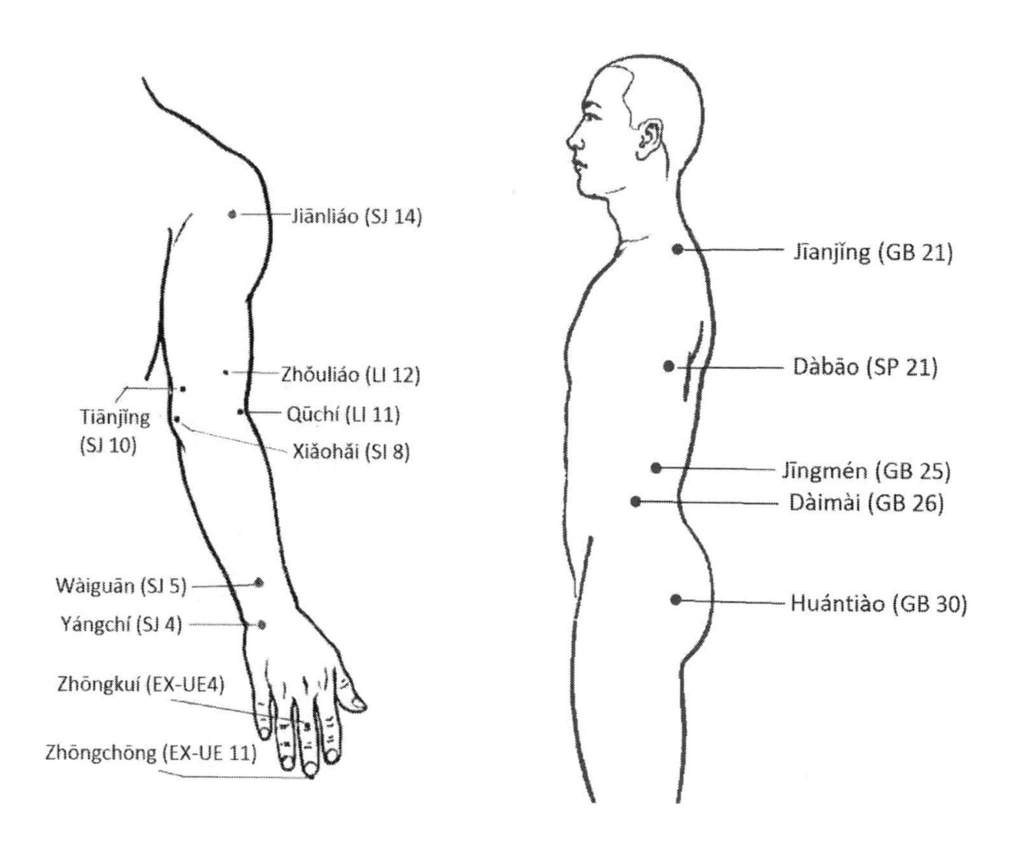

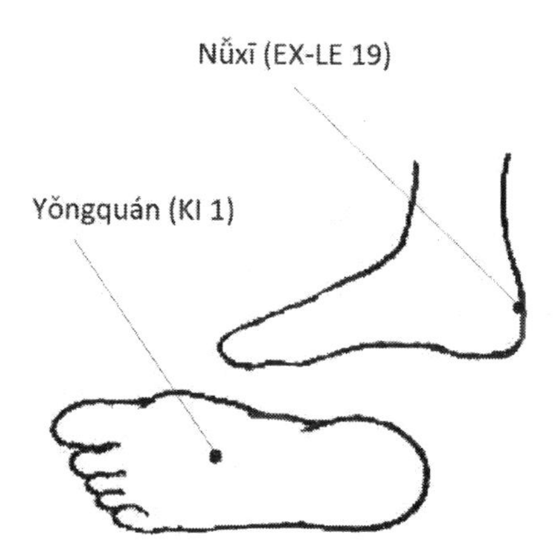

Acupuncture Points

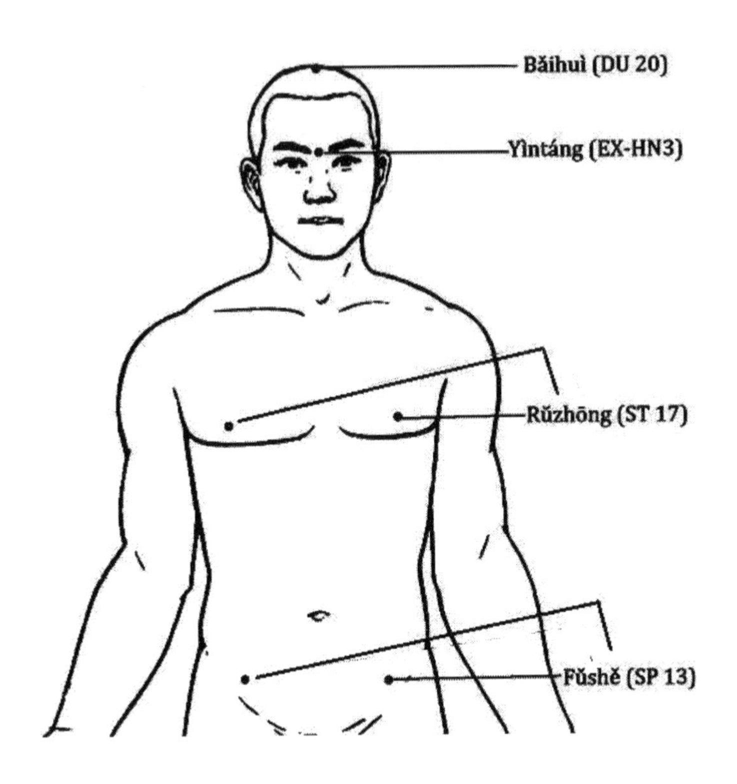

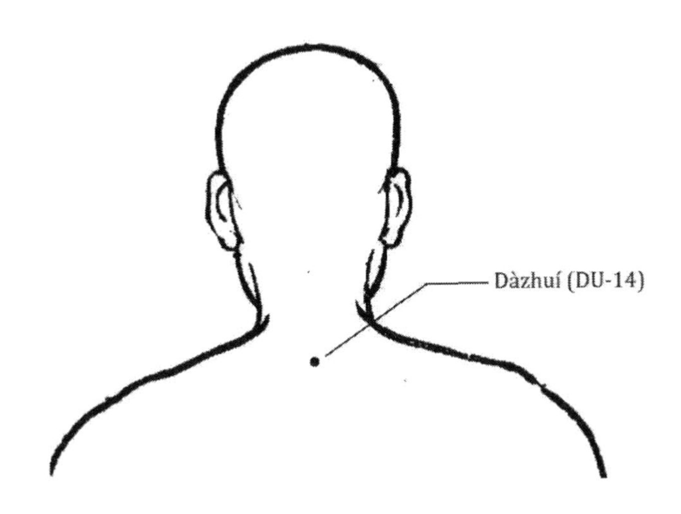

Small Seven Stars

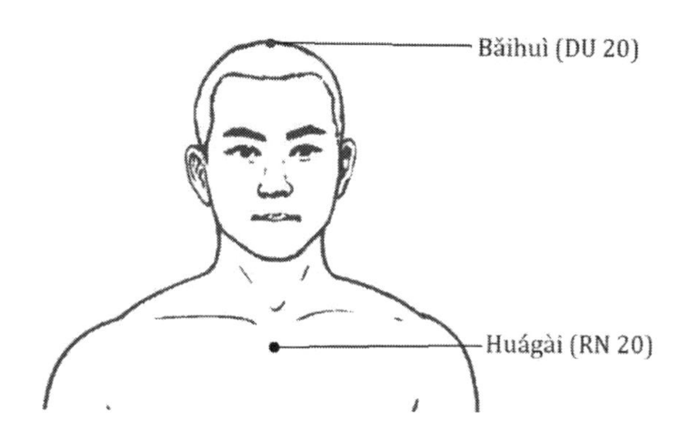

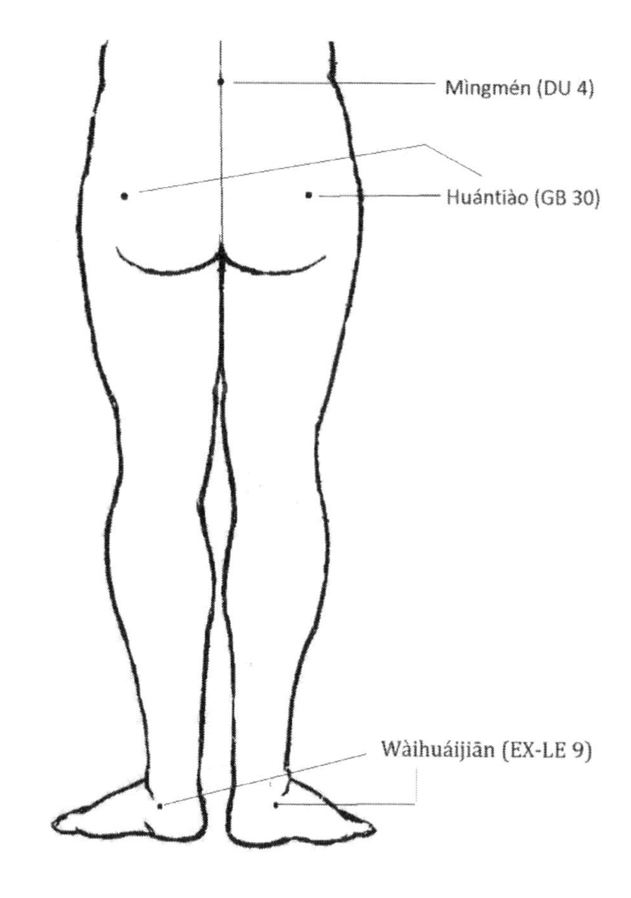

Big Seven Stars

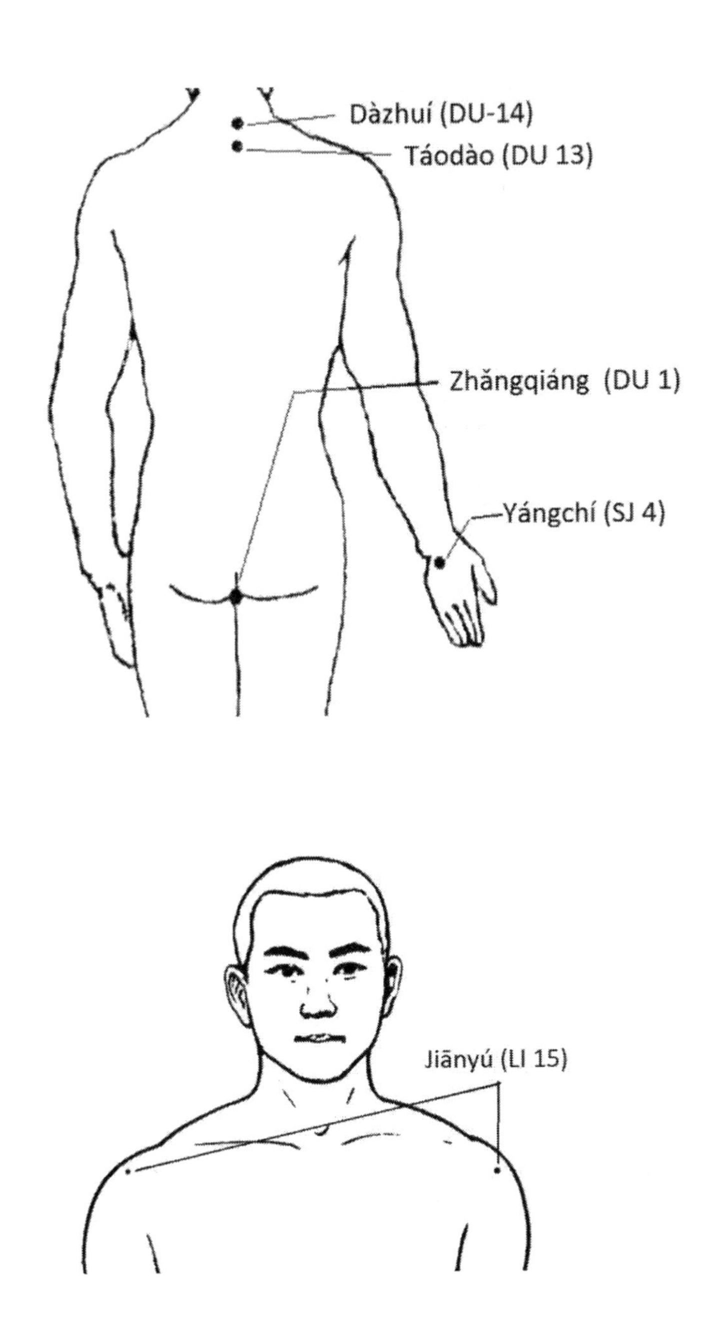

Reverse Seven Stars

GLOSSARY: QÌGŌNG TERMS

Prepared by B. J. Kish Irvine, Ph.D., with additions, revisions, and indexing from Chan Hou Hee Lǎoshī's translation.

Bǎihuì (Bǎi Huì) 百會穴, Governor Vessel 20 (GV 20), top of head, 65, 66, 68, 69, 74, 76, 88, 89, 92-96, 104, 123, 129, 130, 136, 141-146, 164, 171, 174, 175, 195, 203.

Belt Meridian, Dàimài (Dài Mài) 帶脈, along the waist. The Dài Mài is one of the eight Extraordinary Meridians. It regulates the twelve main meridians, 92, 96, 203.

Chì or Qì 氣, see Qì.

Chì Field 氣場, see Qì Field.

Chìhù 氣戶, see Qìhù.

Coccyx, tailbone, 73, 128-131, 142, 143, 146.

Dàbāo大包, on the Spleen Meridian, between the sixth and seventh ribs below the center of the armpit. It regulates the lateral meridians, 83, 86, 88, 146, 165, 172, 175, 188, 199.

Dān 丹, pill or "ball." 6.

Dāng 襠 crotch, 73, 74, 142.

Dāntián 丹田, it is an area for storage of Qì. They are three Dāntiáns in the body, Lower Dāntián or just Dāntián, normally refers to the area between the navel and the Mìngmén; Middle Dāntián refers to the chest area between the nipples, and Upper Dāntián refers to the center area of the head. 22, 24, 28, 36, 38, 39, 42- 44, 49, 67, 72, 73, 79, 82, 83, 86-88, 96, 114, 117, 118, 129-131, 143, 145, 150, 166, 171, 172, 187, 188, 200.

Dào 道, nature, encompasses methodology, purpose and virtue, 3, 12, 13, 78,

Dùchì (Dù Qì) 肚臍, navel.

Dū Mài 督脈, Governor Vessel Meridian (also called Governing Vessel Meridian).

Eight Essential Guidelines of Zhineng Qigong, 75-80.

Five Elements Method, Third Step Gong, 30-33, 41.

Gōng 功, method or practice, 30, 31, 32, 38, 41-44,

Governor Meridian, see Dū Mài.

Tiger Mouth (Hǔkǒu) 虎口, the area between the thumb (Lung Meridian) and the index finger (Large Intestine Meridian), 152.

Wan Yuán Chì 混元氣, see Hùn Yuán Qì.

Wěi Lú 尾閭, see coccyx.

Wèi Qì 衛氣, coarse Qi that acts like energy, relates to Traditional Chinese Medicine. 4, 5, 27, 68.

Xìng 性, essence, nature, soul, 8.

Xíng 形, appearance, shape, body, physical materials, 23, 24, 36, 41-43, 59, 62, 174, 176, 177.

Xū kōng (Xūkōng) 虛空, space/sky or horizon, 49, 75, 76, 79, 80, 85-87, 175, 180,

Xué 穴, acupuncture point.

Xué Wéi 穴位, acupressure points, position of the acupuncture point.

Yáng 陽, active, light, masculine polarity (tendency), the Yáng organs (large intestine, small intestine, gall bladder, bladder, stomach), 4, 29, 73, 76, 105, 126.

Yīn 陰, passive, dark, feminine polarity (tendency), the Yīn organs (lung, heart, pericardium, liver, kidney, spleen), 29, 42, 76, 88.

Yuán Qì 元氣, see Hùn Yuán Qì.

Zhìnéng Qìgōng 智能氣功, founded in 1980 by Dr. Páng Míng. A Qìgōng practice which includes Lift Chì Up Pour Chì Down Method, Three Centers Merge Standing Method, and Lā Chì.

Zhuāng 庄, posture, also means method, 59, 60, 174.

ABOUT THE AUTHOR:
CHAN (FAMILY NAME) HOU HEE a.k.a. FRANK CHAN

In the 1990s, Chan Lǎoshī and his brother Luke Chan were among the first teachers to officially introduce Zhìnéng Qìgōng, a medical Qìgōng famous in China for healing thousands with "incurable" diseases, to students in the United States. They named their organization Chilel (meaning Qì Therapy) Qìgōng with the approval of Dr. Páng Míng, founder and grandmaster of Zhìnéng Qìgōng.

Drawing from over 40 years of training and practice in Taiji and Qìgōng and his background as an engineer, the hallmark of Chan Lǎoshī's teaching is his ability to explain to his students HOW and WHY a movement is performed in terms that they are able to understand. Chan Lǎoshī's philosophy is that Qìgōng is not something that is mysterious. He defines Qìgōng as "physical therapy or exercise with mindfulness." Qìgōng is what we practice once we become aware of our body and aware of how we move our body.

To complement the physical forms of Qìgōng, he teamed up with Eva Lew, M.D. who provides insights into the mental and emotional parts of Qìgōng practice as well as the relationship of Qìgōng to Western Medicine. Their collaboration resulted in the release of "Medicine Begins with Me: A Holistic Approach to Healthcare." This program is designed to train healthcare providers as well as the general public in effective, easy to learn Qìgōng techniques.

CHILEL QÌGŌNG TITLES

Zhìnéng Qìgōng: Overview and Foundation Methods

Zhìnéng Qìgōng: Hun Yuan Wholistic Theory

Medicine Begins With Me:
A Holistic Approach to Health Care DVD, by Eva Lew M.D. and Hou Hee Chan

Medicine Begins With Me:
Wellness in Motion DVD, by Eva Lew M.D. and Hou Hee Chan

Chilel Qìgōng: Body and Mind Method Book, by Hou Hee Chan

101 Miracles of Natural Healing Book, by Luke Chan

101 Miracles of Natural Healing DVD, by Luke Chan

Chilel Qìgōng, Body & Mind Method DVD, by Luke Chan

Secrets of Tai Chi Circle: Journey to Enlightenment, by Luke Chan

101 Lessons of Dào, by Luke Chan

For information on workshops, products (DVDs, CDs, books) and practice tips, please visit our website:

www.chilelwellness.com
or
www.chilel.com